HOLT

Elements of Language

SIXTH COURSE

Grammar, Usage, and Mechanics

Language Skills Practice for Chapters 1–16

- Lesson Worksheets
- Chapter Reviews

HOLT, RINEHART AND WINSTON
A Harcourt Education Company
Orlando • Austin • New York • San Diego • London

Copyright © by Holt, Rinehart and Winston

All rights reserved. No part of this publication may be reproduced or transmitted in any form or by any means, electronic or mechanical, including photocopy, recording, or any information storage and retrieval system, without permission in writing from the publisher.

Teachers using ELEMENTS OF LANGUAGE may photocopy blackline masters in complete pages in sufficient quantities for classroom use only and not for resale.

ELEMENTS OF LANGUAGE, HOLT, HRW, and the **"Owl Design"** are trademarks licensed to Holt, Rinehart and Winston, registered in the United States of America and/or other jurisdictions.

Printed in the United States of America

If you have received these materials as examination copies free of charge, Holt, Rinehart and Winston retains title to the materials and they may not be resold. Resale of examination copies is strictly prohibited.

Possession of this publication in print format does not entitle users to convert this publication, or any portion of it, into electronic format.

ISBN 978-0-03-099419-7
ISBN 0-03-099419-5

5 6 7 8 1689 14 13 12 11 10

4500228972

Contents

Grammar, Usage, and Mechanics: Language Skills Practice

Chapter 1

PARTS OF SPEECH OVERVIEW: IDENTIFICATION AND FUNCTION

Chapter 2

THE PARTS OF A SENTENCE: SUBJECT, PREDICATE, COMPLEMENT

Chapter 3

THE PHRASE: KINDS OF PHRASES AND THEIR FUNCTIONS

Chapter 4

THE CLAUSE: INDEPENDENT AND SUBORDINATE CLAUSES, SENTENCE STRUCTURE

Copyright © by Holt, Rinehart and Winston. All rights reserved.

Contents

Chapter 5

AGREEMENT:
SUBJECT AND VERB, PRONOUN AND ANTECEDENT

Chapter 6

USING PRONOUNS CORRECTLY:
CASE FORMS OF PRONOUNS; SPECIAL PRONOUN PROBLEMS

Chapter 7

CLEAR REFERENCE:
PRONOUNS AND ANTECEDENTS

Copyright © by Holt, Rinehart and Winston. All rights reserved.

Contents

Copyright © by Holt, Rinehart and Winston. All rights reserved.

Contents

Copyright © by Holt, Rinehart and Winston. All rights reserved.

Contents

Copyright © by Holt, Rinehart and Winston. All rights reserved.

Using This Workbook

The worksheets in this workbook provide practice, reinforcement, and extension for Chapters 1–16 of *Elements of Language.*

Most of the worksheets you will find in this workbook are **traditional worksheets** providing practice and reinforcement activities on every rule and on all major instructional topics in the grammar, usage, and mechanics chapters in *Elements of Language.*

The Teaching Resources include the **Answer Key**, which is located on the *Teacher One Stop.*

Copyright © by Holt, Rinehart and Winston. All rights reserved.

Common, Proper, Concrete, and Abstract Nouns

1a. A ***noun*** names a person, a place, a thing, or an idea.

COMMON NOUNS	scientist, artist
PROPER NOUNS	Albert Einstein, Jackson Pollock
CONCRETE NOUNS	moon, calendar, broccoli, Vietnam
ABSTRACT NOUNS	gentility, meekness, Buddhism, hope

EXERCISE In the following sentences, underline the common nouns once and the proper nouns twice. Above each noun write *C* if the noun is *concrete* or *A* if the noun is *abstract.*

Example 1. Beth (C) worked up the courage (A) to eat some of the unfamiliar dish (C).

1. My father believes sunshine can make you smart.
2. The cowboys took the horses to the creek just past Razzleberry Hill.
3. Jon did not have the strength to close the window.
4. I learned to speak Portuguese from my teacher, Dr. Tihonen.
5. That's a good thought, Jacob, but I don't have any plastic bags.
6. From the house, you can see both the waterfall and the stream.
7. It's not about how you hit the baseball; it's about your mental attitude.
8. The province finally won its independence.
9. It takes patience to learn the guitar.
10. Farley, Jack, and I paddled our canoes down the Colorado River.
11. Moving to Pittsburgh caused me a lot of heartache.
12. Why don't you take off your shoes and rest your feet, Lucy?
13. That student has great ambition.
14. Our homework is due tomorrow.
15. My brother is a surgeon in Houston.
16. Robby is an excellent saxophone player.
17. I wish everyone could enjoy the love of a loyal pet.
18. Paul thought the play was about forgiveness.
19. The hippopotamus rested in the cool water.
20. Let's not listen to that song right now.

Copyright © by Holt, Rinehart and Winston. All rights reserved.

NAME CLASS DATE

Collective and Compound Nouns

The singular form of a ***collective noun*** names a group. A ***compound noun*** consists of two or more words used together as one noun. The parts of a compound noun may be written as one word, as separate words, or as a hyphenated word.

COLLECTIVE NOUNS organization, herd, choir, team
COMPOUND NOUNS highway, high school, son-in-law

EXERCISE In the following sentences, underline the collective nouns once and the compound nouns twice.

Example 1. Our class took a field trip last week.

1. On our way to the Museum of Fine Arts, the bus began to overheat.
2. Our bus driver, Mr. Peterson, said we had to pull over to the wayside.
3. One group of students wandered down to see the pond.
4. There was a mother duck with a brood of ducklings.
5. "Look," I said, "a fleet of ducks!"
6. "Silly!" said Lynn. "It's called a flock of ducks."
7. "But they float around like ships," I said. "Maybe we should call them a crew."
8. A few people from the class fed the flock with bread from our lunchboxes.
9. Lynn got too close to the waterside and almost fell in.
10. Some of our classmates walked to the other side of the lake.
11. A group of boys began throwing a football.
12. Some students in the choir decided to practice a song.
13. I'm not in the choir; I'm in the band.
14. The teacher used a cell phone to call the school.
15. After the radiator was fixed, the crowd got back on the bus.
16. When I bent down to retie my shoelace, I noticed a baby duck under the seat.
17. We coaxed the bird back to the duck pond, where its family was waiting.
18. As we drove off, the entire class waved goodbye to the flock through the rear window.
19. I was happy that our group was finally on its way to the museum.
20. However, when we got there, there was a sign on the museum door: "Museum closed due to floodwater."

Copyright © by Holt, Rinehart and Winston. All rights reserved.

Pronouns and Antecedents

1b. A ***pronoun*** takes the place of one or more nouns or pronouns.

The word that a pronoun stands for is the *antecedent* of the pronoun.

EXAMPLES Ruth decorated the room **herself.** [The noun *Ruth* is the antecedent of *herself.*]

The teacher wrote **his** name on the board. [The noun *teacher* is the antecedent of *his.*]

EXERCISE In the following sentences, underline each pronoun once and its antecedent twice.

Example 1. Phillip and Laura live in the town where they both grew up.

1. Uncle Andrew is in this picture; he is on the far left.
2. When Clara was a little girl, she wanted to be an artist.
3. The dishes are in the dishwasher because they are dirty.
4. Mary drove here herself.
5. Clifford will have to hurry; he is late.
6. Where is the screwdriver? It was here a minute ago.
7. Tell George the blue umbrella is for him.
8. Tori is leaving. Will Ed go with her?
9. Andrea had something in her eye.
10. The sign was so small it could not be seen from the road.
11. Dad went with him when Sven took the driving test.
12. Tom built the shed himself.
13. Seth said, "I intend to be president of the class."
14. The students painted the mural themselves.
15. The clock needs to be wound because it has stopped.
16. As they entered the pep rally, Carl and Christopher announced loudly, "The wrestling team has arrived!"
17. Louie and Rachel are tired of their toys.
18. Ms. Young told Jamie, "You were the student voted most likely to succeed."
19. Is Sergio at his job?
20. The factory workers and the managers are happy they get along so well.

Copyright © by Holt, Rinehart and Winston. All rights reserved.

Personal, Reflexive, and Intensive Pronouns

A *personal pronoun* refers to the one(s) speaking *(first person)*, the one(s) spoken to *(second person)*, or the one(s) spoken about *(third person)*.

A *reflexive pronoun* refers to the subject of a verb and functions as a complement or as the object of a preposition.

An *intensive pronoun* emphasizes its antecedent—a noun or another pronoun.

EXERCISE In the following sentences, underline each pronoun. Then, identify each pronoun by writing above it *P* for *personal*, *I* for *intensive*, or *R* for *reflexive*.

Example 1. He said himself that we should be kind to ourselves. (P, I, P, R)

1. They rode the train west for as far as it would carry them.
2. We thought this house was hers.
3. He convinced himself to finish the chores.
4. They themselves made the waffles.
5. I found her house all by myself.
6. Our greatest challenge is ahead of us.
7. His sister went with him to find your dog.
8. I wrote myself a note about their party.
9. You could paint the room yourself.
10. She is my favorite designer.
11. The puppy chased its tail until it tired itself out.
12. Her grandparents live next door to you, don't they?
13. You may help yourself to the buffet.
14. It was so cold that we could see our breath.
15. She fixed the leaking faucet herself.
16. The scientists themselves could not figure out the problem.
17. You and your friends should join us.
18. We are not planning to see the movie ourselves.
19. If she said we would not finish the race, then she does not know us well.
20. Monica herself was there to meet us when we dragged ourselves off the plane after the longest flight of our lives.

Copyright © by Holt, Rinehart and Winston. All rights reserved.

Demonstrative, Interrogative, and Relative Pronouns

A ***demonstrative pronoun*** points out a noun or another pronoun.

An ***interrogative pronoun*** introduces a question.

A ***relative pronoun*** introduces a subordinate clause.

DEMONSTRATIVE PRONOUNS this, that, these, those
INTERROGATIVE PRONOUNS who, whom, which, what, whose
RELATIVE PRONOUNS that, which, who, whom, whose

EXERCISE In the following sentences, underline demonstrative, interrogative, and relative pronouns. Then, above each underlined pronoun, write *D* for *demonstrative, I* for *interrogative,* or *R* for *relative.*

Example 1. "Who stole the diamond-covered shoehorn?" asked the great detective.

1. "We must discover the culprit who is guilty of this crime."
2. "The shoehorn was last seen near a window, which has been broken."
3. "Which is the window that was broken?" asked Ann, the housekeeper.
4. "This must be the one," said Harold, the butler.
5. Harold pointed to a window, which had been shattered.
6. "What are the marks on the ground outside the window?" asked Ann.
7. "Those are footprints," replied the great detective.
8. "They belong to someone whose boots are very large."
9. "Who has boots as big as the footprints?" asked Ann, looking at the butler's feet.
10. "What are you implying?" demanded the butler.
11. "The thief must have large feet. That's all," said Ann, looking down at her small shoes.
12. "These are certainly the footprints of the thief," said the great detective.
13. "However, those were not necessarily the boots of the thief."
14. "What do you mean?" they both asked.
15. "There is one thing that you are forgetting," said the great detective. "Small feet can fit into large boots, too."
16. "That is silly," said Ann.
17. "Why would someone who had small feet wear large boots?"
18. "What could be a better way of disguising your footprints than using someone else's shoes?"
19. "That is right," said the butler. "A pair of my boots is missing."
20. "This is the thief!" cried the great detective, pointing at Ann, the small-footed housekeeper.

Copyright © by Holt, Rinehart and Winston. All rights reserved.

Indefinite Pronouns

An *indefinite pronoun* refers to a person, a place, a thing, or an idea that may or may not be specifically named.

INDEFINITE PRONOUNS all, another, anyone, both, each, everyone, everybody, everything, few, many, neither, nothing, several, such

EXERCISE A Underline the indefinite pronouns in the following sentences.

Example 1. Today, most of us use flatware to eat.

1. However, in the not-too-distant past, eating with one's fingers was nothing unusual.
2. Etiquette dictated that anyone considered "high-class" should use only three fingers to pick up a morsel, leaving out the pinky and ring finger.
3. Someone might, in fact, be mocked for using a utensil rather than just his or her hands.
4. Few know that the fork is a rather recent invention; it was first used for eating in eleventh-century Tuscany, which today is part of Italy.
5. The new utensil spread to other parts of Europe, though it was considered by most to be more a curiosity than a useful tool.
6. Many at the time considered the use of the fork to be strange and even ungodly.
7. It was not until the eighteenth century that the French nobility began to believe it was impolite for one to use fingers at the table.
8. Consequently, most started using forks.
9. The spoon and knife predate the fork, as anyone who studies culinary history could explain.
10. Of the early spoons that have been found, most were made of thin, concave pieces of wood.

EXERCISE B Write appropriate indefinite pronouns to complete the following sentences.

Example 1. Could ___anyone___ imagine eating dinner in a fine restaurant without at least one spoon by the plate?

11. ________ have been found in Asia, while others have been discovered in Egyptian tombs.
12. ________ know that the knife is much older than either the spoon or the fork.
13. ________ knows for sure, but it is believed that the knife has been used for 1.5 million years.
14. People used early knives for ________ from eating to fighting one another.
15. While ________—the fork, the spoon, and the knife—has a different history, they combine to make eating more efficient.

Copyright © by Holt, Rinehart and Winston. All rights reserved.

Adjectives and the Words They Modify

1c. An ***adjective*** modifies a noun or a pronoun.

An adjective tells *what kind, which one, how many,* or *how much.*

WHAT KIND	**green** eyes, **French** perfume
WHICH ONE	**these** pencils, **last** page
HOW MANY	**six** erasers, **few** pennies
HOW MUCH	**some** sand, **enough** sauce

A, an, and *the* are the most frequently used adjectives. They are called ***articles.***

EXERCISE Underline each adjective in the following sentences once. Then, draw an arrow from the adjective to the word it modifies. Do not underline articles.

Example 1. Lumpy oatmeal is the only kind I will eat.

1. Larry brought four suitcases on vacation.
2. I enjoyed the scary movie we saw yesterday.
3. Will we have enough soup for everyone?
4. The dry leaves crunched underfoot.
5. The first time I saw snow, I was in New Mexico.
6. The young skater was surrounded by many admirers.
7. There is less need for caution now.
8. All students must go to the new auditorium.
9. Sunny weather makes me smile.
10. I don't need those notes anymore.
11. We will need some fennel for this recipe.
12. The red wagon is rusting in the rain.
13. The second door on the left is the bathroom.
14. Several children in the group are afraid of clowns.
15. Chloe had three tests on the same day.
16. After the storm, we found the hungry dogs hiding in an old shed.
17. You must have more courage than I do.
18. They made a lemon glaze for the shortbread cookies.
19. This song has twelve verses.
20. The club has little money, so I don't think we can afford an end-of-the-year trip.

Copyright © by Holt, Rinehart and Winston. All rights reserved.

Adjective or Pronoun?

Many of the words that can be used as pronouns can also be used as adjectives.

PRONOUNS **This** is the longest novel I have ever read.
Which of the parking lots is being repaved?

ADJECTIVES **This** novel has really made me think about life.
Which parking lot do you usually use?

EXERCISE A In the following sentences, the same word is used twice, once as an adjective and once as a pronoun. Identify each underlined word by writing above it *A* for *adjective* or *P* for *pronoun.*

Example 1. We should study both (A) chapters because both (P) will be on the test.

1. Few would spend so few hours studying.
2. Which review sheet is which?
3. These notes are better, so we should study these.
4. Any way of remembering these dates would help; can you think of any?
5. This is how I remember this fact.

EXERCISE B In the following sentences, identify each underlined word by writing above it *A* for *adjective* or *P* for *pronoun.*

Example 1. Each (A) student was nervous about the test results.

6. Few had finished the test in the time allowed.
7. Even those students who finished the test had many questions.
8. Several students arrived early for class on Monday.
9. Some even waited in the hall for the teacher to arrive.
10. The students were confused about a statement that had to be identified as either true or false.
11. Either answer could be correct, depending on how one looked at it.
12. However, many thought it was neither.
13. The teacher told them such things occasionally happen on tests.
14. The question, which had been poorly worded, was unclear.
15. Since either was acceptable, students got credit for either answer.

Copyright © by Holt, Rinehart and Winston. All rights reserved.

Adjective or Noun?

Most words that are used as nouns can also be used as adjectives.

NOUNS	table	dog	United States
ADJECTIVES	**table** lamp	**dog** food	**United States** government

EXERCISE Identify each underlined word by writing above it *A* for *adjective* or *N* for *noun*.

Example 1. The tiger habitat at this zoo is beautiful. (A: tiger; N: zoo)

1. The restaurant guide says this place is terrible.

2. The cat ran out through the cat door.

3. I love to make fudge brownies.

4. A group of lions is called a pride.

5. The bedroom closet is too small.

6. The bulldozer made a lot of noise that morning.

7. This mountain is part of a range that stretches for hundreds of miles.

8. Would you like to be a travel writer someday?

9. Camping is my favorite vacation activity.

10. Our town has a harvest festival every year.

11. William is the nicest boy in school.

12. Have you ever heard a really good mandolin player?

13. Apricots look like small peaches to me.

14. May I borrow your toenail clippers?

15. Our neighbor, the beekeeper, collects yard art.

16. Does that store sell plant fertilizer?

17. This huge computer is obsolete now.

18. Birthday decorations covered the entire table.

19. At the picnic, we ate egg salad off paper plates with plastic forks.

20. Let's look for him in the garden.

Copyright © by Holt, Rinehart and Winston. All rights reserved.

NAME _______________ CLASS _______________ DATE _______________

Main Verbs and Helping Verbs

1d. A ***verb*** expresses action or a state of being.

A *main verb* and one or more *helping verbs* (also called *auxiliary verbs*) make up a *verb phrase.* A *modal* is a helping verb that is joined with a main verb to express an attitude such as necessity or possibility.

VERBS A pair of robins **landed** in the tree and **began** to build a nest.

VERB PHRASES The concert **has been canceled,** but it **will** soon **be rescheduled.**

MODALS If you **must** go outside in this weather, you **should** wear a good hat.

EXERCISE Underline each verb phrase in the following sentences and underline each main verb twice.

Example 1. In 1914, when the *Endurance* was sailing to the Antarctic, its crew could not have known what lay ahead of them.

1. Sir Ernest Shackleton, who was the leader of the expedition, was a seasoned explorer who had been on two expeditions to Antarctica.

2. Shackleton and his team were planning a trip across the continent on foot.

3. The trip was delayed first at South Georgia Island, which is near Antarctica.

4. None of the whalers on the island could remember a time when the ice conditions had been as bad.

5. The whalers advised Shackleton that he should wait at least a month and perhaps should even wait another season.

6. After a month's delay, the *Endurance* was continuing south when the ship ran into ice about 80 miles from its destination.

7. The men could not free their ship from the ice.

8. They were slowly being carried farther and farther from land, as the ice pack was drifting with the current.

9. Since they could not sail again until the spring, Shackleton and his men settled in for the winter.

10. It was boring for the men that winter, but at least they had good shelter and enough food.

Copyright © by Holt, Rinehart and Winston. All rights reserved.

Action Verbs

An *action verb* expresses either physical or mental activity.

PHYSICAL ACTIVITY run, draw, push

MENTAL ACTIVITY think, remember

EXERCISE Underline all of the action verbs in the following sentences. Identify each verb by writing above it *P* if it expresses *physical activity* or *M* if it expresses *mental activity.*

Example 1. Please remember (M) that we must wash (P) the car today.

1. I know about every book in that series.
2. I doubt the accuracy of that statement.
3. Herman rides the bus every day.
4. I think I understand this assignment.
5. You will find your keys on the hall table.
6. We should drive to the beach.
7. He thought we were arriving at noon.
8. They have solved the problem.
9. We baked gingerbread cookies.
10. Consider the risks before you start your own business.
11. Who will open this jar for me?
12. The pie cooled on the windowsill.
13. She runs like the wind.
14. I wonder if it will rain.
15. Think of the possibilities!
16. Elizabeth told us about it.
17. Harry will go first today.
18. I usually exercise for an hour.
19. He says he can estimate the number of people who will vote.
20. I suppose the meeting will begin on time.

Copyright © by Holt, Rinehart and Winston. All rights reserved.

Linking Verbs

A *linking verb* connects the subject to a word or word group that identifies or describes the subject. Such a word or word group is called a ***subject complement.***

EXAMPLES This meal **smells** delicious!
Who **is** the new class president?
That **must be** one of the oldest buildings in the city.

EXERCISE Underline the linking verbs in the following sentences.

Example 1. I may be the shortest one here, but I am also the best basketball player.

1. He is the office manager.

2. At first, the problem appeared unsolvable.

3. Hermina seems sad.

4. You are very brave to volunteer for that job.

5. We have been cold all morning.

6. That looks wonderful!

7. She could be president.

8. They felt encouraged after the meeting with the coach.

9. We were the first ones in line today.

10. What would be best?

11. The film became more and more difficult to follow.

12. That movie was an immediate success.

13. Where is the broom that usually sits in the closet?

14. What could be more interesting?

15. Is he really a circus acrobat?

16. The honeysuckle smelled sweet.

17. You grow more beautiful every time I see you.

18. Who is your counselor?

19. This tastes too salty.

20. Your plan sounds as though it will work.

Copyright © by Holt, Rinehart and Winston. All rights reserved.

Transitive and Intransitive Verbs

A ***transitive verb*** has an ***object***—a word that tells who or what receives the action. An ***intransitive verb*** does not have an object.

TRANSITIVE Becky **gave** her speech first. [The object *speech* receives the action of the verb *gave.*]

Frank **has thrown** more touchdown passes than anyone else in the division. [The object *passes* receives the action of the verb *has thrown.*]

INTRANSITIVE Rain **has been falling** for the last three hours.

The detective **is** very perceptive.

EXERCISE In the following sentences, underline each intransitive verb once and underline each transitive verb twice.

Example 1. I can hardly wait for opening night of our production of *King Lear.*

1. I play the character of Regan in our school's production of Shakespeare's tragedy.
2. We rehearse every weeknight.
3. Fortunately, I can memorize lines fairly quickly.
4. My friend Robert plays the character Kent.
5. He always arrives early for rehearsal.
6. The last school play was *Waiting for Godot* by Samuel Beckett.
7. I was not in that play, but I helped the set designers on the weekends.
8. One day I would like to act in a big Broadway musical.
9. I can sing enthusiastically.
10. My mother sings beautifully.
11. She has perfect pitch.
12. She sang in jazz clubs.
13. It was at a performance that she met my father, a piano player.
14. He can really tickle the ivories!
15. They help with tips about show business.
16. Sometimes my mother and I sing a duet while my father plays the piano.
17. "Music comes from the heart, not the head," my dad says.
18. Of course, there is no music in *King Lear,* but I enjoy my part a lot.
19. The next production will be *Romeo and Juliet.*
20. I'll be auditioning for the part of Juliet.

Copyright © by Holt, Rinehart and Winston. All rights reserved.

NAME ______________________ CLASS ______________ DATE ______________

Adverbs and the Words They Modify

1e. An ***adverb*** modifies a verb, an adjective, or another adverb.

An adverb tells *how, when, where,* or *to what extent (how much, how often,* or *how long).*

EXAMPLES He spoke **loudly** and **slowly.** [The adverbs *loudly* and *slowly* modify the verb *spoke,* telling *how.*]
They sat in the **extremely** uncomfortable chairs. [The adverb *extremely* modifies the adjective *uncomfortable,* telling *to what extent.*]
She wrote the answers **very neatly.** [The adverb *very* modifies the adverb *neatly,* telling *to what extent.* The adverb *neatly* modifies the verb *wrote,* telling *how.*]

EXERCISE A Underline each of the adverbs in the following sentences and draw an arrow from the adverb to the word(s) it modifies. Hint: A sentence may have more than one adverb.

Example 1. The original version of this game ran unbelievably slowly.

1. Considering that this video game is fairly old, it has surprisingly good graphics.
2. Is that the surpassingly lovely princess I have to rescue?
3. That was an unusually friendly gnome.
4. My character in the game is an exceptionally skilled archer.
5. At the archery tournament, I shot my arrow almost exactly in the center of the target.
6. I think a goblin is lurking nearby.
7. The castle's towers loom ominously over the treacherously swampy landscape.
8. Rather reluctantly, the gatekeeper let me into the city.
9. My sister mastered this game quickly.
10. The continually elusive high score escaped me again.

EXERCISE B On the line provided, add an adverb to complete each sentence below.

Example 1. After the lecture Jesse and his friends ___quietly___ walked to a nearby cafe.

11. Once seated, they all ________________ began discussing the topic of the lecture.
12. Jesse argued ________________ that the speaker's comments were well supported.
13. Cynthia disagreed ________________ and offered her own views on the subject.
14. Rafael suggested that the lecture would have been ________________ interesting if there had been more time for questions at the end.
15. ________________, they all agreed that they had learned a lot and hoped to attend another lecture soon.

Copyright © by Holt, Rinehart and Winston. All rights reserved.

Noun or Adverb?

Some words that are often used as nouns may also be used as adverbs.

NOUN **Friday** is the day I start my racquetball lessons.

ADVERB I'll be having another lesson every **Friday** for the next two months. [The noun *Friday* is used as an adverb telling *when*.]

EXERCISE In the following sentences, identify the underlined word by writing above it *N* if it is a noun or *ADV* if it is an adverb.

Example 1. Yesterday was exciting. (N)

1. My parents and I arrived in New York City yesterday.
2. First, we went uptown to the Metropolitan Museum of Art.
3. That was wonderful, so I thought that uptown would be my favorite part of New York.
4. Then, we went downtown.
5. Downtown is definitely my favorite, but not because of any of its tourist attractions.
6. It is my favorite because it is my best friend Miriam's home.
7. After only a few days, I certainly was not ready to go home.
8. Miriam and I went to Chinatown and Little Italy today.
9. I think today has been the most fun so far.
10. My family has to leave tomorrow.
11. Tomorrow is the first day of spring.
12. We get to go upstate to see the countryside.
13. My aunt says that upstate is very beautiful.
14. First we will spend two nights in a cabin.
15. I will probably be the first to cook dinner at the cabin.
16. I'm really looking forward to Sunday.
17. Sunday, Miriam and I will visit her aunt who lives on Lake Ontario.
18. If we have time, we'll then drive into Canada.
19. Since we haven't yet spoken to Miriam's aunt about it, we can't really make plans until then.
20. Finally, on Wednesday we'll return to New York City to take an airplane home.

Copyright © by Holt, Rinehart and Winston. All rights reserved.

NAME CLASS DATE

The Preposition

1f. A ***preposition*** shows the relationship of a noun or pronoun, called the ***object of the preposition,*** to another word.

EXAMPLES The water flowed **over** the rocks.
The water flowed **around** the rocks.
The tree stood **next to** the water.

EXERCISE Underline the preposition(s) in the following sentences.

Example 1. Is this phone call about the book you lent me before the holidays?

1. I think it's underneath my bed.

2. If it's not there, then I'm sure it's behind the couch.

3. It might be in my backpack.

4. Wait—I remember leaving it at the bus stop.

5. I got on the bus without your book.

6. It must have slipped out of my backpack onto the ground.

7. Your shoe is beside the table.

8. It could be on the porch.

9. I can't believe I left your jacket out there!

10. At the time, it seemed like a good idea.

11. It's a shame about the rain.

12. I'm sure your favorite jacket is as good as new.

13. There may be a few rips on the sleeve.

14. That jacket is out of style anyway.

15. I washed your T-shirt in the sink.

16. Now the ketchup stain is gone without a trace!

17. Unfortunately, it fell into a bucket of paint.

18. Also, I lent your binoculars to my neighbor.

19. Please accept an apology from the bottom of my heart.

20. Can I borrow your guitar for a few days?

Copyright © by Holt, Rinehart and Winston. All rights reserved.

Adverb or Preposition?

Some of the words that are commonly used as prepositions may also be used as adverbs. Keep in mind that an adverb is a modifier and that it does not have an object. Prepositions always have objects.

ADVERB Did you leave those muddy boots **outside**? [*Outside* modifies the verb *did leave.*]

PREPOSITION Take those boots off while you're **outside** the house. [*Outside* introduces a prepositional phrase and has an object, *house.*]

EXERCISE In each of the following sentences, the underlined word is used once as an adverb and once as a preposition. Identify each underlined word by writing above it *ADV* for *adverb* or *PREP* for *preposition.*

Example 1. Your family is waiting in (PREP) the living room, so you should go in (ADV).

1. After going inside, I realized there was no more room for food inside the refrigerator.
2. By ourselves, we watched the cars go by.
3. The game is over, over there.
4. Get off the court, but don't run off.
5. We must surround that building because the fugitive is within, still within our reach.
6. Before you go out the door, tell me if we are going out tonight.
7. If the show is going to go on, we have to be on time.
8. You can't go across this mountain range in your car, because there is no good road to take you across.
9. After he climbed down the telephone pole, he sat down on the ground.
10. When you go outside, see if there are any snowdrifts outside our fence.
11. We left Ted behind when we went behind the curtain.
12. I cooked the roast throughout the afternoon, until it was well-done throughout.
13. They walked around the park because they like to walk around.
14. Carry on without fear, and don't worry that you will have to go without.
15. Above all, we noticed the helicopter hovering above.
16. Let's climb up, because the best view is from up this hill.
17. Along the side of the road, a dog was ambling along.
18. In 2007, my grandmother moved in.
19. After reading a book about exotic locations, we decided to travel about.
20. Past ninety, but still charming, the man lifted his hat whenever a lady walked past.

Copyright © by Holt, Rinehart and Winston. All rights reserved.

The Conjunction

1g. A ***conjunction*** joins words or word groups.

A *coordinating conjunction* joins words or word groups that are used in the same way.

Correlative conjunctions are pairs of conjunctions that join words or word groups that are used in the same way.

A *subordinating conjunction* begins a subordinate clause and connects it to an independent clause.

EXERCISE Underline every conjunction in the following sentences.

Example 1. My sister has finished her holiday shopping, but I have hardly started mine.

1. Not only am I late getting started, but I also haven't decided what to buy for everyone.
2. I look forward to buying presents for my mother and my father.
3. While I was studying for finals, I didn't have time to think about shopping.
4. Since finals are over, I have to hurry to get caught up.
5. Not only do I typically buy presents for them, but I also get a gift for my sister.
6. Since the emphasis is on giving, no one in my family expects expensive presents.
7. Gifts are a holiday tradition, and everyone in my family enjoys the custom.
8. If I could knit, I would make them each a scarf.
9. While I'm shopping, I should buy a gift for my girlfriend, too.
10. Well, she's not really my girlfriend, though I think she's smart and pretty.
11. I'm planning to buy her either flowers or a book of poems by Yeats.
12. I could write a few poems myself and give her those instead of the book.
13. I think I'll get my dad a new hat or some golf balls.
14. He needs the hat because he usually works outside.
15. Although I want to get my mother a new coat, I only have enough money to buy her a blouse.
16. While my sister probably wants ski boots, I'm going to buy her some earmuffs.
17. Last year I gave my mother an oven mitt and my father a pair of socks.
18. I had even less money then than I do now.
19. Whether I buy them expensive gifts or not, my parents always like what I give them.
20. After I buy everything I want for them, I'm getting a basketball for myself.

Copyright © by Holt, Rinehart and Winston. All rights reserved.

The Interjection

1h. An **interjection** expresses emotion and has no grammatical relation to the rest of the sentence.

An interjection is often set off from the rest of the sentence by an exclamation point or one or more commas. Exclamation points indicate strong emotion. Commas indicate mild emotion.

EXAMPLES **Whoa!** Don't try to carry so much at one time.
I thought that, **well,** you might like to see a movie this weekend.

EXERCISE Underline the interjections in the following sentences.

Example 1. Hey! You stepped on my toe!

1. Oh, do you want to get started?
2. I'll just grab this teakettle—ouch!
3. Uh-oh, where are my keys?
4. Well, that's the best I can do.
5. My! That was a close one!
6. Oh, I'm going to be okay when the bone heals.
7. Oops! That's too much ketchup!
8. Just look at that airplane! Wow!
9. If you don't get it the first time, well, don't give up.
10. Aha! Now I know where I put my lampshade!
11. Yes! That's right!
12. No! You lose!
13. Sure, I believe crocodiles can eat cars.
14. Hey! The garage is on fire!
15. Yippee! We're moving to Texas!
16. That's how I would do it, but, hey, do whatever you think is best.
17. Well, I guess we're stuck with it then.
18. Aha! Now I understand how to finish my science project!
19. I'll just gently move this crystal goblet over to the shelf—oops!
20. I'm glad that's over. Phew!

Copyright © by Holt, Rinehart and Winston. All rights reserved.

Determining Parts of Speech

1i. The way a word is used in a sentence determines what part of speech the word is.

EXAMPLES Have you finished band **practice** yet? [noun]
If you don't **practice** your oboe, you won't get any better. [verb]
Did you leave your oboe in the **practice** hall? [adjective]

EXERCISE A Identify the part of speech of each underlined word in the following paragraphs by writing above it *N* for *noun*, *PRO* for *pronoun*, *ADJ* for *adjective*, *V* for *verb*, *ADV* for *adverb*, *PREP* for *preposition*, *CON* for *conjunction*, or *INT* for *interjection*.

Example **[1]** Oops! I think I blinked.

[1] "Wow! Wait until you see your picture! It's great!" **[2]** Every year at high schools throughout the United States, excitement is the overwhelming response of students as they get their **[3]** first glimpse of the yearbook. Also known as the annual, the yearbook is published in either May or June **[4]** and is regarded **[5]** by seniors as a **[6]** sure sign that graduation is no longer a dream but a reality.

[7] Although the yearbook may seem to appear **[8]** rather magically, it **[9]** represents the combined efforts of **[10]** several in our class.

EXERCISE B In each of the following sentences, underline every word that is used as the part of speech given in parentheses after the sentence.

Example **1.** Planning for the yearbook begins in the spring: Editors are chosen, themes are decided, and budgets are set. *(preposition)*

11. When high school opens for the fall semester, the staff moves at top speed. *(verb)*

12. A flurry of activity marks September and October: organizing the senior section, covering sports and clubs, shooting candids of students and faculty, and running the advertising campaign. *(adjective)*

13. Frazzled but wiser, the staff members meet their first deadline, with the knowledge that it is only the first of many yet to come. *(pronoun)*

14. Then, during the winter months, when deadlines come faster and meetings last longer, deep friendships are often formed. *(adverb)*

15. Finally, by mid-March, the work is finished. *(noun)*

Copyright © by Holt, Rinehart and Winston. All rights reserved.

Review A: Parts of Speech

EXERCISE Identify the part of speech of each underlined word in the following sentences by writing above it *N* for *noun, PRO* for *pronoun, ADJ* for *adjective, V* for *verb, ADV* for *adverb, PREP* for *preposition, CON* for *conjunction*, or *INT* for *interjection*.

Example 1. That is the reason I don't want that one. (PRO, ADJ)

1. As we drew near the light at the end of the road, a light rain was falling.
2. The bird-watcher saw the woodpecker hop off the wooden fence and fly off.
3. After the play had become a success, the director made dinner for the cast and crew after a performance.
4. The gardener plants seeds in the spring and harvests the plants in the fall.
5. According to the school's monthly newsletter, an open meeting of the debate club is held monthly.
6. When the fire alarms sound, you cannot hear the sound of anything else.
7. This indicates that you do not understand this grammatical concept very well.
8. The kite flew high until its string got caught in the high branches of a cottonwood tree.
9. Before the arena's gates opened, you were standing before us in the waiting line.
10. Telephone me when your telephone is repaired.
11. Aretha walked along with us as we enjoyed our hike along the river.
12. If you won't climb up the ladder, then I will have to climb up.
13. This is the first time I have read this book.
14. After I left the room, I remembered my promise to stay after class.
15. I will sled down the hill, and then you can use my sled.
16. Scientists must fully understand the effect before they can effect a correction.
17. Well, I believe my watch just fell down the well.
18. Those are the costumes worn by those actors.
19. The new assistant reports directly to the assistant principal.
20. Put that down; it's an antique down pillow, and you could damage it.

Copyright © by Holt, Rinehart and Winston. All rights reserved.

NAME CLASS DATE

Review B: Parts of Speech

EXERCISE A Each of the following sentences contains either one word or two words of the kind specified before the sentence. Find each of these words and underline it.

Examples **1.** *(verb)* Computers serve many purposes.

2. *(pronoun)* Without them our society would be considerably different.

1. *(conjunction)* As computers have become increasingly common, they have changed our lives and our society.

2. *(pronoun)* Anyone who has played a video game has seen how fascinating a computer program can be.

3. *(adjective)* Of course, providing fun is only one purpose that computers serve.

4. *(verb)* The incredible operating speed of computers accounts in large part for their seemingly uncanny capabilities.

5. *(preposition)* A powerful computer can instantly perform herculean tasks that require days or weeks of a person's time.

6. *(noun)* Someone who has used even a simple pocket calculator is likely to appreciate computer capabilities.

7. *(preposition)* With the appropriate software and the touch of a key, business executives can generate complicated schedules and budgets.

8. *(adverb)* Mechanical engineers can create remarkably detailed drawings of machines.

9. *(pronoun)* Everyone from preschool tots to college professors is using computers.

10. *(adverb)* You may already be able to program computers, or perhaps you would like to learn.

EXERCISE B Identify the part of speech of each underlined word in the following sentences by writing above it *N* for *noun*, *PRO* for *pronoun*, *ADJ* for *adjective*, *V* for *verb*, *ADV* for *adverb*, *PREP* for *preposition*, *CON* for *conjunction*, or *INT* for *interjection*.

Example **[1]** Daniel is an enthusiastic computer hobbyist. (ADJ)

Daniel loves his **[11]** computer. He **[12]** works **[13]** tirelessly to perfect the programs he has designed. **[14]** In his room, Daniel has every kind of **[15]** computer accessory you can imagine. **[16]** He hopes to combine his interests in computers **[17]** and monster movies by working for a special effects company **[18]** someday. **[19]** Wow, **[20]** that sounds like fun!

Copyright © by Holt, Rinehart and Winston. All rights reserved.

Review C: Parts of Speech

EXERCISE Identify the part of speech of each underlined word in the following paragraph by writing above it *N* for *noun, PRO* for *pronoun, ADJ* for *adjective, V* for *verb, ADV* for *adverb, PREP* for *preposition, CON* for *conjunction*, or *INT* for *interjection*.

Example Read the passage **[1]** carefully.

From 1853 to 1857, Nathaniel Hawthorne was a United States **[1]** consul **[2]** in England. **[3]** He traveled extensively and kept a series of journals in which he commented **[4]** shrewdly on the English landscape and **[5]** English character. After his return to the United States, he gathered together a number of excerpts from these journals and **[6]** published them as a **[7]** book. **[8]** One excerpt recounts an experience he had **[9]** while he was journeying in the Lake District of England. He was traveling **[10]** between the villages of Grasmere and Windermere in a stagecoach that was greatly overloaded; there were fifteen **[11]** outside passengers, **[12]** besides the four inside passengers. The road was rough and **[13]** hilly, and **[14]** Hawthorne expected that the coach would topple any minute since **[15]** it was creaking and swaying **[16]** dangerously. He **[17]** became convinced that he was going to be thrown headlong from the coach against the high stone fence that **[18]** bordered the road. **[19]** Ouch! He determined that at the moment of catastrophe he would fling his heavy shawl **[20]** about his head to give himself some protection. With this decision, he settled back to await his fate.

Copyright © by Holt, Rinehart and Winston. All rights reserved.

NAME CLASS DATE

Sentences and Sentence Fragments

2a. A ***sentence*** is a word group that contains a subject and a verb and that expresses a complete thought.

SENTENCE FRAGMENT Last summer on my vacation.

SENTENCE Last summer on my vacation, I went to Arizona.

EXERCISE If one of the following word groups is a sentence, add appropriate capitalization and punctuation and write *S* before the item number. If the word group is a sentence fragment, add or delete words to make it a sentence. Then, add appropriate capitalization and punctuation.

Example 1. did think of the class field trip to the American Indian reservation

What did you think of the class field trip to the American Indian reservation?

1. oraibi is one of the oldest continually inhabited villages in America

2. according to the guide's lecture, the Hopi reservation is surrounded by the Navajo reservation

3. a remarkable description given about the life of the Hopi people

4. situated near several massive stone mesas, the eleven villages by the canyon

5. found on the protected Hopi reservation in the beautiful Arizona desert

6. tewa, Sichomovi, and Walpi are three villages atop the mesa

7. breathtaking cliff-side stone houses they are

8. the villages, also called "pueblos"

9. are some villages known for pottery

10. a pleasant visit to this ancient reservation, a sight to behold

Copyright © by Holt, Rinehart and Winston. All rights reserved.

Subjects and Predicates

2b. Sentences consist of two basic parts: *subjects* and *predicates*. The ***subject*** is a word or word group that tells whom or what the sentence is about. The ***predicate*** is a word or word group that tells something about the subject.

SUBJECT **The western coast of England** will provide the setting for the story.

PREDICATE The western coast of England **will provide the setting for the story.**

EXERCISE For each of the following sentences, identify the underlined words as the subject or the predicate. Write *S* for *subject* or *P* for *predicate*.

Example 1. Before leaving the southern coast, my brother and I took wonderful photos of the sun sinking into the sea. P P

1. The four-star general examined the maps and other strategic information.
2. The writer will strive to be more thorough and accurate in her work.
3. Was Carla at the bowling alley or the movie theater?
4. The skilled guide dog waited attentively for the traffic light to change.
5. Along the winding road through the woods, we made our way to the cabin.
6. Was the jewel heist at the department store the top story on the evening news?
7. Under the current policy, soft drinks and snacks are not permitted in Ms. Garcia's classroom.
8. The search turned up nothing but a pencil and sixty-five cents in change.
9. Did Perry get on the subway at 96th Street and Broadway?
10. The girls' gymnastics squad at my high school is training for the district championship.
11. At the top of the page, the writer listed the sources that he had used.
12. After storing our backpacks in the cabin, we sat and watched the sun set over the water.
13. The tiny restaurant, tucked in the corner of the square, had only sandwiches on the menu.
14. The movie starred two mermaids, an alien, and a lovable dog named Ralph.
15. Under the neon sign, the portrait artist waited for another customer.
16. Just beyond the train station and the information booth, Adam found the youth hostel.
17. Is this it?
18. The tour bus will be making another stop soon.
19. Three books, a coffee mug, slippers, a chess set, and a toothbrush were all he owned.
20. The actors dressed as pirates exited the stage.

Copyright © by Holt, Rinehart and Winston. All rights reserved.

NAME CLASS DATE

Simple and Complete Subjects

2c. The ***simple subject*** is the main word or word group that tells whom or what the sentence is about.

The ***complete subject*** consists of the simple subject and any word or word groups used to modify the simple subject.

SIMPLE SUBJECT A summer **trip** to the beaches of sunny Thailand sounds wonderful.

COMPLETE SUBJECT **A summer trip to the beaches of sunny Thailand** sounds wonderful.

EXERCISE In the following sentences, underline the complete subject once and the simple subject twice.

Example 1. Doesn't every student in this classroom like to exercise?

1. Regular exercise helps prevent certain diseases.
2. People in excellent health also feel better emotionally.
3. Sedentary people risk developing health problems.
4. Sensible, safe, low-impact exercise is ideal.
5. The capacity of the lungs to take in air can be increased.
6. With exercise, a person's muscles can grow stronger.
7. A consistent exercise regimen helps people stay in shape.
8. Top athletes pay close attention to their exercise routines.
9. Everyone, not just top athletes, needs to be physically active.
10. Even the best-conditioned athletes should stretch before a workout.
11. Proper, careful stretching helps prevent injuries.
12. People young and old need to exercise each day.
13. Do your high school classmates exercise?
14. Even simple, everyday activities like climbing stairs are good for you.
15. Low-impact workouts include walking, swimming, and cycling.
16. People with health conditions should talk to their doctors first.
17. Your doctor or physical therapist may be able to design an exercise program just for you.
18. Some daily form of exercise can improve your endurance.
19. The flow of oxygen to the heart can be increased.
20. What a difference a little exercise can make!

Copyright © by Holt, Rinehart and Winston. All rights reserved.

Simple and Complete Predicates

2d. The ***simple predicate,*** or verb, is the main word or word group that tells something about the subject.

The *complete predicate* consists of the simple predicate and all of the words used to modify the simple predicate and complete its meaning.

SIMPLE PREDICATE The cheering fans **were parading** around the stadium floor.

COMPLETE PREDICATE The cheering fans **were parading around the stadium floor.**

EXERCISE In the following sentences, underline the complete predicate once and the simple predicate twice.

Example 1. After two hours, the doctors finished the surgical operation.

1. Gary, Joan, and Lisa want their own company.
2. This new museum will certainly attract more visitors.
3. Will they do more research into the proposed ecology initiative?
4. I was born in the small California coastal town of Mendocino.
5. The perfect sandwich needs mustard and mayonnaise on two slices of rye bread.
6. An innovative, unusual work of art can provoke thought.
7. Is the science project focusing on the latest developments in energy conservation?
8. Phillip does not give in easily.
9. In the morning, the tour group will begin a train trip through Mexico's Copper Canyon.
10. The antique lamp seems dignified and grand.
11. Can you see the playing field from the upper level of the stadium?
12. Carpeting is needed only in the cabin's bedrooms and hallway.
13. The black mastiff in the backyard is running along the fence.
14. We bought these tasty apricots at the store.
15. After midnight, the moon crept out from behind the clouds.
16. Truck drivers travel long distances with their payloads.
17. The delivery from the sporting goods store was late as always.
18. Among the professor's many reference books were ten dictionaries for ten different languages.
19. Next to my cat sat a tiny stuffed mouse.
20. When will the ceremony in the school auditorium end?

Copyright © by Holt, Rinehart and Winston. All rights reserved.

Complete and Simple Subjects and Predicates

2c. The ***simple subject*** is the main word or word group that tells whom or what the sentence is about.

The *complete subject* consists of the simple subject and any word or word groups used to modify the subject.

2d. The ***simple predicate,*** or verb, is the main word or word group that tells something about the subject.

The *complete predicate* consists of the simple predicate and all of the words used to modify the simple predicate and to complete its meaning.

EXERCISE In the following sentences, underline the complete subject once and the complete predicate twice. Then, circle and label the simple subject (SS) and the simple predicate (SP).

Example 1. The small, isolated nation of Iceland is a republic with a long and proud history.

SS SP

1. Before the tenth century, not many foreigners had visited Iceland.
2. One of the early Norse settlers was Eric the Red.
3. A kind of parliament, the Althing was established in 930.
4. The island nation had much turmoil in its early days.
5. The stories of early Icelanders are recorded in long narratives called *sagas*.
6. One famous saga is called the *Laxdaela Saga*.
7. Pirates from other countries often raided the coastal towns.
8. In the late 1800s, a measure of stability returned to the island.
9. For centuries, the small nation of Iceland remained under the Danish crown.
10. During World War II, the Allied forces sent troops to Iceland in case of a German attack.
11. Toward the end of the war came an almost unanimous Icelandic vote for independence from Denmark.
12. The people of Iceland, nearly all highly literate, are some of the world's most avid readers.
13. The oldest book club in Iceland was founded in 1816.
14. The fishing industry is one of Iceland's most important.
15. Only about one fourth of the island is suitable for human habitation.
16. Many of Iceland's two hundred volcanoes are active to this day.
17. In 1963, a new island was formed by volcanoes off the southern coast.
18. The island was named Surtsey after Sutur, the god of fire in Icelandic mythology.
19. Deep canyons, called *fjords*, cut into the island's coasts.
20. The island's residents sometimes keep warm in the natural hot springs.

Copyright © by Holt, Rinehart and Winston. All rights reserved.

Compound Subjects and Verbs A

2e. A ***compound subject*** consists of two or more subjects that are joined by a conjunction and that have the same verb.

2f. A ***compound verb*** consists of two or more verbs that are joined by a conjunction and that have the same subject.

COMPOUND SUBJECT **Terence, Michelle,** and **Alan** are going to be late.

COMPOUND VERB They **had stopped** and **bought** flowers on their way.

EXERCISE A In the following sentences, underline the compound subjects.

Example 1. Phillip, Kate, and Spot left an hour ago.

1. Chocolate and strawberry are the two flavors available.
2. Jim, his sister, Louise, and I went to the Grand Canyon.
3. Will the Cougars or the Rockets win the regional championship?
4. Jennifer and Amy took the couch, the bookshelf, and the floor lamp.
5. Carter and his dog swam across the lake.
6. My ankle and knee ache because of the workout.
7. The reporter and his editor discussed the committee's findings.
8. Wind and rain, not to mention hail, made the trip hazardous.
9. In the meantime, Kenny and I put on our hats and boots.
10. Eugene, Noah, Harold, Louis, Glen, and Paul slept on the bus.

EXERCISE B In the following sentences, underline the compound verbs.

Example 1. Would you rather run or swim today?

11. The quarterback passed the football and ran for more than 200 yards.
12. Can your cat meow and purr at the same time?
13. Carla took the money and flew to Hawaii for a much-needed vacation.
14. Kelly will study and memorize the material.
15. My brother found an old radio and donated it to the Salvation Army.

Copyright © by Holt, Rinehart and Winston. All rights reserved.

GRAMMAR

NAME ______________________ CLASS ______________ DATE ______________

Compound Subjects and Verbs B

2e. A ***compound subject*** consists of two or more subjects that are joined by a conjunction and that have the same verb.

2f. A ***compound verb*** consists of two or more verbs that are joined by a conjunction and that have the same subject.

COMPOUND SUBJECT **Glenda** and **Tido** had a great time at the club's annual banquet.

COMPOUND VERB They **ate** dinner, **watched** the awards ceremony, and **spoke** to the president of the club.

EXERCISE In the following sentences, underline the compound subjects once and the compound verbs twice.

Example 1. The trials and tribulations they endured did not frighten or deter them.

1. Did you and Carla fly or drive to New Mexico?
2. Bob and his father ate heartily and enjoyed themselves at the Thanksgiving dinner.
3. Sally and I knocked on the door and called through the window.
4. Paper clips and rubber bands bind and organize my documents and notes.
5. He or she should not add or delete any information in this essay.
6. When did James and Brooke win the tennis match and advance to the next level?
7. Before the game, the coach and the players stretched and waited in the locker room.
8. Gabe, Rochine, and the other club members planned and organized the awards ceremony.
9. Would you and your brother rather prepare lunch or wash the dishes?
10. In the triathlon, professional athletes and novice competitors run, bike, and swim.
11. My brother and my father both went to Yale and studied architecture.
12. Violet and sage are my favorite colors and appear in most of my artwork.
13. My cousin and I mostly slept and watched TV.
14. From the top of the volcano, lava and ash surged and threatened the campers.
15. Jake and I found the fossil and gave it to the geology teacher.
16. Jennifer, Darla, Sandi, and Ben are competing and have been selected as our four finalists.
17. In the gymnasium, retired teachers and former students congregated and conversed.
18. Both Wyoming and Idaho have rugged terrain and are great camping destinations.
19. The employees and volunteers must wipe and polish every single statue in the exhibit.
20. Will you and your twin brother please be quiet during the movie or go outside to play?

Copyright © by Holt, Rinehart and Winston. All rights reserved.

Finding Subjects in Sentences

To find the subject of a sentence, ask *Who?* or *What?* before the verb.

EXAMPLES The **train** was delayed. [What was delayed? The *train* was delayed.]
Anna and Paul voted for me. [Who voted for me? *Anna and Paul* voted for me.]
Go to your room! [Who should go? The understood *you* should go.]

EXERCISE In the following sentences, underline each simple subject and indicate whether it answers the question *Who?* or *What?* If the understood *you* is the subject, write *you* after the sentence.

Example 1. When is the varsity debate team leaving town? *Who*

1. A partial eclipse of the moon will take place tonight.
2. Carry the books, please.
3. What year did your cousin buy his new computer?
4. A panel of experts oversaw the research.
5. From the crashing waves came a veteran surfer.
6. Are these two coffee mugs clean?
7. My house is on Far West Boulevard.
8. Under the tree behind the house was Kerry's missing bicycle.
9. As for the old tenement building, several influential council members want it destroyed.
10. Hand that eraser to me, please.
11. Many classic lunchboxes from the '60s are now very valuable.
12. Before the meeting, however, no one on the team had met the volunteers.
13. During the first part of the century, my great-grandmother on my mother's side worked as a nurse.
14. The condition of the garment was very poor.
15. Last winter, my brothers made several huge snowmen.
16. Here is your new semester class schedule.
17. Are these books on the front shelf for sale?
18. Last night at the track meet, Amy got a first-place trophy.
19. According to the legend in the fairy tale book, the brave and honest knight triumphed.
20. Growing three inches in one year is no surprise for Tom.

Copyright © by Holt, Rinehart and Winston. All rights reserved.

GRAMMAR

Complements

2g. A ***complement*** is a word or word group that completes the meaning of a verb.

Complements may be nouns, pronouns, or adjectives. Be careful not to mistake an adverb for a complement. The object of a prepositional phrase is not a complement.

COMPLEMENT	John Irving and Alice Walker are **novelists.**
ADVERB	The firefighter acted **bravely.**
OBJECT OF A PREPOSITION	The audience cheered for the **cast** during three curtain calls.

EXERCISE Identify the underlined word in each of the following sentences as a complement, an adverb, or the object of a preposition. Write *C* for *complement, A* for *adverb,* or *OP* for *object of a preposition.*

Example 1. Susan reacted modestly when she was presented an award.

1. Managing money and being financially responsible are challenging goals.

2. Courage under stress is essential for an emergency-rescue worker.

3. Rafael considered carefully his choices of universities to attend in the fall.

[illegible] The journalist's reasons were many for keeping his inside sources confidential.

[illegible] [illegible]id Mariah speak calmly during the debate round?

6. [illegible]e Koran is the sacred scripture of the Muslim faith.

7. T[illegible] list of prizes for the geography quiz show seems quite impressive.

8. Th[illegible] sent me the information in the mail.

9. My [illegible]vorite documentary show on PBS starts at eight o'clock in the evening.

10. I thin[illegible] drew the peach accurately in my still-life drawing class.

11. It seem[illegible] that the trouble with the car is the transmission.

12. Did she throw the ball perfectly into the hoop in the last quarter of the game?

13. Through the front door the hornets flew in a whirlwind.

14. I gave my book to Ralph's sister to read during her bus trip.

15. My mom bought contact lenses for me when I joined the basketball team.

16. I left the faucet running in the upstairs bathtub this morning!

17. Why not take the book with you to school?

18. The judge declared her candidacy for state office.

19. Your dad seems happy that he won the amateur golf tournament.

20. Until recently, Joe drove his truck to Philadelphia at the end of each month.

Copyright © by Holt, Rinehart and Winston. All rights reserved.

Direct Objects

2h. A ***direct object*** is a complement that tells who or what receives the action of a verb or shows the result of the action.

A direct object may be a noun, a pronoun, or a word group that functions as a noun. To find a direct object, ask *Whom?* or *What?* after a transitive verb. Direct objects may be compound.

DIRECT OBJECT Edgar chose the easiest **task.** [Chose what? *Task.*]

Your grandmother misses **you and your sister.** [Misses whom? *You and your sister.*]

EXERCISE Underline the direct objects in the following sentences. Then, indicate whether the direct object answers *Whom?* or *What?*

Example 1. Will this class include a section on short-film production? (what)

1. John Le Carré writes suspenseful spy stories about international intrigue.
2. You are eating a nutritious meal this morning.
3. Elizabeth sold me her computer for a very reasonable price.
4. Ramón entertained Sam and me with an account of his vacation.
5. Andrés Segovia transcribed pages of classical music for the guitar.
6. After a lengthy campaign process, the students elected Miguel.
7. Doing word puzzles makes Tien and his grandfather happy.
8. Ms. Hamilton appointed Bill and me.
9. You may pick up an information sheet at the front desk.
10. Open this envelope and please read it to me.
11. Ted and I will carry the tent during the weekend camping trip.
12. Before the storm, we all filled sandbags.
13. Please sign your name at the bottom of the registration form.
14. Lindsey received her pilot's license last year.
15. Miss Webber has canceled the meeting of the student dance committee.
16. Karen left her coat in Mr. Singh's restaurant the other night.
17. Did Tina and Tranh finish Ms. Yanez's homework?
18. A robin has built its nest on the stone ledge outside my window.
19. Unfortunately, I have lost my mother's car keys again!
20. The flamenco dancer from Paraguay practiced his dance steps last night before the show.

Copyright © by Holt, Rinehart and Winston. All rights reserved.

Indirect Objects

2i. An ***indirect object*** is a complement that often appears in sentences containing direct objects and that tells *to whom* or *to what* or *for whom* or *for what* the action of a transitive verb is done.

An indirect object may be a noun, a pronoun, or a word group that functions as a noun. To find an indirect object, ask *To whom?* or *To what?* or *For whom?* or *For what?* after a transitive verb. Indirect objects may be compound.

INDIRECT OBJECT Mother gave **me** the rest of the chores. [Gave the rest of the chores to whom? *Me.*]

EXERCISE Underline the indirect object(s) in each of the following sentences. Then, circle the direct object(s) of each sentence.

Example 1. Perhaps your English teacher would write you a letter of recommendation.

1. Would you lend me your umbrella?
2. I sent Bill and Norine a card for their anniversary.
3. At Thanksgiving, I gave my aunt a basket of fruit and some flowers.
4. Please lend Allison your sheet music for that chorus.
5. Did Mr. Terry write you a dramatic role in the school play?
6. Maria taught her family's dogs some clever tricks.
7. I am sure we can find Al a tennis racket.
8. Raul assigned me the role of secretary.
9. Derrick offered the three of us tickets to the school concert.
10. After three months of procrastination, Lani finally sent Janet a letter.
11. I picked my mom a bouquet of flowers for her birthday.
12. The chef offered everyone bread, cheese, and fruit after dinner.
13. Worrying about his college entrance exam gave Arthur headaches.
14. Can you and your sister show Dora the right bus?
15. Clara built her older sister's children a treehouse in the backyard.
16. Samuel gave our hiking group detailed directions to the campsite.
17. The judges awarded Tina the first-place prize in the spelling competition even though she could not attend the ceremony.
18. My veterinarian gave my cat a fuzzy new toy.
19. His adventure in Mr. McGregor's garden taught Peter Rabbit a lesson.
20. Ilse brought our entire family some Christmas gifts from Germany.

Copyright © by Holt, Rinehart and Winston. All rights reserved.

Objective Complements

2j. An ***objective complement*** is a complement that helps complete the meaning of a transitive verb by identifying or modifying the direct object.

An objective complement may be a noun, a pronoun, an adjective, or a word group that functions as a noun or an adjective. Only a few verbs take objective complements. These verbs are *consider, make,* and any verbs that can be replaced by *consider* or *make,* such as *appoint, believe, call, find, keep, name, choose, elect, paint, render,* and *sweep.* An objective complement may be compound.

EXAMPLES I consider Jane my closest **friend.**

The article called Andrew Jackson **energetic** and **self-confident.**

EXERCISE Underline the objective complement(s) in each of the following sentences.

Example 1. Did they name Joyce secretary and treasurer of the committee?

1. I find his collection of antiques outstanding.
2. Would you call her actions heroic or foolish?
3. Her dazzling performance as Joan of Arc rendered the audience speechless.
4. We must consider the defendants innocent unless we can prove them otherwise.
5. The novelist made his villain dynamic and enigmatic.
6. In his recommendation, Mr. Gatwood, my English teacher, called me hard-working and conscientious.
7. Hillary painted her clay sculpture indigo, tangerine, and bright green.
8. The governor named Lisa her personal assistant during the campaign.
9. I found the story of the Trail of Tears sad and moving.
10. Will they elect Jeffrey treasurer for a second term?
11. We consider Terence's behavior authentic and inspiring.
12. I find cooking, which is one of my favorite hobbies, challenging and creative.
13. The critics called her performance spontaneous and funny.
14. I made the chili mildly spicy just for you.
15. That conversation made me happy about my choice of university.
16. After his comedy routine in the cafeteria, we voted Charlie class clown.
17. The court's ruling rendered that law virtually unenforceable.
18. I found that kind of glue ineffective for building model airplanes.
19. Do you think this gift appropriate for a graduation party?
20. Most of the viewers found the global-travel series fascinating and informative.

Copyright © by Holt, Rinehart and Winston. All rights reserved.

Complements

2h. A ***direct object*** is a complement that tells who or what receives the action of a verb or shows the result of the action.

2i. An ***indirect object*** is a complement that often appears in sentences containing direct objects and that tells *to whom* or *to what* or *for whom* or *for what* the action of a transitive verb is done.

2j. An ***objective complement*** is a complement that helps complete the meaning of a transitive verb by identifying or modifying the direct object.

EXERCISE In the following sentences, underline each direct object once, underline each indirect object twice, and circle each objective complement.

Example 1. My mother, a zoologist, often tells me obscure facts about animals.

1. I find these stories fascinating.
2. She told me one about the blue-ringed octopus.
3. She called the small creature "dangerous."
4. The poison from a tiny, blue-ringed octopus could kill a person.
5. My mom gave me a book with more interesting animal trivia.
6. Some hummingbirds beat their wings eighty times a second.
7. A 4,000-pound hippopotamus can outrun a human.
8. A python in Indonesia once ate a fourteen-year-old boy.
9. Scientists consider the whale shark the largest fish in the world.
10. Experts gave the world's biggest frog the name "Goliath."
11. The hefty amphibian tips the scales at about seven pounds.
12. My husky cat Shadow gives Goliath a challenge, though.
13. My mom calls Shadow a "big but agile" kitty.
14. We usually feed him special dry cat food or tuna.
15. We consider Shadow a beloved and valued member of the family.
16. Sometimes I walk my big kitty on a generous leash.
17. He's not happy about the leash, but he accepts it.
18. I gave my dearest friend, Kim, a tiny kitten for her most recent birthday.
19. Much to my dismay, she named the feisty tabby Torvald.
20. What name would you give a cat?

Copyright © by Holt, Rinehart and Winston. All rights reserved.

Predicate Nominatives

2k(1). A ***predicate nominative*** identifies or refers to the subject of a linking verb.

A predicate nominative may be a noun, a pronoun, or a word group that functions as a noun. Predicate nominatives may be compound.

PREDICATE NOMINATIVE A college degree is a lifelong **asset.**

EXERCISE Underline the predicate nominative in each of the following sentences.

Example 1. The purpose of the painting exercise is to paint outside the lines.

1. Troy is a carpenter of the highest level.
2. Laura will be captain and manager of the team while I am away.
3. Who was the President of the United States in 1916?
4. The things that got us through the competition were hope and hard work.
5. This is a mystery to me!
6. The first ones in line were Bill, Grace, and Albert.
7. That noise must have been the wind whipping at the shutters.
8. Is Kevin a drummer, guitarist, and vocalist?
9. My uncle is the principal of a high school in Georgia.
10. My favorite places to go on vacation are Virginia Beach and Martha's Vineyard.
11. This is the way home from the stadium.
12. Our dog Cora is a mother of five puppies.
13. The winner of the chess tournament was she.
14. The eldest of our three parrots is Edgar.
15. The book we found on the bench is hers.
16. The only thing I want for my birthday is that.
17. The solution to this plant's problem is better security.
18. She became the new district attorney for the southern district.
19. One hindrance to completing the project was the dean's opposition.
20. This is the last exercise we have to complete.

Copyright © by Holt, Rinehart and Winston. All rights reserved.

NAME _______________ CLASS _______________ DATE _______________

Predicate Adjectives

2k(2). A ***predicate adjective*** is an adjective that is in the predicate and that modifies the subject of a linking verb.

Predicate adjectives may be compound.

PREDICATE ADJECTIVES This week has been unusually **chilly** and **rainy.**

EXERCISE In each of the following sentences, underline the predicate adjectives.

Example 1. Worthy and precious is knowledge.

1. The sidewalk is always slippery right after a rain shower.
2. The darkness was impenetrable but oddly comforting.
3. The soil was too chalky to grow the crops we wanted.
4. The solution to Jake's problem was obvious to me.
5. It was foggy outside earlier, but now it is fine.
6. Astonished by the news of the election, Milly and I were absolutely ecstatic.
7. This puzzle is difficult to solve.
8. High, clear, and beautiful was her singing voice.
9. It is dark in the basement, so we should bring our flashlights.
10. Were you happy about the good fortune you had?
11. Our cat was tired and listless after the surgery.
12. My new dress is black-and-white striped and long.
13. My, how cheery Mr. Morris seems today!
14. Fragile and helpless were the newly hatched chicks.
15. These confetti eggs certainly are delicate and colorful!
16. Mike's story about his photo safari in Africa was quite captivating and inspiring.
17. The melted wax for the art project was sticky and gooey.
18. It is refreshing to go for a swim on such a hot and humid afternoon.
19. The librarian said that the old textbook is excellent and thorough as a reference.
20. Their negligence in this case was not surprising, considering their busy schedules.

Copyright © by Holt, Rinehart and Winston. All rights reserved.

Predicate Nominatives and Adjectives

2k(1). A ***predicate nominative*** identifies or refers to the subject of a linking verb.

A predicate nominative may be a noun, a pronoun, or a word group that functions as a noun.

2k(2). A ***predicate adjective*** is an adjective that is in the predicate and that modifies the subject of a linking verb.

Predicate nominatives and predicate adjectives may be compound.

PREDICATE NOMINATIVE He was a **hero.**

PREDICATE ADJECTIVES The landscape was **yellow, green,** and **blue.**

EXERCISE In each of the following sentences, underline any predicate nominative(s) once and any predicate adjective(s) twice.

Example 1. Adrian is not only creative, but she is also a brilliant mathematician.

1. In 1776, Patrick Henry became the first governor of Virginia.
2. The Wren Building is the oldest building on campus.
3. The gust of wind felt icy against our unprotected faces.
4. Geographically, Alaska is the largest state in the United States.
5. Tony must have been nervous before that interview.
6. Willis appeared disoriented and dazed when he walked into the room.
7. The bite of a tarantula can be painful.
8. The next captain of our soccer team will be either Julia or I.
9. This year, Mr. Pinkham's sociology course is my favorite class.
10. How delicious this soup tastes!
11. Suddenly I was the center of attention.
12. For me, acting is exciting and fulfilling.
13. On our soccer team, Alex always seems most daring.
14. Is she a crossing guard?
15. Sandy and Dave were lucky and grateful this time.
16. This after-school job is a great responsibility.
17. Are you excited about something?
18. This folder is too flimsy; a sturdy one would be better.
19. I may be shy, but I am not frightened.
20. Such lively cities are New York and New Orleans.

Copyright © by Holt, Rinehart and Winston. All rights reserved.

Parts of a Sentence

EXERCISE For each of the following sentences, identify whether the underlined word is a subject (S), a verb (V), a direct object (DO), an indirect object (IO), an objective complement (OC), a predicate nominative (PN), or a predicate adjective (PA).

Example **1.** A Fulbright grant can open a person's eyes to a larger world. S

1. My sister won a Fulbright when she graduated from college.

2. She was the only Fulbright winner at her school.

3. For one year, the program allowed her to live and study in Germany.

4. She studied European history at a university in Marburg.

5. She tells everyone she meets that she loved it.

6. She found the city of Marburg charming.

7. The U.S. Congress started the program in 1946.

8. It helps promote cultural exchange and mutual understanding between the United States and other nations.

9. Thousands of Americans have studied in more than one hundred nations thanks to the Fulbright.

10. J. William Fulbright was the senator who sponsored the legislation.

11. He was popular in his home state of Arkansas.

12. He gave the nation a great gift.

13. My sister considers the German language somewhat guttural.

14. The Spanish language is very beautiful to my ear.

15. "Educational exchange can turn nations into people."

16. My sister told me that quote is from Senator Fulbright.

17. The program sponsors students, artists, and professionals.

18. It is interesting to learn about other countries.

19. Someday, I will be a world traveler.

20. Are you going to apply for a Fulbright?

Copyright © by Holt, Rinehart and Winston. All rights reserved.

NAME ______ CLASS ______ DATE ______

Review A: Fragments and Complete Sentences

EXERCISE Identify each of the following items as a complete sentence (S) or as a sentence fragment (F). If an item is a sentence fragment, add, change, or delete words to make it a complete sentence.

Example 1. Inside the heavy-duty carton, the fragile but intact egg. *(F) Inside the heavy-duty carton, the fragile but intact egg sat.*

1. Late for the plane to Chicago. ______

2. It left without me! ______

3. Of course now the meeting in Chicago about a new toothpaste for whiter teeth. ______

4. Food at the airport is expensive. ______

5. Eight dollars for a hamburger! ______

6. While waiting at my gate, an old friend from high school. ______

7. We went to the prom together. ______

8. The rented limousine with the sunroof and the windows heavily tinted. ______

9. Matching my vest to her dress color and all of that fuss. ______

10. She now pilots helicopters. ______

Copyright © by Holt, Rinehart and Winston. All rights reserved.

NAME CLASS DATE

Review B: Sentence Parts

EXERCISE The following sentences contain at least one complement. Underline each complement and indicate what kind of complement each one is. Use the following abbreviations: *DO* for direct object, *PN* for predicate nominative, *OC* for objective complement, *IO* for indirect object, or *PA* for predicate adjective.

Example 1. At the Munich conference of 1938, France and Great Britain gave Hitler (IO) a number (DO) of concessions.

1. Nazi Germany had threatened an armed invasion of Czechoslovakia.
2. Hitler wanted the Sudetenland, a highly industrialized region of Czechoslovakia.
3. The Sudetenland was the land near the border of Germany and Czechoslovakia.
4. The unification of the German people under one flag was the excuse presented by Hitler for this demand.
5. The majority of the inhabitants of the Sudetenland were Germans.
6. Hitler considered the Sudetenland part of Germany.
7. France and Britain were uneasy about Nazi Germany's demands for territory.
8. However, the French and the British remembered vividly the terrible destruction of World War I.
9. Therefore, they made the annexation of the Sudetenland possible.
10. British Prime Minister Neville Chamberlain and French Premier Édouard Daladier met Hitler in Munich and gave him everything he wanted.
11. Hitler gave them his word that Germany's aggressive expansion would cease.
12. Within a few months, however, German troops occupied the rest of Czechoslovakia.
13. Poland's treatment at the hands of the Nazis was similar.
14. On September 1, 1939, Nazi Germany invaded Poland.
15. The German "blitzkrieg" strategy left Poland little chance.
16. The country's flat terrain made the Germans' new tactic very successful.
17. The German tactic dealt the Poles an overwhelming defeat.
18. The Germans and their ally the Soviet Union divided Poland between them.
19. Hitler's Germany scored important early victories against the Czechs and the Poles.
20. War between Germany on one side and Britain and France on the other soon became inevitable.

Copyright © by Holt, Rinehart and Winston. All rights reserved.

Review C: Sentence Parts

EXERCISE Identify whether the underlined word in each of the following sentences is a subject (S), a verb (V), a direct object (DO), an indirect object (IO), an objective complement (OC), a predicate nominative (PN), or a predicate adjective (PA).

Example 1. I enjoy classical music. DO

1. Aaron Copland is my favorite composer.
2. One of Copland's highest achievements, *Appalachian Spring,* is a ballet.
3. The versatile Copland wrote songs in many styles.
4. Last week I bought a Philip Glass CD.
5. A serious composer, Glass has also written TV jingles and film scores.
6. My friend Lenny told me Glass's music is very hypnotic.
7. Glass is more popular than many of his contemporaries.
8. Glass's style is usually referred to as "minimalism."
9. Along with Robert Wilson, Glass produced the four-hour opera *Einstein on the Beach.*
10. As a would-be composer, I consider his music inspiring.
11. Right now, I am taking guitar lessons and listening to different styles of music.
12. I enjoy classical music, rock, and jazz.
13. My guitar teacher gave me a book about scales and chords.
14. I hope to memorize all the scales by the end of the year.
15. Judging by the complexity of the fingering patterns, this is going to be a difficult task.
16. It should be less difficult than learning the violin!
17. My grandfather was a violinist.
18. I think my love of music comes from him.
19. Thinking about him keeps me enthusiastic about learning guitar.
20. Music has helped me become a more well-rounded human being.

Copyright © by Holt, Rinehart and Winston. All rights reserved.

Review D: Sentence Parts

EXERCISE A Decide whether each of the following items is a sentence (S) or a sentence fragment (F).

Example 1. Did their new custom van with the shiny chrome wheel rims? *(F)*

1. She left.

2. My friend from Birmingham, Alabama, with the pickup truck and the dog named Dan.

3. Get on Interstate 35 and then take the Palmer Lane exit.

4. A few of them over near the bus station.

5. When you consider the options, the solution seems obvious.

EXERCISE B In each of the following sentences, underline the complete subject once and the complete predicate twice. Circle and label the simple subject (SS) and simple predicate (SP).

Example 1. I voted for the man with the best record and the most integrity. *(SS: I; SP: voted)*

6. The drive from here to Phoenix is long and desolate.

7. Did the truck arrive at the depot?

8. We moved across the bridge to the other side of town last year.

9. Many of the builders who worked on the project became ill.

10. Kayaking is an immensely enjoyable sport.

EXERCISE C Identify the underlined word(s) in each of the following sentences as a subject (S), a verb (V), a direct object (DO), an indirect object (IO), an objective complement (OC), a predicate nominative (PN), or a predicate adjective (PA).

Example 1. The temperature in the room was ten degrees above normal. *(S)*

11. People from the neighboring village gave Lewis some corn and water.

12. Out of the cave came a giant bear with a steady gaze and quick gait.

13. All of the pilots were trained on flight simulators.

14. A triple play in baseball is a very rare feat.

15. My dog is much smarter than most animals.

16. Eddie's plan simply will take some hard work.

17. We received eight dollars for mowing Mr. Crabtree's backyard.

18. The doctor's poor handwriting made the prescription indecipherable.

19. The brother of the former president sings at special occasions.

20. The top surgeon at our local hospital is also an excellent singer.

Copyright © by Holt, Rinehart and Winston. All rights reserved.

Identifying Phrases

3a. A ***phrase*** is a group of related words that is used as a single part of speech and that does not contain both a verb and its subject.

PREPOSITIONAL PHRASE Several accidents occurred **over the weekend.** [*Over the weekend* is used as an adverb modifying the verb *occurred.*]

VERBAL PHRASE **Standing at the podium,** Jalen practiced his speech. [*Standing at the podium* is used as an adjective modifying the noun *Jalen.*]

APPOSITIVE PHRASE **The first in line,** Mia bought two tickets. [*The first in line* identifies the noun *Mia.*]

EXERCISE A On each of the lines provided below, write *P* if the underlined word group is a phrase and *NP* if it is not a phrase.

Example __P__ 1. We have finally discovered the secret of delicious pizza.

_____ 1. Last Friday evening, we decided to make our own pizza.

_____ 2. We thought pizza, my favorite food, would be easy to make.

_____ 3. We found a recipe book, dog-eared and worn, and turned the pages.

_____ 4. Mixing the dough was the first task that gave us trouble.

_____ 5. It was hard to measure just the right amount of flour, and the dough became sticky.

_____ 6. The dough, sticking to the countertop, didn't rise as the cookbook said it should.

_____ 7. We pressed the lumpy mass into the pizza pan anyway and forged on.

_____ 8. When we took the mozzarella out of the refrigerator, we saw that it had grown mold.

_____ 9. Frustrated by too many problems, we dumped our "creation" into the garbage can.

_____ 10. For us, the easiest way to get the perfect pizza is to call the local pizza place and then wait for the delivery person!

EXERCISE B For each of the following sentences, write a phrase that correctly completes the sentence.

Example 1. Ms. Goldstein, __my next-door neighbor__, is running in a marathon next week.

11. ______________________, we rushed toward the burning bridge.

12. The chipmunk quickly ran ______________________.

13. I have promised Laura ______________________.

14. That old convertible, ______________________, could run if we replaced its transmission.

15. ______________________ is more difficult than it looks.

Copyright © by Holt, Rinehart and Winston. All rights reserved.

NAME ________________ CLASS ________________ DATE ________________

Prepositional Phrases

3b. A ***prepositional phrase*** includes a preposition, the object of the preposition, and any modifiers of that object.

EXAMPLES The bloodhounds tracked the criminal **through the thick, still woods.** [The noun *woods* is the object of the preposition *through.*]

According to this article, the highway will be completed soon. [The noun *article* is the object of the compound preposition *According to.*]

EXERCISE A Underline each prepositional phrase in the following sentences. If a sentence does not contain a prepositional phrase, write *none* on the line provided.

Example ______ **1.** It is a well-known fact that camels can go many days without water.

______ **1.** Many people used to believe that camels stored water in their humps.

______ **2.** In 1954 a research team set out to study the camel's water-storing capacities.

______ **3.** The results of their research indicated, surprisingly, that a camel does not actually store extra water.

______ **4.** Instead, the camel's body conserves the water that it contains.

______ **5.** Human beings and many other animals must depend on an evaporation process to keep their body temperatures constant.

______ **6.** When a horse is hot, it perspires, and the evaporation of this water cools its body.

______ **7.** A camel's body temperature, however, need not remain constant.

______ **8.** Therefore, a camel rarely needs to expend precious water on any cooling system.

______ **9.** During a long, hot day, a camel's temperature may rise ten degrees, but the animal does not suffer any ill effects.

______ **10.** Can you imagine having a temperature of 108 degrees and feeling healthy?

EXERCISE B For each item, use the nouns in parentheses to write a sentence that gives directions for putting away groceries. Do not use any verb or preposition more than once.

Example 1. (pasta, pantry) *Store the pasta in the pantry.*

11. (coffee, canister) ______________________________

12. (cinnamon, spice rack) ______________________________

13. (detergent, sink) ______________________________

14. (split peas, shelf) ______________________________

15. (vitamins, medicine cabinet) ______________________________

Copyright © by Holt, Rinehart and Winston. All rights reserved.

The Adjective Phrase

3c. A prepositional phrase that modifies a noun or a pronoun is called an ***adjective phrase.***

EXAMPLE Someone **from the American Red Cross** will give a presentation **about disaster preparedness.** [*From the American Red Cross* modifies the pronoun *Someone. About disaster preparedness* modifies the noun *presentation.*]

EXERCISE A Underline the adjective phrase in each of the following sentences. Then, circle the word or words it modifies.

Example 1. The (sense) <u>of smell</u> can evoke old memories.

1. I remember Grandmother when I smell freshly baked bread with butter.
2. The aroma of my grandmother's baking was often strong.
3. When I was young, Grandmother let me help make soft rolls with butter.
4. She also made breads such as wheat rolls and cranberry muffins.
5. Grandfather would say that his favorite of all the rolls was the batch I had helped to make.
6. I remember the tickle of flour and baking powder when I breathed it in.
7. My grandmother would say that I was the "best baker of the bunch."
8. Now, years later, the smell of rising bread brings back these memories.
9. I can almost see Grandmother wearing her dress with the roses.
10. Whenever I get the chance, I bake one of Grandmother's specialties.

EXERCISE B On the lines below, rewrite each sentence by adding an adjective phrase that modifies the underlined word.

Example 1. Giuli followed the <u>trail</u>. *Giuli followed the trail of stone markers.*

11. The trail led to a <u>hilltop</u>. _______________

____

12. Giuli could see the <u>town</u>. _______________

____

13. <u>Lights</u> were flickering. _______________

____

14. The setting sun illuminated the <u>horizon</u>. _______________

____

15. Giuli rested and watched the <u>meadow</u>. _______________

____

Copyright © by Holt, Rinehart and Winston. All rights reserved.

The Adverb Phrase

3d. A prepositional phrase that modifies a verb, an adjective, or an adverb is called an ***adverb phrase.***

EXAMPLES **After school** I rode my bicycle **to the neighborhood park.** [The adverb phrases *After school* and *to the neighborhood park* modify the verb *rode.*]

Early **on that cold, gray morning** the ship left the harbor. [The adverb phrase *on that cold, gray morning* modifies the adverb *Early.*]

EXERCISE A Underline the adverb phrase in each of the following sentences. Then, draw a circle around the word or words it modifies.

Example 1. Many teenagers work part-time during high school.

1. Some work at fast food restaurants, while others work outdoors.
2. One important skill students learn at part-time jobs is communication.
3. Students can earn extra cash and experience at a part-time job.
4. Those who contribute to a savings account regularly can watch their money grow quickly.
5. Throughout the nation, many teens have career-related part-time jobs.
6. Students may find career-related jobs in a vocational catalogue.
7. Students can check with their guidance counselors, who will help them investigate possibilities.
8. A student who wants to study veterinary medicine could work for a local veterinarian.
9. Students who hope to practice law someday could volunteer at the attorney general's office.
10. Any part-time job can be helpful for the future.

EXERCISE B Complete each sentence by adding an adverb phrase that answers the question posed in the parentheses.

Example 1. *(Why?)* Mircea bought an inexpensive camera for her beach trip.

11. *(When?)* Did you ask Cooper to help us __________.
12. *(How?)* Call your cousin __________.
13. *(How far?)* Drew pitched the ball __________.
14. *(Where?)* We saw the fire trucks __________.
15. *(To what extent?)* I tried __________.

Copyright © by Holt, Rinehart and Winston. All rights reserved.

Identifying Adjective and Adverb Phrases

3c. A prepositional phrase that modifies a noun or a pronoun is called an ***adjective phrase.***

EXAMPLE The irises **of her mysterious eyes** are flecked with gold. [The adjective phrase *of her mysterious eyes* modifies the noun *irises.*]

3d. A prepositional phrase that modifies a verb, an adjective, or an adverb is called an ***adverb phrase.***

EXAMPLE The politician talked **with eloquence and animation.** [The adverb phrase *with eloquence and animation* modifies the verb *talked.*]

EXERCISE A For each of the following sentences, draw an arrow from the underlined prepositional phrase to the word that it modifies. Then, identify the underlined phrase by writing *ADJ* for *adjective phrase* or *ADV* for *adverb phrase* on the line provided.

Example ADV 1. My little cousin speaks clearly for a two-year-old.

_____ **1.** The ice on the plane's wings made the mechanics uneasy.

_____ **2.** Ariadne spoke with great confidence and enthusiasm about her favorite subject, fishing.

_____ **3.** Throughout the school year, Ms. Cruz has tracked the students' progress.

_____ **4.** Is Mr. Toyoda still active in local politics?

_____ **5.** A large group of uniformed six-year-olds descended upon the shrine.

EXERCISE B In the parentheses following each sentence, a type of phrase is identified. Locate and underline that type of phrase in the sentence.

Example 1. Golf is a popular sport with a long history. *(adjective)*

6. Golf balls have changed a lot over the years. *(adverb)*

7. The earliest balls were made of wood. *(adverb)*

8. The first big breakthrough in golf balls was the "feathery" ball. *(adjective)*

9. This ball debuted in the early seventeenth century. *(adverb)*

10. "Featheries" were tightly stuffed, as you might guess, with feathers that had been boiled. *(adverb)*

11. By the mid-nineteenth century, the gutta-percha ball was being used. *(adverb)*

12. Gutta-percha is a latex of several South American and South Pacific island trees. *(adjective)*

13. Gutta-percha balls, unfortunately, were hard, brittle, and difficult to get into the air. *(adverb)*

14. The rubber ball, which was invented early in the twentieth century, provided better control. *(adverb)*

15. Because of the rubber ball, many more people began playing golf. *(adverb)*

Copyright © by Holt, Rinehart and Winston. All rights reserved.

NAME CLASS DATE

The Participle

3e. A ***participle*** is a verb form that can be used as an adjective.

(1) Present participles end in *–ing.*

EXAMPLES No one could comfort the **crying** baby. [*Crying* modifies the noun *baby.*]

Smiling broadly, Josh handed her the flowers. [*Smiling* modifies the noun *Josh.*]

(2) Most past participles end in *–d* or *–ed.* Others are irregularly formed.

EXAMPLES The money **raised** by the band members will help pay for the trip. [*Raised* modifies the noun *money.*]

The **fallen** leader was later forced to leave the country. [*Fallen* modifies the noun *leader.*]

EXERCISE A Underline the participle in each of the following sentences. Then, write above it *present* for a present participle or *past* for a past participle.

Example 1. Smiling children are easy to photograph. *(present)*

1. Working as a children's photographer is a challenging job.

2. On some charmed days, all the children who come in for pictures are happy and cooperative.

3. Their faces light up when I show them a stuffed animal, and the pictures are keepers.

4. Their delighted parents happily order photos for family and friends.

5. On the frustrating days, however, the children cry and complain.

6. My annoyed assistant tempts them with promises of a treat after the photo session.

7. Sometimes this bribery calms a crying child.

8. Sometimes the despairing parents must take the child home without having pictures made.

9. I remind them that another day will be the perfect time to photograph their fussing baby.

10. In the end, this rewarding job never ceases to surprise me!

EXERCISE B Complete each of the following sentences by adding a modifying participle above the caret. Use the verb provided in parentheses to form the participle.

Example 1. The ^ traffic intimidated the new drivers. (*rush*) *(rushing)*

11. Sean ignored the ^ passengers in the backseat. (*fidget*)

12. He carefully checked the ^ traffic behind him. (*adjust*)

13. "Let the fire truck pass," came an ^ word from one of the passengers. (*advise*)

14. With ^ lights, the fire truck drove past. (*flash*)

15. Finally, Sean merged slowly into the ^ traffic. (*congest*)

Copyright © by Holt, Rinehart and Winston. All rights reserved.

The Participial Phrase

3f. A ***participial phrase*** consists of a participle and its modifiers and complements. The entire phrase is used as an adjective.

EXAMPLES **Making their way through the thick brush,** the hikers soon grew tired. [The participial phrase modifies the noun *hikers*.]

The trophy **won by the volleyball team** will be displayed in the lobby. [The participial phrase modifies the noun *trophy*.]

An *absolute phrase* consists of (1) a participle or a participial phrase, (2) a noun or a pronoun that the participle or participial phrase modifies, and (3) any other modifiers of that noun or pronoun. The entire word group is used as an adverb to modify a clause.

EXAMPLE **The weather being so dismal,** we decided to stay inside. [The participial phrase *being so dismal* modifies the noun *weather*. The entire absolute phrase modifies the independent clause *we decided to stay inside*, telling why we decided to stay inside.]

EXERCISE A Underline the participial phrase in each of the following sentences. Then, circle the word or words it modifies.

Example 1. A geological (formation) called Enchanted Rock has inspired several legends.

1. Located an hour or so from Austin, Texas, the domes of Enchanted Rock are batholiths, underground rock formations that erosion has slowly revealed.

2. Many years ago, Tonkawas living nearby said that a pale man had been swallowed by the rock and reborn as rock.

3. Ghostly lights sometimes flicker from the domes' surfaces—the pale man weaving enchantments, said the Tonkawa.

4. Today, visitors know that the lights come from water puddles reflecting moonlight.

5. Hiking the path to the summit, I am struck by the beauty of the rock.

EXERCISE B Underline the absolute phrase in each of the following sentences. Be prepared to tell how the phrase modifies the whole clause—does it tell *when*, *why*, or *how*?

Example 1. My feet having become tingly from the cold, I decided to go inside.

6. The clock striking the hour of noon, I thought that a brisk walk would be pleasant.

7. I bundled up and left the house, our excited dog straining at the leash.

8. The walk began beautifully, snow crunching underfoot.

9. We crossed the stream, the water rushing with new-melted snow.

10. Back at home, I relaxed by the fire, my hot chocolate steaming deliciously.

Copyright © by Holt, Rinehart and Winston. All rights reserved.

NAME ______________________ CLASS ______________ DATE ______________

Participles and Participial Phrases

3e. A ***participle*** is a verb form that can be used as an adjective.

EXAMPLES Several of the **falling** branches hit the house, but no damage was done. [*Falling* modifies the noun *branches*.]

Frightened by the noise, I looked up. [*Frightened* modifies the pronoun *I*.]

3f. A ***participial phrase*** consists of a participle and its modifiers and complements. The entire phrase is used as an adjective.

EXAMPLE The swimmer, **shaking with cold,** clambered out of the water. [*Shaking with cold* modifies the noun *swimmer*.]

EXERCISE A Complete each sentence by adding a participle or participial phrase. Use the verb indicated in parentheses to form the participle.

Example 1. Swinging gently, the ceiling fan spun slowly. *(Swing)*

1. The ____________ summer heat bore down. *(wilt)*
2. ____________, cicadas filled the trees. *(Hum)*
3. The glasses of ____________ lemonade sweated on the table. *(sweeten)*
4. All in all, it was a typical ____________ summer day. *(swelter)*
5. I escaped for a while into the ____________ cool water of the pool. *(refresh)*

EXERCISE B Underline the participial phrase in each of the following sentences. Then, draw an arrow from the participial phrase to the noun or pronoun it modifies.

Example 1. Down the alley came a large pickup truck loaded with boxes and furniture.

6. Clearing his throat, the tenor began his rehearsal.
7. The weary hikers spent the next night at a cabin stocked with food and blankets.
8. Moving with grace and stealth, the Siamese cat was stalking the mouse.
9. The sandwiches, shared with the children on the playground, provided a moment of peace for the teacher.
10. Checking her hair in the mirror, the actor practiced the first lines of her speech.
11. Repaired just weeks before, the radiator had developed yet another leak.
12. The German shepherd lying by that man's feet is a guide dog.
13. The head coach, discussing the call with the official, remained calm.
14. Ms. Ortiz whispered something to the lady sitting next to her.
15. The blankets piled on the bed are clean.

Copyright © by Holt, Rinehart and Winston. All rights reserved.

The Gerund

3g. A ***gerund*** is a verb form ending in *–ing* that is used as a noun.

Like nouns, gerunds can be used as subjects, direct objects, indirect objects, predicate nominatives, and objects of prepositions.

SUBJECT	**Diving** can be dangerous.
DIRECT OBJECT	Mattie has always enjoyed **jogging** in the park.
INDIRECT OBJECT	Always give **driving** your full attention.
PREDICATE NOMINATIVE	One of his favorite pastimes is **skiing.**
OBJECT OF A PREPOSITION	Make an outline before **drafting** your paper.

EXERCISE A In each sentence, underline the gerund. Above it, write *S* if it is a subject, *DO* if it is a direct object, *IO* if it is an indirect object, *PN* if it is a predicate nominative, or *OP* if it is an object of a preposition.

Example 1. People benefit from relaxing (OP) at the end of a busy day.

1. Choosing from among many refreshing activities can be difficult.

2. Some people enjoy gardening.

3. Others combine relaxation and health improvement by exercising.

4. Still others would far rather give playing chess their attention.

5. Reading continues to hold its own among leisure activities.

6. Since somebody has to make dinner anyway, one favorite hobby is cooking.

7. There will always be those who prefer watching television.

8. Chatting on the phone is a very popular activity, especially with cell phone use on the rise.

9. Simply enjoying conversation together is a critical part of most families' days.

10. Whatever people choose to do, developing a hobby can ease the day's stress, both physically and mentally.

EXERCISE B For each item below, write a sentence that uses a gerund formed from the verb provided.

Example 1. vote *Because voting is important to Al, he votes in every election.*

11. run ______

12. sing ______

13. divide ______

14. design ______

15. invent ______

Copyright © by Holt, Rinehart and Winston. All rights reserved.

NAME ______________________ CLASS ______________ DATE ______________

The Gerund Phrase

3h. A ***gerund phrase*** consists of a gerund and its modifiers and complements. The entire phrase is used as a noun.

EXAMPLES **Training your dog consistently** will improve your bond with the animal. [The gerund phrase is the subject of the verb phrase *will improve*. The noun *dog* is the direct object of the gerund *Training*. The adverb *consistently* modifies *Training*.]

What are some of the benefits of **spending time with pets?** [The gerund phrase is the object of the preposition *of*. The noun *time* is the direct object of the gerund *spending*. The adverb phrase *with pets* modifies *spending*.]

EXERCISE A In each sentence, underline the gerund phrase. Above it, write *S* if it is a subject, *DO* if it is a direct object, *IO* if it is an indirect object, *PN* if it is a predicate nominative, or *OP* if it is an object of a preposition.

Example 1. Recognizing cinema excellence is the goal of the Academy Awards. *S*

1. At the founding of the Academy of Motion Picture Arts and Sciences in 1927, Hollywood began to consider how to reward excellence.

2. Staying abreast of cinematic developments is challenging, and the number of annual awards has fluctuated throughout the years since 1929.

3. The Oscar statuette was cast in bronze and gold-plated for many years, but World War II brought on the waning of U.S. metal supplies, so for a time the figure was made of plaster that was painted gold.

4. Today the technique used to make the statuette is covering a britannium base with gold plating.

5. Untold numbers of Americans have given the fateful ripping of each envelope their full attention.

EXERCISE B Use the directions given in parentheses to write five sentences containing gerund phrases.

Example 1. (Use *arriving* as a subject.)
Arriving late to the interview may cost you the job!

6. (Use *applying* as a direct object.) ______________________

7. (Use *focusing* as a predicate nominative.) ______________________

8. (Use *predicting* as the object of a preposition.) ______________________

9. (Use *borrowing* as a subject.) ______________________

10. (Use *flinging* as a subject.) ______________________

Copyright © by Holt, Rinehart and Winston. All rights reserved.

NAME ____________ CLASS ____________ DATE ____________

Gerunds and Gerund Phrases

3g. A ***gerund*** is a verb form ending in *–ing* that is used as a noun.

EXAMPLE Mario places great importance on **listening.**

3h. A ***gerund phrase*** consists of a gerund and its modifiers and complements. The entire phrase is used as a noun.

EXAMPLE Their highest priority is **serving customers efficiently and courteously.**

EXERCISE A Underline the gerund or gerund phrase in each of the following sentences. Then, identify its function in the sentence by writing, on the line provided, *S* for *subject, PN* for *predicate nominative, DO* for *direct object, IO* for *indirect object,* or *OP* for *object of a preposition.*

Example OP **1.** During the summer Mae earns money by mowing people's lawns.

______ **1.** One of the most exciting experiences my family ever had was adopting my baby brother.

______ **2.** Translating from Chinese to English is a rare and valuable skill.

______ **3.** The coach was praised for treating each of her players with respect.

______ **4.** Emilio taught Cajun cooking in an adult education class.

______ **5.** Tanya, a conscientious person, gives caring for her new puppy top priority.

EXERCISE B On the line provided, write a sentence using each of the following gerunds in a gerund phrase. Follow the instructions in parentheses.

Example 1. *preparing* (Use the gerund phrase as an object of a preposition.) Leslie devoted the evening to preparing her presentation.

6. *painting* (Use the gerund phrase as a subject.) ______________________

____

7. *complaining* (Use the gerund phrase as a predicate nominative.) ______________________

____

8. *swimming* (Use the gerund phrase as a direct object.) ______________________

____

9. *saving* (Use the gerund phrase as an object of a preposition.) ______________________

____

10. *caring* (Use the gerund phrase as an indirect object.) ______________________

____

Copyright © by Holt, Rinehart and Winston. All rights reserved.

NAME ______________________ CLASS ______________ DATE ______________

Identifying Participial and Gerund Phrases

3f. A ***participial phrase*** consists of a participle and its modifiers and complements. The entire phrase is used as an adjective.

3h. A ***gerund phrase*** consists of a gerund and its modifiers and complements. The entire phrase is used as a noun.

EXERCISE A In each of the following sentences, identify the underlined phrase by writing above it *gerund phrase* or *participial phrase.*

Example 1. Cleaning a house from top to bottom is a big job! (*gerund phrase*)

1. Some tasks, such as putting away clutter, involve much walking from room to room.
2. Using the recycling bin judiciously, you can make your way through the piles of paper that have been collecting for weeks.
3. It's easy to place the dishes into the patiently waiting dishwasher.
4. Who wants to undertake the tedious task of ironing all the cotton clothes?
5. Personally, I've always found folding warm towels to be a soothing task.
6. One good way to pass the time pleasantly while working is listening to good music.
7. Working together, two people can quickly get the trash gathered and put out.
8. Two people cleaning the bathroom, however, soon run out of room!
9. Cleaning experts agree that vacuuming the floors is a task best left till last.
10. After cleaning the house, I'm going out for dinner!

EXERCISE B Compose five sentences, using the verb and the type of phrase indicated in the parentheses.

Example 1. (Use *flit* in a participial phrase.) *Flitting across the meadow, the fireflies delighted us.*

11. (Use *thrive* in a participial phrase.) ______________________

12. (Use *argue* in a gerund phrase.) ______________________

13. (Use *permit* in a gerund phrase.) ______________________

14. (Use *concentrate* in a participial phrase.) ______________________

15. (Use *whine* in a participial phrase.) ______________________

Copyright © by Holt, Rinehart and Winston. All rights reserved.

The Infinitive

3i. An ***infinitive*** is a verb form that can be used as a noun, an adjective, or an adverb. Most infinitives begin with *to.*

NOUN **To graduate** is her primary goal. [subject of *is*]

ADJECTIVE Mr. Tanger would be the one **to ask.** [adjective modifying the pronoun *one*]

ADVERB The guests stood **to leave.** [adverb modifying the verb *stood*]

In addition to the present form, infinitives have a ***present perfect*** form.

EXAMPLES **To have solved** the problem would have made the research worthwhile.

The original goal was **to have been finished** with the project by noon.

The word *to,* the sign of the infinitive, is sometimes omitted.

EXAMPLE Please let me [to] **finish** my story.

EXERCISE A In each sentence, underline the infinitive. Above it, write *N* if it is a noun, *ADJ* if it is an adjective, or *ADV* if it is an adverb.

Example 1. To forgive is sometimes difficult. (N)

1. At the party, the toddler wanted to eat first.

2. The large dog needs to go to the vet for shots.

3. To have finished early would have required more help.

4. Call me if you have any questions to ask.

5. Was Pauli really prepared to leave?

EXERCISE B Compose five sentences using infinitives. Use the infinitive and part of speech indicated in the parentheses.

Example 1. (Use *to wait* as an adverb.) We settled in to wait.

6. (Use *to see* as an adverb.) ____________________

7. (Use *to find* as an adjective.) ____________________

8. (Use *to nurture* as a noun.) ____________________

9. (Use *to investigate* as an adjective.) ____________________

10. (Use *to crawl* as a noun.) ____________________

11. (Use *to give* as a noun.) ____________________

12. (Use *to win* as an adverb.) ____________________

13. (Use *to begin* as an adjective.) ____________________

14. (Use *to have gone* as a noun.) ____________________

15. (Use *to have been recognized* as a noun.) ____________________

Copyright © by Holt, Rinehart and Winston. All rights reserved.

NAME ______________________ CLASS ______________ DATE ______________

The Infinitive Phrase

3j. An ***infinitive phrase*** consists of an infinitive and its modifiers and complements. The entire phrase can be used as a noun, an adjective, or an adverb.

NOUN Bruce's dream is **to travel to Africa.** [The infinitive phrase is a predicate nominative identifying the subject *dream.*]

ADJECTIVE Have you had a chance **to sample this authentic tortilla soup**? [The infinitive phrase modifies the noun *chance.*]

ADVERB Are you ready **to give Chamique her instructions**? [The infinitive phrase modifies the adjective *ready.*]

EXERCISE In each sentence, underline the infinitive phrase. Above it, write *N* if it is used as a noun, *ADJ* if it is used as an adjective, or *ADV* if it is used as an adverb.

Example 1. ADV To keep up with the growing population's demand for food, many farmers are developing new methods.

1. For many decades, farmers have continued to use artificial pesticides on their crops.
2. However, recent concerns about toxicity have convinced many farmers that they should seek ways to avoid the use of such pesticides.
3. To think of organic farming as a recent idea, however, is incorrect.
4. In the 1930s, a British agri-scientist, Sir Albert Howard, presented the world with a new farming method to examine for possible use.
5. He developed a system of farming in which wastes were used to fertilize crops.
6. Manure, compost, straw, and organic waste from crops work to improve soil conditions for growing plants.
7. Eager to improve nutrition without reducing crop yields, some farmers choose organic methods.
8. Rotating crops, releasing insect predators, and sowing pest-resistant plants are options to employ for pest control.
9. To improve sustainable agriculture is one of the goals of organic farming.
10. More and more people are beginning to buy and enjoy organic foods each year.

Copyright © by Holt, Rinehart and Winston. All rights reserved.

Infinitives and Infinitive Phrases

3i. An ***infinitive*** is a verb form that can be used as a noun, an adjective, or an adverb. Most infinitives begin with *to.*

NOUN The hyena began **to laugh.** [direct object of *began*]
ADJECTIVE Toyoko is a runner **to watch.** [modifies the noun *runner*]
ADVERB Rodrigo said that he came **to dance.** [modifies the verb *came*]

3j. An ***infinitive phrase*** consists of an infinitive and its modifiers and complements. The entire phrase can be used as a noun, an adjective, or an adverb.

NOUN I want **to see that film again.** [direct object of *want*]
ADJECTIVE Melissa didn't have time **to read my paper.** [modifies the noun *time*]
ADVERB Are you eager **to go to the park**? [modifies the adjective *eager*]

EXERCISE A Underline the infinitive or infinitive phrase in each of the following sentences. Then, tell how the infinitive is used by writing, on the line provided, *N* for *noun, ADJ* for *adjective,* or *ADV* for *adverb.* If a sentence does not contain an infinitive or infinitive phrase, write *none* on the line.

Example __N__ **1.** If you go for a bike ride, don't forget to wear your helmet.

______ **1.** To go to law school is Mai's goal.
______ **2.** Chucha is happy to be part of the Zuni ceremony.
______ **3.** Many Cubans immigrated to the United States after the 1959 revolution.
______ **4.** Imala spoke to her teacher about an independent study project.
______ **5.** The seamstress likes to see the needlework done by her talented son.
______ **6.** Because of the howling wind and creaking shutters, Jamila was unable to sleep.
______ **7.** The player to emulate is Manuel.
______ **8.** Halfway across the rock face, Nina began to lose her footing.
______ **9.** If you ask me, this little gray kitten should be eager to go home with you.
______ **10.** Chantel and Ricki have both offered to help with the park cleanup.

EXERCISE B Follow the instructions to write sentences that contain infinitives or infinitive phrases.

Example 1. (Use *to make* as a noun.) Karli hopes to make better grades this year.

11. (Use *to dream* as a noun.) ______
12. (Use *to keep* as an adjective.) ______
13. (Use *to travel* as an adverb.) ______
14. (Use *to listen* as a noun.) ______
15. (Use *to leave* as an adverb.) ______

Copyright © by Holt, Rinehart and Winston. All rights reserved.

Identifying Prepositional and Verbal Phrases

3b. A ***prepositional phrase*** includes a preposition, the object of the preposition, and any modifiers of that object.

EXAMPLE The hiker tripped **over the old tree limb.**

3f. A ***participial phrase*** consists of a participle and its modifiers and complements. The entire phrase is used as an adjective.

EXAMPLE The car, **covered with fresh snow,** looked like a mysterious mound.

3h. A ***gerund phrase*** consists of a gerund and its modifiers and complements. The entire phrase is used as a noun.

EXAMPLE Have you finished **painting the trim** yet?

3j. An ***infinitive phrase*** consists of an infinitive and its modifiers and complements. The entire phrase can be used as a noun, an adjective, or an adverb.

EXAMPLE The workers have come **to repair the roof.**

EXERCISE Identify each underlined word group in the following paragraph by writing above it *PREP* for *prepositional phrase, PART* for *participial phrase, GER* for *gerund phrase,* or *INF* for *infinitive phrase.*

Example [1] With his catchy nickname, Charlie "Yardbird" Parker was and is a well-known jazz figure. (PREP)

[1] Considered by many the best jazz improviser, Yardbird Parker played alto sax, composed music, and originated bebop, [2] regarded as the pace-setting jazz style [3] of the mid-twentieth century. Parker collaborated [4] with Dizzy Gillespie [5] to define jazz [6] for two decades. [7] Listening to swing music in the 1930s moved Parker [8] toward his own new style. He also gained experience [9] playing with various bands. However, [10] to follow their own musical ideas, he and Gillespie founded their own ensemble [11] in 1945. Parker incorporated many musical voices [12] into his music, [13] from African-American folk songs [14] to modern concert music. His style, [15] punctuated by quick tempos and [16] accented by sudden pauses and endings, became the root style [17] of many subsequent jazz musicians. Sadly, Parker's death [18] at the young age [19] of thirty-four ended a career [20] of remarkable music-making.

Copyright © by Holt, Rinehart and Winston. All rights reserved.

for **CHAPTER 3: THE PHRASE** *pages 119–120*

The Appositive

3k. An ***appositive*** is a noun or pronoun placed beside another noun or pronoun to identify or describe it.

An appositive usually follows the word it identifies or describes.

EXAMPLES My sister **Deborah** started college this year.
Our class president, **Alan Rodriguez,** will give a speech.

An appositive is sometimes placed at the beginning of a sentence for emphasis.

EXAMPLE A **gazehound,** the whippet hunts by sight and can run extremely fast.

EXERCISE A Underline the appositive in each of the following sentences. Then, circle the word or words it describes or identifies.

Example 1. The best source for word meanings, the dictionary, describes a palindrome as a word or sentence that reads the same forward or backward.

1. *Civic,* one example, reads the same no matter which end of the word you begin with.
2. *Desserts stress Ed* and *Sit on a potato pan, Otis!* are amusing examples, real gems, of sentence-length palindromes.
3. The word *palindrome* comes from Greek and means "running back again."
4. Palindromes are little word games now but once had deeper significance to a superstitious people, the Romans.
5. They inscribed palindromes on decorative charms—amulets—to ward off harm.

EXERCISE B Complete each sentence by inserting an appositive to describe or identify the noun or noun phrase.

Example 1. Danae's sister, ______Maya______ , just bought a used car.

6. She worked as a legal assistant at the company ____________________ to save money for the down payment.
7. The car's color, ____________________, is one of my favorites.
8. Maya will take her driver's test tomorrow, ____________________, in the morning.
9. If she passes, she plans to drive her new car to a special place, ____________________.
10. Her friend ____________________ will go with her.

Copyright © by Holt, Rinehart and Winston. All rights reserved.

NAME ______________________ CLASS ______________ DATE ______________

for CHAPTER 3: THE PHRASE page 120

The Appositive Phrase

3l. An ***appositive phrase*** consists of an appositive and its modifiers.

EXAMPLE The silver pendant, **a gift from her best friend,** hung on a thin, short chain.

An appositive phrase usually follows the word it identifies but may precede it.

EXAMPLE **A favorite food of my father,** tempura is often served at our house.

EXERCISE A Underline the appositive phrase in each of the following sentences. Circle the word or words it describes or identifies.

Example 1. Many animals were housed at Cameron Critter Haven, our local animal shelter.

1. Volunteers, excited children and experienced adults, gathered for a day of cleaning cages, stocking supplies, and visiting with the animals.
2. Each animal would be kept here until those special people, its new family, chose it.
3. We called on my particular friend at the Haven, a playful Irish Setter named Redbeard.
4. Most Irish Setters, slightly nervous dogs, calm down once they get to know people.
5. Some animals needed medical attention, a healing touch from our veterinary volunteers.
6. Generous donors, financial supporters without whom the Haven would have to close, provide for each pet to be spayed or neutered.
7. Still, now and then we take in a litter of bright-eyed kittens, mischievous balls of fur.
8. We keep the kittens till each finds just what it needs, a loving and safe home.
9. Some volunteers foster animals in their own houses, temporary homes-away-from-home.
10. I often wish I could keep every animal I foster, but my landlord, the man with the deciding vote in the matter, would not approve!

EXERCISE B Complete each of the following sentences by adding an appositive phrase to describe or identify the noun or noun phrase.

Example 1. It's important to take the time, _fifteen minutes or so_, to write thank-you notes.

11. Though a phone call is nice, receiving written thanks, ______________, means more.
12. Also, unlike a phone call, ______________, one can read a thank-you note again later.
13. It's all too easy to take a friend, ______________, for granted.
14. Thank-you notes, ______________, say the words that sometimes don't get past our lips.
15. There are bad habits and good habits, and writing thank-you notes, ______________, is definitely one of the latter!

Copyright © by Holt, Rinehart and Winston. All rights reserved.

Appositives and Appositive Phrases

3k. An ***appositive*** is a noun or a pronoun placed beside another noun or pronoun to identify or describe it.

EXAMPLE Have you read Gary Soto's short story **"The Jacket"**?

3l. An ***appositive phrase*** consists of an appositive and its modifiers.

EXAMPLE Akela, **the youngest in our family,** wants to become a trapeze artist.

EXERCISE A Underline the appositive or appositive phrase in each of the following sentences, and draw an arrow to the word or word group it identifies.

Example 1. Emilio is knowledgeable about nutrition, a widely discussed topic in his home.

1. We finally convinced Rashard's friend Casey to join the team.
2. Yori's letter, a poem about our friendship, made my birthday unforgettable.
3. Charlie Belliveau, the high school custodian, convinced a boy not to quit school, and that boy eventually became the mayor of our city.
4. Without Blair, the housekeeper, nobody in that family would know how to get through their days.
5. Those overalls, my favorites, have been mended and patched dozens of times.
6. This grandfather clock, an oak masterpiece of handiwork, is an antique.
7. My cousin Amanda is a veterinarian who works at a wildlife park.
8. A hardy perennial, the grape hyacinth comes from a bulb that is planted in the fall and blooms in the spring.
9. The party, a celebration of my friend's eighteenth birthday, was held at a local swimming pool.
10. Lanelle's favorite song, "Moondance," is a jazz rock tune sung by Van Morrison.

EXERCISE B Add meaning to each sentence below by turning the underlined appositive into an appositive phrase. Write the appositive phrase on the line provided.

Example 1. That long-awaited ceremony, graduation, is fast approaching.
graduation from our alma mater

11. Do we all have to wear those hats, mortar boards? ______
12. At least our robes will be a beautiful color, blue. ______
13. Soon we will be leaving for our next adventure, college. ______
14. Mr. Longmire and Dr. Terry, professors, will give speeches. ______
15. Graduation ceremonies, rituals, can be very meaningful. ______

Copyright © by Holt, Rinehart and Winston. All rights reserved.

NAME CLASS DATE

Review A: Phrases

EXERCISE A Classify the underlined phrase in each of the following sentences. In the space above the phrase, write *PREP* for *prepositional phrase*, *PART* for *participial phrase*, *GER* for *gerund phrase*, *INF* for *infinitive phrase*, or *APP* for *appositive phrase*.

Example 1. Blessed by a mild climate, southern California produces flowers all year long. (PART)

1. California, a state famous for its natural beauty, takes great pride in its flowers.
2. If you want to see the world's greatest flower show, watch the annual New Year's Day parade in Pasadena.
3. Watching this parade is one way that many people start the new year.
4. Some enthusiasts take up vantage spots along the parade route the day before New Year's.
5. Bearing thousands of flowers on a framework of wooden braces and wire netting, a large float may take many weeks to design and build.
6. One float featured an artificial tree decorated with approximately 40,000 orchids.
7. The task of providing the flowers for the decoration of the floats falls on the shoulders of local florists and nursery workers.
8. Even in the balmy climate of southern California, one major problem is having enough flowers in bloom at the right time.
9. Hundreds of thousands of people wait for hours to enjoy this beautiful spectacle.
10. The pageant, the result of many months of cooperative effort, is well worth seeing.

EXERCISE B Identify the underlined phrase in each of the following sentences. Above the phrase, write *PREP* for *prepositional phrase*, *PART* for *participial phrase*, *GER* for *gerund phrase*, *INF* for *infinitive phrase*, or *APP* for *appositive phrase*.

Example 1. Babylon, one of the greatest of ancient cities, had two periods of glory. (APP)

11. These two periods, separated by a thousand years, are known for their strong leaders.
12. Hammurabi, as king of Babylon, did not wish to maintain an uneasy peace with unfriendly neighboring rivals.
13. The author of a famous code of laws, Hammurabi was an outstanding king.
14. More than a thousand years after Hammurabi's reign, Nebuchadnezzar, another great Babylonian leader, came to power.
15. One of Nebuchadnezzar's greatest achievements was overseeing the reconstruction of the city of Babylon.

Copyright © by Holt, Rinehart and Winston. All rights reserved.

for **CHAPTER 3: THE PHRASE** ***pages 105–120***

Review B: **Phrases**

EXERCISE A Above each underlined phrase, write *PREP* for *prepositional phrase, PART* for *participial phrase, GER* for *gerund phrase, INF* for *infinitive phrase,* or *APP* for *appositive phrase.*

Example 1. The football sitting near the goal-post is Ahmed's. *PART*

1. Smiling broadly, Anthony showed us the sizable amount of interest he had earned on his savings account.
2. The librarian, asked about enjoyable fitness activities, recommended the new book about tai chi.
3. Gabriel García Márquez, the brilliant Colombian novelist, was awarded the Nobel Prize in literature in 1982.
4. Donya wants to ride her bicycle from Washington, D.C., to Seattle, Washington.
5. Kai's ambition is to drive a tractor-trailer.
6. Marnie made an appointment to audition for a part in the play this morning.
7. Many of us in biology class have mixed emotions about dissecting frogs.
8. Moving their vehicles to the right, all of the drivers let the ambulance pass.
9. My cousin, who is hard of hearing, prefers watching closed-captioned television programs.
10. My friends Alecca and Leon sent me a postcard from Rome.

EXERCISE B Compose ten sentences, using the verb to create the type of verbal or verbal phrase indicated in parentheses.

Example 1. (*take*, gerund phrase) *The first item on the agenda was taking roll.*

11. (*revise*, participial phrase) __________
12. (*consider*, infinitive phrase) __________
13. (*joke*, gerund phrase) __________
14. (*fan*, participial phrase) __________
15. (*abhor*, infinitive phrase) __________
16. (*stand*, gerund phrase) __________
17. (*speak*, participial phrase) __________
18. (*write*, infinitive phrase) __________
19. (*explain*, gerund phrase) __________
20. (*understand*, participial phrase) __________

Copyright © by Holt, Rinehart and Winston. All rights reserved.

Review C: Phrases

EXERCISE In the paragraph below, identify each underlined phrase by writing above it *PREP* for *prepositional phrase, PART* for *participial phrase, GER* for *gerund phrase, INF* for *infinitive phrase,* or *APP* for *appositive phrase.*

Example **[1]** Have I told you yet about my bear encounter? (PREP)

I was camping **[1]** in the Guadalupe Mountains last spring. I'd heard the stories that campers tell, **[2]** tall tales aggrandizing each camper's own bravery, I figured. Mountain lions and whole packs **[3]** of bears starred **[4]** in these exaggerated stories, so I ignored them as I huffed **[5]** up the path. **[6]** Exhausted in every muscle, I tossed down my gear and set up camp. **[7]** Sleeping deeply and soundly was the main thing **[8]** on my mind, and **[9]** having dismissed the bear scare stories, I neglected **[10]** to hang my pack **[11]** from a rope **[12]** over a tree branch, as one is supposed to do if bears might be around. I fell asleep right away, but minutes later, or so it seemed, I woke **[13]** to hear a snuffling, grunting, scratching noise **[14]** near my tent flap. Adrenaline flooded my system as I regretted not listening **[15]** to the more experienced campers' stories. However, I had heard how **[16]** to protect myself: I charged up my camera flash, leapt **[17]** through the tent door, and, aiming at the bear, set off the flash. Then I scrambled back **[18]** into the tent and listened hopefully as the confused bear loped off **[19]** through the woods. I learned something that night: Skip the camera if you like, but never go camping **[20]** without the camera flash!

Copyright © by Holt, Rinehart and Winston. All rights reserved.

Identifying Clauses

4a. A ***clause*** is a word group that contains a verb and its subject and that is used as a sentence or as part of a sentence.

EXAMPLES where the **airplane landed** (S above airplane, V above landed)

before **we finish** our visit (S above we, V above finish)

Every clause has both a subject and a verb, but not every clause expresses a complete thought.

SENTENCE A cockapoo is a dog that is part cocker spaniel and part poodle.

CLAUSE A **cockapoo is** a dog. [complete thought] (S above cockapoo, V above is)

CLAUSE **that is** part cocker spaniel and part poodle [incomplete thought] (S above that, V above is)

EXERCISE Identify the subject and verb of each clause below. Write *S* above the subject and *V* above the verb. If you do not find both a subject and its verb, write *not a clause* after the sentence.

Examples **1.** the dog has been digging in the garden again (S above dog, V above been)

2. how to stop him *not a clause*

1. the dog prefers the marigold patch
2. sleeping in the bushes by the front door
3. where the dog buries its bones
4. the afternoon sun winks through the pear tree's branches
5. the shadows dance and play on the dog's gold fur
6. known to many in the neighborhood
7. the birds splash in the birdbath
8. because the dog keeps an eye on them
9. the dog would never chase or bite them
10. if it sees a cat

Copyright © by Holt, Rinehart and Winston. All rights reserved.

NAME ______________________ CLASS ______________________ DATE ______________________

The Independent Clause

4b. An ***independent*** (or ***main***) ***clause*** expresses a complete thought and can stand by itself as a sentence.

EXAMPLES **The patrons raved about the chilis rellenos.** [one independent clause]

The restaurant had been open for only a few weeks, but **already it had a reputation for delicious food and good service.** [two independent clauses joined by *but*]

After we had tasted the salsa, **we knew** that we had found a quality restaurant. [an independent clause combined with two subordinate clauses]

EXERCISE A In the following sentences, underline the independent clauses. For each independent clause you underline, identify the subject and verb by writing *S* above the subject and *V* above its verb.

Example 1. I always order guacamole, but Fern is not fond of avocados.

1. The wait staff wear brightly embroidered clothing.
2. Stuffed jalapeños make an excellent appetizer, but the black bean nachos are good, too.
3. I sometimes eat chips and salsa before the entrée arrives.
4. Fern likes enchiladas, but I like tacos.
5. I always leave a good tip, for the wait staff are attentive and quick.
6. The pico de gallo stings my mouth a bit, but it tastes good.
7. Is Mexican food your favorite, or do you prefer Italian?
8. Some people prefer bland foods.
9. I enjoy the soothing atmosphere and the delicious food.
10. I don't particularly like, on the other hand, the arrival of the bill.

EXERCISE B Compose five sentences about the kind of food you like best. Each sentence should include at least one independent clause. Underline each independent clause. Then, for each independent clause you underline, identify the subject and verb by writing *S* above the subject and *V* above its verb.

Example 1. I often crave a chef salad with all the trimmings.

11. ____
12. ____
13. ____
14. ____
15. ____

Copyright © by Holt, Rinehart and Winston. All rights reserved.

NAME ______________________ CLASS ______________ DATE ______________

The Subordinate Clause

4c. A ***subordinate*** (or ***dependent***) ***clause*** does not express a complete thought and cannot stand by itself as a sentence.

EXAMPLE which was sent to the wrong address

The meaning of a subordinate clause becomes clear only when the subordinate clause is combined with an independent clause.

EXAMPLE The registration form, **which was sent to the wrong address,** was late.

EXERCISE On the lines provided, write independent clauses to complete the meaning of each of the following subordinate clauses.

Example 1. who open the exhibition

The skaters who open the exhibition carry flags of the city, state, and nation.

1. who purchased tickets to the figure-skating contest

____

2. while we waited in line

____

3. if there were still six seats together

____

4. that the semifinals were not sold out

____

5. until we paid for our seats

____

6. which events were scheduled for Monday

____

7. as if we could afford front-row seats

____

8. which includes backstage passes

____

9. whoever wants to learn to skate

____

10. because we enjoy the competition so much

____

Copyright © by Holt, Rinehart and Winston. All rights reserved.

NAME CLASS DATE

Independent and Subordinate Clauses

4b. An ***independent*** (or ***main***) ***clause*** expresses a complete thought and can stand by itself as a sentence.

EXAMPLE **I like Indian food,** but **my sister prefers Chinese or Thai dishes.** [two independent clauses joined by *but*.]

4c. A ***subordinate*** (or ***dependent***) ***clause*** does not express a complete thought and cannot stand by itself as a sentence.

EXAMPLE **before Tim arrived**

The meaning of a subordinate clause becomes clear only when the subordinate clause is combined with an independent clause.

EXAMPLE **Before Tim arrived,** we had washed ten cars.

EXERCISE For each of the following sentences, classify the underlined word group by writing above it *IC* for *independent clause* or *SC* for *subordinate clause.*

Example **1.** Roberto has almost finished his term paper, which is about the Moorish empire.

1. The Muslims, who were known in Spanish history as the Moors, invaded Spain from North Africa in A.D. 711.

2. Moorish Spain, which is known as Andalusia, grew very prosperous.

3. When al-Hakam II became caliph, or ruler, a renaissance of learning took place.

4. In addition, Andalusia's economy expanded as agriculture, mining, and industry all made strides forward.

5. Andalusia set up trade with North Africa, further increasing economic growth.

6. The Moors brought new crops—apricots, almonds, and sugar cane—to the region, which they irrigated with complicated structures.

7. Arab Muslims, Spanish Christians, and Jews collaborated in Andalusia to create celebrated centers of science at a time when much of Europe was still mired in the Dark Ages.

8. The Alhambra, which was a Moorish fortress and palace in Granada, drew the admiration of many people.

9. Moorish power in Andalusia began to fall apart after the Christian armies of King Alfonso VIII defeated the Moorish army in 1212.

10. When the capital, Córdoba, surrendered to the Christian king Ferdinand III in 1236, the Moorish empire in Spain was weakened significantly.

Copyright © by Holt, Rinehart and Winston. All rights reserved.

The Adjective Clause

4d. An ***adjective clause*** is a subordinate clause that modifies a noun or a pronoun.

An ***adjective clause*** usually follows the word or words it modifies and tells *what kind* or *which one.*

EXAMPLE The Inca, **who were great weavers,** often used threads spun of birds' feathers and gold. [The adjective clause *who were great weavers* modifies the noun *Inca.*]

EXERCISE A In each of the following sentences, underline the adjective clause and circle the word or words the adjective clause modifies.

Example 1. Mr. Mendoza, who traveled to Sri Lanka, has prepared a slide show of his trip.

1. Sri Lanka is an island nation that lies off the coast of the southern tip of India.
2. This island, which was formerly called Ceylon, is famous for its tea.
3. It is a country where both the land and the people present dramatic contrasts.
4. Mount Pidurutalagala, which rises to a height of 8,281 feet (2,524 meters), stands in contrast to the coastal lowlands.
5. The teachings of the principal religion, Buddhism, contrast with the civil war that has ravaged the country in recent years.

EXERCISE B In each of the following sentences, underline the adjective clause and circle the word or words the adjective clause modifies.

Example 1. My grandparents can remember a time when computers did not even exist.

6. It is futile to worry about things that are in the past.
7. Chinua Achebe is a Nigerian author whose books I enjoy.
8. I hardly recognized the house where I had spent my childhood.
9. The red maple that grows in our backyard turns a beautiful shade of red in the autumn.
10. The 1960s was an era when many young people debated government policies.
11. Astronomy is a subject that I would like to study in more depth.
12. The Shang people of ancient China imported jade, which they laboriously carved into objects of exquisite beauty.
13. The rain forests where the cockatoos live are being destroyed.
14. Felicia explained the terminology that the programmers had used in the manual.
15. Thailand, which provides the world with much of its rice and teak, is one of the largest countries in Southeast Asia.

Copyright © by Holt, Rinehart and Winston. All rights reserved.

Relative Pronouns

An adjective clause is usually introduced by a ***relative pronoun*** such as *that, which, who, whom,* or *whose.* An adjective clause may be introduced by a ***relative adverb***, such as *when* or *where.*

EXAMPLES Have you seen the African sculptures **that are on display at the museum**? [The relative pronoun *that* refers to the noun *sculptures* and serves as the subject of the verb *are.*]

Do you know the street **where the museum is located**? [The relative adverb *where* relates the adjective clause to its noun antecedent, *street*, and modifies *is located.*]

EXERCISE A In each sentence, underline the adjective clause. Circle the noun or pronoun that the clause modifies. Then, above each relative pronoun or relative adverb, write *S* for *subject, DO* for *direct object, OP* for *object of preposition,* or *ADV* for *relative adverb.*

Example 1. Taste, which is called the gustatory sense, works hand in hand with smell.

1. Taste buds, which help make the sense of taste possible, are located on the tongue.

2. Each taste bud is made of fifty to seventy cells that are arranged in clusters called papillae.

3. The different tastes that you experience come from the interplay between food, your taste buds, and your brain.

4. The tip of the tongue is the spot where we taste sweetness.

5. Have you ever experienced a time during which your sense of taste wasn't functioning properly?

EXERCISE B In each sentence, underline the adjective clause. Circle the noun or pronoun that the clause modifies. Then, above each relative pronoun or relative adverb, write *S* for *subject, DO* for *direct object, OP* for *object of preposition, M* for *modifier,* or *ADV* for *relative adverb.*

Example 1. The piano that Carol's mother donated to the school has a beautiful tone.

6. Susan is a girl who always tries to focus on the positive aspects of a difficult situation.

7. The field where I used to play soccer is now a shopping mall.

8. Kelly, whose poem was published, was asked to recite it during graduation.

9. Henry found it difficult to think of a time when cars didn't exist.

10. The toddler accidentally dropped the large tumbler of water that his mother gave him.

11. People who are allergic to aspirin are usually able to take aspirin substitutes.

12. Helen decided to give the books to the person who asked her first.

13. The baseball league in which Shelly plays is hosting a tournament this weekend.

14. The store, the site where an infamous robbery took place, is located across the street.

15. Jennifer is a smart and friendly student whom many people simply call "Jen."

Copyright © by Holt, Rinehart and Winston. All rights reserved.

Essential and Nonessential Clauses

Depending on how it is used, an adjective clause is either essential or nonessential. An *essential clause* provides information that is necessary to the meaning of the sentence.

EXAMPLE Everyone **who played for Coach Mendoza last year** attended a banquet in the coach's honor. [Omitting the adjective clause would change the basic meaning of the sentence.]

A *nonessential clause* provides additional information that can be omitted without changing the basic meaning of the sentence. A nonessential clause is set off by commas.

EXAMPLE Coach Mendoza, **who has gained the admiration of students and teachers alike,** will retire next year. [The adjective clause gives extra information. Omitting the clause would not change the basic meaning of the sentence.]

EXERCISE Above each underlined adjective clause, write an *E* if the clause is essential to the sentence's meaning or *N* if the clause is not essential to the sentence's meaning. If the clause is not essential, insert commas where they belong.

Example 1. The dog that my grandmother gave me won a blue ribbon in last week's county dog show. (E)

1. Tim is one friend on whom I know I can always count.
2. Call out the numbers that you draw from the basket.
3. The women whose opinions I've always valued are talking with each other by the door.
4. The students are busily decorating the room in which the school dance is to be held.
5. Mrs. Tate whom I admire always offers constructive criticism.
6. The house where we will meet has a blue car in the driveway.
7. One speaker who seemed rather nervous provided thorough information about the task of seeking scholarships.
8. Fifteen repetitions with each arm is the number that my coach recommends.
9. She's a clever girl who can figure out solutions to many problems.
10. I'm allergic to Bermuda grass which is planted all around my neighborhood.

Copyright © by Holt, Rinehart and Winston. All rights reserved.

The Noun Clause

4e. A ***noun clause*** is a subordinate clause that is used as a noun.

A noun clause may be used as a subject, a predicate nominative, a direct object, an indirect object, an object of a preposition, or an appositive.

EXAMPLES **How the Colosseum was built** was the topic of discussion. [subject]

My opinion is **that he should be given an award.** [predicate nominative]

I know **that hieroglyphics were used by the ancient Egyptians.** [direct object]

The library is giving **whoever wishes to come** free tickets for a tour of the museum. [indirect object]

Give the money to **whomever you want.** [object of a preposition]

The belief **that the earth is flat** was refuted a long time ago. [appositive]

EXERCISE Underline the noun clause in each sentence. Then, identify how the noun clause is used by writing above it *S* for *subject, DO* for *direct object, IO* for *indirect object, OP* for *object of a preposition,* or *PN* for *predicate nominative.*

Example 1. No one can predict when the problem of pet overpopulation will finally be solved. DO

1. You can discuss your report with whichever teacher is available.
2. A little praise from time to time is what most children need.
3. The mayor will give whoever passes the finish line first a key to the city.
4. The teacher said that this little chunk of granite is over four billion years old.
5. What happened to the fabled city of Atlantis remains a mystery.
6. We will donate whatever we do not need to the Salvation Army.
7. The committee's decision was that solar power cells should be installed.
8. Deke expounded his weird theories to whoever would listen to them.
9. Marie Curie discovered that radium is an element.
10. How whales hunt by means of echolocation will be our subject for today.

Copyright © by Holt, Rinehart and Winston. All rights reserved.

for **CHAPTER 4: THE CLAUSE** *pages 136–137*

The Adverb Clause

4f. An ***adverb clause*** is a subordinate clause that modifies a verb, an adjective, or an adverb.

An adverb clause tells *how, how much, when, where, why, to what extent,* or *under what conditions.*

EXAMPLES **Before you leave Japan,** take a picture of the family with whom you are staying.
The rice paddies were dry **because the rains had not come.**
Daryl plays the guitar better **than he plays the violin.**

EXERCISE A In each of the following sentences, underline the adverb clause and circle the word or words the clause modifies.

Example 1. Danika likes riding her bicycle (more) than she likes jogging.

1. After I eat lunch, I will clean my room.
2. This hat is prettier than that one is.
3. When you get home, please clean your room.
4. Do you really watch tennis on TV more than you watch basketball?
5. George Bernard Shaw did not write a play until he was thirty-five years old.
6. Karen makes friends wherever she goes.
7. If you like the music of Mozart, you will love Beethoven's first symphony.
8. Don't open that present early unless you want to ruin the surprise.
9. Because Keith was born in Tokyo, his parents gave him a Japanese middle name.
10. Provided that you complete the training, you can start work next week.

EXERCISE B Use each of the subordinating conjunctions in parentheses to compose a sentence with an adverb clause.

Example 1. *(as soon as)* As soon as we heard the thunder in the distance, we cut our hike short and turned back toward the car.

11. *(if)* ____________
12. *(as long as)* ____________
13. *(because)* ____________
14. *(unless)* ____________
15. *(while)* ____________

Copyright © by Holt, Rinehart and Winston. All rights reserved.

NAME ______ CLASS ______ DATE ______

Subordinating Conjunctions

An adverb clause is introduced by a *subordinating conjunction*—a word or word group that shows the relationship between the adverb clause and the word or words it modifies.

COMMON SUBORDINATING CONJUNCTIONS

after	as long as	before	since	unless	where
although	as soon as	if	so that	until	wherever
as	as though	in order that	than	when	whether
as if	because	provided that	though	whenever	while

EXERCISE Underline the adverb clauses and circle the subordinating conjunctions in the sentences below. Then, on the lines provided, identify how the adverb clause functions in each sentence. Does the adverb clause tell *how, how much, when, where, why, to what extent,* or *under what conditions?*

Example 1. (As) students prepare to graduate from high school, they also prepare to enter the working world. *when*

1. Although many teens work during high school, they usually earn only a modest amount of money. ______

2. However, they will have to start paying income taxes as soon as they begin to work. ______

3. Whether teens know it or not, the practice of taxing income in the United States goes back to the Civil War. ______

4. In 1873, the federal income tax ceased, until President Grover Cleveland reinstated it in 1894. ______

5. Because the Supreme Court declared the personal income tax unconstitutional, those who supported the tax had to alter the Constitution. ______

6. This they did in 1913 when the Sixteenth Amendment was ratified. ______

7. Provided that a citizen made at least $3,000 a year, he or she was required to pay tax. ______

8. When World War II ended, the minimum tax rate was 23 percent and the maximum tax rate was 94 percent. ______

9. So that they can raise revenue for schools and roads, some states also have a personal income tax. ______

10. Since we have to work to pay for food, rent, clothing, and school, we will all end up paying taxes at some point! ______

Copyright © by Holt, Rinehart and Winston. All rights reserved.

The Elliptical Clause

4g. Part of a clause may be left out when its meaning can be clearly understood in the context of the sentence. Such a clause is called an ***elliptical clause.***

EXAMPLES **Although** [he was] **ill,** Matthew managed to finish his essay.
When [you are] **visiting the ruins,** do not disturb anything.
Why is this tree so much taller **than the others** [are tall]?

EXERCISE A In each sentence below, part of the clause has been omitted to produce an elliptical clause. On the line provided, insert a word or words that would complete the clause.

Example 1. You know that I don't like horror movies as much _as you do._

1. The runners, though _______________ tired, completed the last lap of the race.

2. Buy your popcorn and drink before _______________ the movie.

3. Whenever _______________ singing, you must support the tone with ample breath.

4. He likes reading Dickens more than _______________ Hawthorne.

5. Count and exhale while _______________ lifting the weight bar.

EXERCISE B For each of the following adverb clauses, draw a line through a word or words to produce an elliptical clause.

Example 1. When ~~you are~~ setting up the computer, read the instructions carefully.

6. Unless they are frightened of clowns, children generally enjoy circuses.

7. While you are turning off the lights, check the doors, too.

8. I usually listen to the radio while I am studying.

9. Do you like chocolate as much as you like vanilla?

10. Jacob is taller than the other players are tall.

Copyright © by Holt, Rinehart and Winston. All rights reserved.

NAME ______________________ CLASS ______________ DATE ______________

Identifying Adjective and Adverb Clauses

4d. An ***adjective clause*** is a subordinate clause that modifies a noun or a pronoun.

EXAMPLES The movie **that I saw yesterday** really made me think.
I discussed the film with Bianca, **who reviews movies for the school newspaper.**

4f. An ***adverb clause*** is a subordinate clause that modifies a verb, an adjective, or an adverb.

EXAMPLES **When Nari heard about the stranded animals,** she volunteered to help.
Do not try to handle a strange dog or cat **unless you have been properly trained.**

EXERCISE In each sentence, underline the subordinate clause. Above each subordinate clause, write *ADJ* if the clause functions as an adjective or *ADV* if the clause functions as an adverb.

Example 1. Jeff is the one <u>whose brother works overseas.</u> (ADJ)

1. Although some people have had access to the Internet for only a short time, its beginnings can be traced back to the 1960s.
2. The Internet, which is a network connecting many computers using a common communications protocol, was once used mostly by academics.
3. The ARPAnet, which was established in 1969, was the predecessor of the Internet.
4. ARPAnet is an acronym that stands for Advanced Research Projects Agency Network.
5. The Department of Defense established ARPAnet when they wanted to connect computers at military installations and universities.
6. Later, in 1974, the Xerox Corporation adapted the communications network for use in its business because it could inexpensively send information throughout the company.
7. The people at Xerox, who called their adaptation an Ethernet, cut the cost of installation with new wiring techniques.
8. Although such communication nets were once used only by military personnel, academics, and business people, today anyone can use the Internet.
9. Provided that you have a library card, you can access the Internet at many public libraries.
10. You can even go to an Internet café and have a snack while you browse the World Wide Web.

Copyright © by Holt, Rinehart and Winston. All rights reserved.

NAME _______________ CLASS _______________ DATE _______________

Identifying and Classifying Subordinate Clauses A

4c. A ***subordinate*** (or ***dependent***) ***clause*** does not express a complete thought and cannot stand by itself as a sentence.

4d. An ***adjective clause*** is a subordinate clause that modifies a noun or a pronoun.

4e. A ***noun clause*** is a subordinate clause that is used as a noun.

4f. An ***adverb clause*** is a subordinate clause that modifies a verb, an adjective, or an adverb.

EXERCISE A Underline each subordinate clause in the following sentences. Then, classify each subordinate clause by writing above it *ADJ* for *adjective clause*, *N* for *noun clause*, or *ADV* for *adverb clause*.

Example 1. Did you know that some birds are skilled ventriloquists? (N)

1. The American bittern, a member of the heron family, is a bird that practices ventriloquism.
2. The call of the bittern should be familiar to anyone who has ever explored a marshland.
3. Although the bittern's call is easy to identify, the source of the sound is usually hard to locate.
4. Whoever tries to spot a bittern or find its nest may have a difficult job.
5. The call seems to come from one location while the bird is actually somewhere else.
6. Bird experts tell us that the bittern also uses protective coloration.
7. When a bittern is alarmed, it stands motionless and points its bill upward.
8. Its neck, which is marked with a vertical black stripe, then fades in with the marsh reeds.
9. The nest in which the bittern lays its eggs is also difficult to spot.
10. Since the nest is made of reeds, it is easily mistaken for a tangled patch of marsh grass.

EXERCISE B Add a descriptive clause of the type indicated in the parentheses to each sentence. If the clause is nonessential, set it off from the sentence with one or two commas, as needed.

Example 1. (Use *which* to begin an adjective clause.) Camouflage, which means an ability to blend in with one's surroundings, has long been a defense of many birds.

11. (Use *because* to begin an adverb clause.) It protects them from predators.
12. (Use *that* to begin an adjective clause.) Birds may be difficult for predators to see.
13. (Use *while* to begin an adverb clause.) Hunters wear camouflage clothing.
14. (Use *that* to begin a noun clause.) Fashion designers who use camouflage colors know.
15. (Use *who* to begin an adjective clause.) People aren't seeking protection from anything!

Copyright © by Holt, Rinehart and Winston. All rights reserved.

Identifying and Classifying Subordinate Clauses B

4c. A ***subordinate*** (or ***dependent***) ***clause*** does not express a complete thought and cannot stand by itself as a sentence.

4d. An ***adjective clause*** is a subordinate clause that modifies a noun or a pronoun.

EXAMPLE We finally arrived at the village **where Grandmother had grown up.**

4e. A ***noun clause*** is a subordinate clause that is used as a noun.

EXAMPLE **Why the village had become so deserted** was hard to understand.

4f. An ***adverb clause*** is a subordinate clause that modifies a verb, an adjective, or an adverb.

EXAMPLE **When I looked at the architecture and the landscape,** I was overwhelmed by the beauty of this place.

EXERCISE In each sentence, underline the subordinate clause. If the subordinate clause functions as a noun, indicate the clause's function by writing above it *S* for *subject, DO* for *direct object, IO* for *indirect object, OP* for *object of a preposition,* or *PN* for *predicate nominative.* If the clause functions as a modifier, indicate its function by writing above it *ADJ* for *adjective* or an *ADV* for *adverb.*

Example 1. Monopoly, which has worldwide popularity, has been around since 1934. (ADJ)

1. The fact is that Monopoly was invented during the financially difficult years of the Depression.
2. Clarence B. Darrow, who invented the game, didn't succeed with it at first.
3. Darrow invented the game while he dreamed of real fame and fortune.
4. The game was rejected by one company because it had "fifty-two design errors."
5. That the first company refused the game did not deter Darrow.
6. As soon as he had sold 5,000 handmade sets, however, game companies began to take interest.
7. It's not hard to understand why Monopoly was the bestselling game in 1935.
8. Since then, an estimated 500 million people who enjoy games have played it.
9. You might not know that one Monopoly game lasted seventy straight days!
10. Monopoly terms have entered popular conversation, so that trademark protection of the tokens, cards, and game-board corners has become necessary.

Copyright © by Holt, Rinehart and Winston. All rights reserved.

Sentences Classified According to Structure

4h. Depending on its structure, a sentence can be classified as simple, compound, complex, or compound-complex.

(1) A ***simple sentence*** contains one independent clause and no subordinate clauses.

EXAMPLE Andrés Segovia revolutionized the classical guitar.

(2) A ***compound sentence*** contains two or more independent clauses and no subordinate clauses.

EXAMPLE Segovia brought classical guitar music to a wide audience, and he talked many composers into writing for the guitar.

(3) A ***complex sentence*** contains one independent clause and at least one subordinate clause.

EXAMPLE When he played, it sometimes seemed that two or three guitars were playing.

(4) A ***compound-complex sentence*** contains two or more independent clauses and at least one subordinate clause.

EXAMPLE He was a master of technique, and when he wanted, he could make the guitar weep.

EXERCISE Classify each of the following sentences according to its structure. On the line provided, write *S* for *simple, CD* for *compound, CX* for *complex,* or *CD-CX* for *compound-complex.*

Example CD-CX **1.** Heather was nervous at first, but she calmed down as soon as the game got underway.

______ **1.** This crystal comes from England and is handmade.

______ **2.** We particularly enjoyed the exhibition of Turner's paintings that we saw in London.

______ **3.** Spike Lee is an acclaimed filmmaker who writes, directs, and acts in his own movies.

______ **4.** Confucianism, which is known to the Chinese as *Ju Chaio,* teaches that people should behave according to their proper roles—father and son, ruler and subject, master and servant.

______ **5.** When we arrived at the campsite, Roger set up the tent and Mom searched for firewood.

______ **6.** The puppet show bored the children, but their parents thoroughly enjoyed it.

______ **7.** There are more possible connections between cells in one human brain than there are grains of sand on all of the world's beaches.

______ **8.** When it is done correctly, scuba diving is great fun, but it can also be dangerous if attempted without proper training.

______ **9.** The air temperature rose to 100 degrees, and tempers rose as well.

______ **10.** On the tip of the island of Sicily, high above the crashing surf, sits the mysterious walled city of Erice.

Copyright © by Holt, Rinehart and Winston. All rights reserved.

NAME ____________ CLASS ____________ DATE ____________

Sentences Classified According to Purpose

4i. Depending on its purpose, a sentence can be classified as declarative, imperative, interrogative, or exclamatory.

(1) A ***declarative sentence*** makes a statement and ends with a period.

EXAMPLE The police have been using dogs to help them find contraband items**.**

(2) An ***imperative sentence*** gives a command or makes a request. Most imperative sentences end with a period. A strong command ends with an exclamation point.

EXAMPLES Please explain the concept of operant conditioning**.** [request]
Watch out for that car**!** [command]

(3) An ***interrogative sentence*** asks a question and ends with a question mark.

EXAMPLE In what country was Gloria Estefan born**?**

(4) An ***exclamatory sentence*** shows excitement or expresses strong feeling and ends with an exclamation point.

EXAMPLE What a great idea he had**!**

EXERCISE For each of the following sentences, identify its purpose as *de*clarative, *imp*erative, *int*errogative, or *ex*clamatory. Then, supply the proper end mark.

Example 1. Why do some people so enjoy thrill rides? ___int.___

1. I once rode a roller coaster that flipped the riders upside down and then ran around a steel loop ________
2. What a strange feeling that was ________
3. I expected my sandals to fly off and land on people in line below us ________
4. Have you ever ridden a coaster in which the riders must stand up ________
5. No, this will be my first ride on a stand-up roller coaster ________
6. Be sure to secure all loose items in your pockets before boarding the ride ________
7. Don't forget to scream on the way down the hill ________
8. I much prefer calmer rides ________
9. How do you feel about those water rides that soak you to the bone ________
10. What a relief it is to cool off on a hot day ________

Copyright © by Holt, Rinehart and Winston. All rights reserved.

NAME ______________________ CLASS ______________ DATE ______________

GRAMMAR

for **CHAPTER 4: THE CLAUSE** *pages 128–138*

Review A: Clauses

EXERCISE Classify each underlined clause by writing, in the space above it, *I* for *independent* or *S* for *subordinate*. For each subordinate clause, also tell how the clause is used by writing *ADJ* for *adjective clause*, *N* for *noun clause*, or *ADV* for *adverb clause*.

Example 1. Anyone who is visiting Pasadena, California, on New Year's Day should make a point of seeing the Tournament of Roses. (S—ADJ)

1. Pasadena's Tournament of Roses has been held annually since it was established in 1890.

2. The floats are the greatest attraction, but spectators also enjoy the bands that march past.

3. To reserve a spot for viewing the parade, many people camp out along the parade route.

4. The Rose Queens ride on the floats, and equestrians ride atop magnificent horses.

5. The floats are judged before the parade, and the spectators know which ones have won prizes.

6. Floats that are entered by commercial firms are judged separately from those prepared by other organizations.

7. The floats are left on display after the parade is over.

8. A group of officials decides who the tournament queen will be.

9. Preparations for the parade are quite involved.

10. Some years ago the length of the parade had to be limited because the parades were beginning to take too much time.

11. The big sports event of the Tournament of Roses is, of course, the Rose Bowl game, which is played in the afternoon.

12. Traditionally, the Pacific Ten and the Big Ten conferences determined which teams would participate.

13. Teams that are invited to play in the Rose Bowl are highly honored.

14. The Rose Bowl, which seats about 100,000 people, is one of the largest stadiums in the world.

15. It is usually filled to capacity when the Rose Bowl game gets underway.

16. The income from the football game is what covers the cost of the parade.

17. The game is a long-standing tradition that most fans take very seriously.

18. The entire country today can follow the Tournament of Roses on television.

19. Some of those who now watch it on television formerly had to rely on published pictures.

20. Each year millions of viewers enjoy the spectacle, which is ideal for television.

Copyright © by Holt, Rinehart and Winston. All rights reserved.

NAME CLASS DATE

Review B: Clauses

EXERCISE Underline each subordinate clause in the following sentences. Then, classify each subordinate clause by writing, in the space above it, *ADJ* for *adjective clause*, *N* for *noun clause*, or *ADV* for *adverb clause*. If a sentence contains no subordinate clause, write *none* before the item number.

Example 1. Ms. Neeley led a fascinating discussion about why some writers use pseudonyms. (N)

1. Do you know who George Sand was?
2. I learned that she was born Amandine Aurore Lucie Dupin.
3. Her pen name is one of the most famous pseudonyms in the history of literature.
4. When people choose pseudonyms, they do so for a variety of reasons.
5. A pseudonym, or fictitious name, is not always one that conceals a person's identity.
6. After all, nearly everyone knows who Mark Twain was.
7. That he was really Samuel Langhorne Clemens is not a matter of great significance.
8. Some writers may conceal their gender, though, as Mary Ann Evans did by assuming the name George Eliot.
9. A modern writer who has done the same without a pseudonym is P. D. James.
10. When men write romantic fiction, they sometimes assume a woman's name.
11. Of course, entertainers often change their names in order to appear more glamorous to their fans.
12. Cary Grant, who grew up as Archibald Leach, was one such entertainer.
13. Another was Henry John Deutschendorf, Jr., better known as John Denver, a singer whose pseudonym comes from the name of a city.
14. Quite a few other entertainers, such as Donna Fargo and Conway Twitty, have chosen the names of cities and towns as their pseudonyms.
15. Whenever a sports star has a hard-to-pronounce name, the athlete may feel some pressure to change it to something easier.
16. Even some avid baseball fans may not know who Aloysius Szymanski was.
17. He was the great Hall of Fame outfielder Al Simmons, a player who also had a well-known nickname, "Bucketfoot Al."
18. There are "ordinary" people, too, with names they wish to change.
19. Supposedly, a man by the name of Messerschmitt, living in England during World War II, asked to change his name because *Messerschmitt* was the name of a German airplane.
20. He wanted to be called Spitfire in honor of the famous British fighting plane.

Copyright © by Holt, Rinehart and Winston. All rights reserved.

Review C: Sentences Classified According to Structure

EXERCISE A In the following sentences, draw one line under each independent clause and two lines under each subordinate clause. Then, classify the sentence by structure. On the line provided, write *S* for *simple, CD* for *compound, CX* for *complex,* or *CD-CX* for *compound-complex.*

Example CX **1.** The Droughtmaster, which is a popular breed of cattle in Australia, is a cross between a Brahman and a Shorthorn.

______ **1.** Cattle raisers have long used the technique of crossbreeding to produce animals that combine the best qualities of two different breeds.

______ **2.** The Hereford breed, for instance, originated in England in the eighteenth century; it was a cross between native Herefordshire cattle and cattle from the Netherlands.

______ **3.** More recently, American breeders have crossed Herefords and Brahmans in order to produce a breed called Brafords.

______ **4.** The Hereford is a beef breed originally from England, and the Brahman, a breed native to India, is a type noted for its resistance to heat and to disease.

______ **5.** One of the most unusual animals that American breeders have produced is the cattalo; it is a cross between a buffalo and a cow.

EXERCISE B Classify each of the following sentences according to its structure. On the line provided, write *S* for *simple, CD* for *compound, CX* for *complex,* or *CD-CX* for *compound-complex.*

Example CX **1.** Though it may not be as well-known as other cities in Australia, Perth has an appealing mix of city life and nature.

______ **6.** The capital city of Western Australia, Perth is part of a metropolitan area that contains about three fourths of Western Australia's population.

______ **7.** This city, which has a sunny climate, stands out because of its natural formations; it lies on the Swan River and contains a thousand-acre area of vegetation called King's Park.

______ **8.** Along with access to nearby beaches, Perth has a cultural center that is just north of its business district.

______ **9.** Founded in 1829, Perth grew quickly after the discovery of gold near the area in the late 1800s.

______ **10.** Visitors can reach Perth by highway, or they can get there by airplane or transcontinental railroad.

Copyright © by Holt, Rinehart and Winston. All rights reserved.

NAME ______ CLASS ______ DATE ______

Review D: Sentences Classified According to Purpose

EXERCISE On the line provided, identify each sentence by its purpose, as *dec*larative, *imp*erative, *int*errogative, or *excl*amatory. Some sentences also contain a subordinate clause. Underline the clause, or, if the sentence has no subordinate clause, write *no clause* on the line provided.

Example **1.** Many words in our language have histories that are interesting to know.

dec.

1. For instance, the word *panorama,* which names a type of painting invented in 1787, comes from two Greek words. ______
2. *Pan* in Greek means "all," and *horama* means "a view" and comes from the Greek word *horan,* "to see." ______
3. Have you ever seen a panorama that depicts a famous place or event? ______
4. In the nineteenth century, panoramas as large as three hundred feet long and fifty feet tall were popular. ______
5. Hold on to the rails if you ever see a "cyclorama," a panorama that revolves on rollers. ______
6. Speaking of odd words, consider the word *farb.* ______
7. Reenactors re-creating historical battles and former ways of life use this word to describe people whose costumes are not historically accurate. ______
8. After all, would a Civil War soldier have worn sunglasses or carried a cellphone? ______
9. Perhaps this word comes from the German word for color, *farbe,* because inauthentic costumes are often much more brightly colored than the more accurate dull-colored ones. ______
10. What a sight it is to see a Civil War wife cooking in a microwave run by a generator! ______

Copyright © by Holt, Rinehart and Winston. All rights reserved.

Number

Number is the form a word takes to indicate whether the word is singular or plural.

5a. A word that refers to one person, place, thing, or idea is ***singular*** in number. A word that refers to more than one is ***plural*** in number.

SINGULAR	cowboy	belief	child	this	each	she
PLURAL	cowboys	beliefs	children	these	both	they

EXERCISE A On the line before each of the following words, write *S* for *singular* or *P* for *plural.*

Example __P__ **1.** wives

______ **1.** they

______ **2.** creature

______ **3.** windshield

______ **4.** hurricanes

______ **5.** brothers-in-law

______ **6.** amendment

______ **7.** pulleys

______ **8.** himself

______ **9.** basketball

______ **10.** willows

______ **11.** inference

______ **12.** castles

______ **13.** it

______ **14.** danger

______ **15.** geese

______ **16.** crater

______ **17.** illness

______ **18.** wolves

______ **19.** we

______ **20.** theorems

EXERCISE B Write a singular or plural word to complete each word group correctly.

Example 1. two dozen __eggs__

21. three ripe ______

22. many honest ______

23. a more expensive ______

24. another bright red ______

25. both successful ______

26. every single ______

27. too few ______

28. either ______

29. a traditional ______

30. at least fifteen ______

Copyright © by Holt, Rinehart and Winston. All rights reserved.

Subject-Verb Agreement A

5b. A verb should agree in number with its subject.

(1) Singular subjects take singular verbs.
(2) Plural subjects take plural verbs.

5c. The number of a subject is not changed by a word in a phrase or a clause following the subject.

EXAMPLES That **plan sounds** feasible to me. [singular subject and verb]
The **girls** and **boys** on the tennis team **are having** a car wash. [plural subject and verb]
To finish three chapters **is** my goal.
The lead **singer,** as well as the band members, **is rehearsing.**
The **funds** that they raise from this event **are** for charity.

EXERCISE A In each of the following sentences, underline the subject of the verb in parentheses. Then, underline twice the verb in parentheses that agrees in number with the subject.

Example 1. My parents, who both enjoy editorials, often *(has, have)* interesting discussions about the columns.

1. Opinions on the editorial page *(is, are)* often diverse.

2. Ellen Goodman, as well as other writers, *(speaks, speak)* on political issues.

3. A person who reads daily newspapers *(keeps, keep)* up on the issues.

4. One writer of humorous columns *(is, are)* Art Buchwald.

5. Government policy, along with rising taxes, *(receives, receive)* his barbs.

EXERCISE B Proofread the following sentences for errors in subject-verb agreement. Cross out each incorrect verb form, and write the correct form in the space above it. If a sentence is already correct, write C at the end.

Example 1. Prince Olaf, accompanied by many members of his court, ~~were~~ *was* seen shopping at the mall.

6. Her answer to all requests of this kind are the same.

7. A few members of the club usually dominate the proceedings.

8. The editorials in a newspaper often reflect the editor's personal bias.

9. The coach of the team, as well as the student co-captains, are going to speak at the banquet.

10. The success of amateur productions depend largely on the producer.

Copyright © by Holt, Rinehart and Winston. All rights reserved.

Subject-Verb Agreement B

5b. A verb should agree in number with its subject.

(1) Singular subjects take singular verbs.
(2) Plural subjects take plural verbs.

5c. The number of a subject is not changed by a word in a phrase or a clause following the subject.

EXAMPLES Our **cat** always **cleans** itself thoroughly after a meal. [singular subject and verb]
The **cashiers are being paid** $10.00 per hour. [plural subject and verb]
Getting fit **is** his reason for joining the gym.
The **apple** in your lunch box **is** a Granny Smith.
These blue **flowers,** which are from the garden, **have** a lovely fragrance.

EXERCISE In each of the following sentences, underline the subject of the verb in parentheses. Then, underline twice the verb in parentheses that agrees in number with the subject.

Example 1. The girl wearing the dark glasses *(is, are)* my sister.

1. The color of those daisies *(was, were)* bright yellow.
2. Did you know that Principal White, together with the school board, *(has, have)* approved the plan for the new gymnasium?
3. Alan said that the dogs in this obedience class *(was, were)* rescued from the shelter.
4. The drapery fabric that they finally decided upon *(contains, contain)* tiny flecks of yellow and green.
5. Searching for your lost earrings *(is, are)* making us late for the party.
6. My twin brother, whom you met yesterday, *(skis, ski)* better than I do.
7. To return the tiny robin safely to its nest *(was, were)* our goal.
8. In our family, Uncle Jeb, who brings us presents from all over the world, *(is, are)* the most popular of the aunts and uncles.
9. The smoke detector, as well as our noses, *(was, were)* telling us that something was on fire.
10. The paint for these rooms *(arrives, arrive)* tomorrow at the hardware store.

Copyright © by Holt, Rinehart and Winston. All rights reserved.

NAME ______________________ CLASS ______________ DATE ______________

for **CHAPTER 5: AGREEMENT** *pages 155–156*

Subject-Verb Agreement: Indefinite Pronouns A

USAGE

5d. Some indefinite pronouns are singular, some are plural, and some can be singular or plural depending on how they are used.

EXAMPLES **Neither** of those films **is** available on video.

Few who have read that book **praise** it.

Most of the movie **is** exciting. [*Most* refers to the singular noun *movie*.]

Most of the action scenes **are** exciting. [*Most* refers to the plural noun *scenes*.]

EXERCISE A In each of the following sentences, circle the subject of the verb in parentheses and above it write *S* for *singular* or *P* for *plural*. Then, underline the verb in parentheses that agrees in number with the subject.

Example 1. Did you know that no one from our school *(are, is)* going to that college next year?

1. Anybody who had his or her parents' permission *(were, was)* allowed to go on the field trip.
2. Several of our neighbor's puppies *(have, has)* found good homes.
3. Some of the puzzle pieces *(is, are)* missing, but you can still figure out what the picture is.
4. Everything you've advised me to do *(has, have)* been for the best.
5. Something to think about *(is, are)* where you expect to be in five years.

EXERCISE B Most of the following sentences contain an error in agreement between a subject and a verb. First, circle the simple subject of each sentence. Then, draw a line through each incorrect verb, and above it write the form that agrees with the subject. If a sentence is correct, write *C* at the end.

Example 1. Everybody in the junior and senior English classes ~~have~~ has already seen the films on American dialects.

6. Some of the members of the safety patrol is not satisfied with the current regulations.
7. All of the marigolds was blooming.
8. Everyone with high marks are eligible for the scholarship.
9. Only a few of the class members has applied.
10. None of the equipment were salvaged after the devastating flood.
11. Both of those answers is correct.
12. Neither of the pitchers were able to stop the Hawks from winning the game.
13. Most of the incident was captured on videotape.
14. Each of the gymnasts has completed the entry form.
15. Of all the blouses on sale, several was my size.

Copyright © by Holt, Rinehart and Winston. All rights reserved.

Subject-Verb Agreement: Indefinite Pronouns B

5d. Some indefinite pronouns are singular, some are plural, and some can be singular or plural depending on how they are used.

EXAMPLES **Everyone** who votes **receives** a lapel button to wear.
Many who apply to Ivy League schools **get** turned down.
Some of the story **is** set in France. [*Some* refers to the singular noun *story*.]
Some of the characters **are** not very believable. [*Some* refers to the plural noun *characters*.]

USAGE

EXERCISE A In each of the following sentences, circle the subject of the verb in parentheses, and above it write *S* for *singular* or *P* for *plural*. Then, underline the verb in parentheses that agrees in number with the subject.

Example 1. Some of our friends *(are, is)* throwing Eli a surprise party for his birthday.

1. Most of the ingredients for our supper *(were, was)* fresh vegetables from our garden.
2. None of the documentary *(have, has)* been cut from this videotape.
3. Several in the crowd *(is, are)* waving banners and hoping to be noticed by the band.
4. Everything on television tonight *(has, have)* been on before; I'm tired of re-runs.
5. All of us in the forensics society *(is, are)* going to the regional competition.

EXERCISE B Most of the following sentences contain an error in agreement between a subject and a verb. First, circle the simple subject of each sentence. Then, draw a line through each incorrect verb, and above it write the form that agrees with the subject. If a sentence is correct, write *C* at the end.

Example 1. Somebody in the judo or karate class ~~have~~ has already reserved the practice room for next Thursday.

6. Some of the kittens in this litter is gray tabbies like their mother.
7. All of the backpacks was on sale at Edelmann's Sporting Goods Store.
8. Anyone answering all the homework questions correctly are excused from taking the quiz.
9. Several of the daffodils has already sprouted.
10. One of the finalists in the diving competition was born in China.
11. Either of these tuxedos are suitable for the prom, Ernesto.
12. Both of the car dealerships is offering special deals on financing.
13. After the potluck supper, some of Mom's rhubarb pie was left.
14. Neither of these applicants have the experience necessary, Ms. Chao.
15. Few of the pages in that old history book has pictures.

Copyright © by Holt, Rinehart and Winston. All rights reserved.

USAGE

Agreement with Compound Subjects A

A ***compound subject*** consists of two or more subjects that are joined by a conjunction and that have the same verb.

5e. Subjects joined by *and* usually take a plural verb.

Some compound subjects joined by *and* name only one person or thing and take singular verbs.

EXAMPLES **Andrea, Benjamin,** and **Danny were** present at the awards show.
The **producer** and **director** of the movie **was** she.

5f. Singular subjects joined by *or* or *nor* take a singular verb.

EXAMPLE Neither **Danny** nor **Nick has appeared** on stage before.

5g. When a singular subject and a plural subject are joined by *or* or *nor,* the verb agrees with the subject nearer the verb.

EXAMPLES Neither the team **members** nor the **coach has been** to the Super Bowl.
Neither the **coach** nor the team **members have been** to the Super Bowl.

EXERCISE In each of the following sentences, underline once the simple subjects that are part of the compound subject. Then, underline twice the verb in parentheses that agrees in number with the compound subject.

Example 1. To pay for child care and to save for retirement *(take, takes)* a large amount of Aunt Rita's salary.

1. Either the dogs or some wild animal *(has, have)* dug a hole under the fence in the backyard.
2. In the past, *(have, has)* juggling and mime been taught at the performing arts summer school?
3. A cup of sugar and three cups of whole wheat flour *(have, has)* been measured and set aside.
4. Either Rick or his brother *(walks, walk)* their dog, Buster, every morning and evening.
5. *(Has, Have)* working at the movie theater and doing your homework been taking up most of your time?
6. *(Is, Are)* Anna or Elise making the costumes for the senior class play?
7. Jonathan, Dana, Leroy, and I *(are, is)* planning a road trip for spring break.
8. Steak and potatoes *(were, was)* my dad's favorite meal until his doctor told him to reduce the amount of cholesterol in his diet.
9. Talking with clients and designing furniture for them *(make, makes)* up most of Dan's day.
10. The large oak tree in the front yard and the smaller one in the back *(are, is)* not in danger of getting oak wilt disease.

Copyright © by Holt, Rinehart and Winston. All rights reserved.

Agreement with Compound Subjects B

A *compound subject* consists of two or more subjects that are joined by a conjunction and that have the same verb.

5e. Subjects joined by *and* usually take a plural verb.

Some compound subjects joined by *and* name only one person or thing and take singular verbs.

EXAMPLES The **parrot** and the **cockatoo do** not **like** to be left alone very long.
The **writer** and **director** of that popular new play **is** he.

5f. Singular subjects joined by *or* or *nor* take a singular verb.

EXAMPLES Either the letter **opener** or a sharp **knife is** what I need to open this package.
Neither **Wanda** nor **June knows** about the surprise party we are planning for them.

5g. When a singular subject and a plural subject are joined by *or* or *nor,* the verb agrees with the subject nearer the verb.

EXAMPLES Either the **twins** or **Alice washes** the dishes after supper.
Either **Alice** or the **twins wash** the dishes after supper.

EXERCISE Each of the following sentences contains an error in agreement between a subject and a verb. First, underline once the simple subjects that are part of the compound subject. Then, draw a line through the incorrect verb, and above it write the form that agrees with the subject.

Example 1. Many of Alan's friends and some of his coworkers ~~has~~ *have* arranged to bring him meals while he recuperates at home from his surgery.

1. The oboists and the band director is scheduled to have the practice room this afternoon.

2. Two physicians or an emergency room nurse have agreed to speak to our science class about careers in medicine.

3. Twenty geraniums and an entire flat of petunias is what we planted in the window boxes.

4. A good book and a shady hammock is going to help me relax this Saturday.

5. Our boss, cheerleader, and role model are our store manager, Kris.

6. The student council and their faculty advisor has chosen the theme for the prom.

7. During every appointment, the assistants or the veterinarian advise me on tooth care for my basset hound.

8. Cookies or a chocolate cake are a good dessert to bring to a potluck supper.

9. Macaroni and cheese are my little sister's favorite main dish.

10. A dropcloth or even some newspapers helps prevent painting accidents.

Copyright © by Holt, Rinehart and Winston. All rights reserved.

USAGE

Special Problems in Subject-Verb Agreement A

5h. The contractions *don't* and *doesn't* should agree with their subjects.

EXAMPLES **Darnell doesn't** play baseball anymore.
The **tamales don't** seem too spicy to me.

5i. When the subject follows the verb, find the subject and make sure that the verb agrees with it.

EXAMPLES In my opinion, there **are** several good **reasons** to vote for that candidate.
Have Shanda and **Melanie returned** from the polls yet?

The contractions *here's, there's, when's,* and *where's* incorporate the singular verb *is* and therefore should be used only with singular subjects.

NONSTANDARD Where's the tomatoes for the gazpacho?
STANDARD Where **are** the **tomatoes** for the gazpacho?

EXERCISE In the following sentences, underline every subject. Then, draw a line through any incorrect verb, and above it write the form that agrees with the subject.

Example 1. ~~Here's~~ *Here are* the keys you've been looking for, Denise.

1. By the way, where's the tapes that you borrowed last week?
2. Doesn't the fountain and the bird bath freeze in the winter?
3. There's the exchange students from Germany and Romania.
4. Here's the ingredients for the vegetarian lasagna.
5. Is Jenny and her sister both in the choral ensemble?
6. Where's Brent and Joey going over spring break?
7. In addition to your family, was there any friends and neighbors at your grandfather's birthday party?
8. As you know, there's several items on tonight's PTA agenda that concern us seniors.
9. Don't this leather-bound journal from the Netherlands belong to you?
10. Here's the books about World War II that Ms. Ramos put on reserve for us.

Copyright © by Holt, Rinehart and Winston. All rights reserved.

Special Problems in Subject-Verb Agreement B

5j. A collective noun may be either singular or plural, depending on its meaning in a sentence.

A collective noun is singular when it refers to the group as a unit and plural when it refers to the individual members or parts of a group.

SINGULAR The **club meets** on Tuesday. [*Club* is thought of as a unit.]

PLURAL The **club have cast** their votes. [*Club* is thought of as individuals.]

EXERCISE In each of the following sentences, underline the collective noun once. Then, underline twice the verb in parentheses that agrees in number with the collective noun.

Example 1. I still believe that the public (*vote, votes*) their conscience at election time.

1. The team (*plan, plans*) to share their best memories of the coach at his retirement party.
2. At the meeting the staff (*were, was*) remarking on the new furniture in the conference room.
3. I think the orchestra (*sound, sounds*) off-key tonight.
4. How often (*have, has*) our school choir performed at the regional music festival?
5. Principal Smith has asked whether the school safety committee (*want, wants*) to present their reports.
6. The pride of lions (*were, was*) resting in the shade of a tree.
7. That litter of puppies (*have, has*) all different colored coats—brown, black, and white.
8. For this maneuver, the squadron (*fly, flies*) in a tight formation.
9. The herd (*was, were*) tagged and vaccinated against common bovine illnesses.
10. The chamber ensemble (*play, plays*) only music written before 1800.
11. A hive of bees (*work, works*) hard to feed and protect its queen.
12. The couple that moved in next door (*do, does*) yard work every Saturday.
13. After a win, the team (*celebrate, celebrates*) by going out for pizza.
14. The audience usually (*bring, brings*) their opera glasses with them.
15. Before starting to march, the band (*tune, tunes*) their instruments.
16. After the closing arguments, the jury (*seem, seems*) to be taking a long time to reach its verdict.
17. The team usually (*donates, donate*) their old uniforms to a group of disadvantaged youth.
18. After lunch the staff (*is, are*) going to meet to discuss ways to enhance interdepartmental relationships.
19. The faculty (*is, are*) meeting to decide what to do with the grant money they received.
20. Before the play, the cast (*get, gets*) together to do warm-up vocal exercises.

Copyright © by Holt, Rinehart and Winston. All rights reserved.

Special Problems in Subject-Verb Agreement C

5k. An expression of an amount (a measurement, a percentage, or a fraction, for example) may be singular or plural, depending on how it is used.

EXAMPLES **Five dollars is** the price of the buffet lunch. [The amount is thought of as a unit.]

Five dollars were in the bag. [The amount is thought of as separate parts.]

About **two thirds** of the audience **has been seated.** [The fraction refers to the singular noun *audience.*]

About **two thirds** of the guests **have been seated.** [The fraction refers to the plural noun *guests.*]

Thirty-two yards was the distance of the Rams' last touchdown pass. [The amount is thought of as a unit.]

Thirty-two yards were measured off in one-yard sections. [The amount is thought of as separate parts.]

EXERCISE In each of the following sentences, underline the verb in parentheses that agrees in number with its subject.

Example 1. Ten kilometers *(was, were)* the distance we biked.

1. Twenty-five dollars *(is, are)* the cost of a ticket to the upcoming concert.

2. *(Do, Does)* six fluid ounces of water weigh the same as six fluid ounces of tomato juice?

3. Recently, about five percent *(have, has)* been the interest rate for money market accounts.

4. If four cents *(are, is)* my change, just keep it.

5. Three quarters of a cup *(were, was)* all the sugar called for in that recipe.

6. Two blocks from Beech Street *(were, was)* the closest I had been to the arena until tonight.

7. Since I last checked them, twelve percent of the beans in my experiment *(has, have)* sprouted.

8. Fifty miles an hour *(seem, seems)* to be too fast a speed limit for that twisty section of road.

9. Almost one third of my classmates *(participate, participates)* in after-school activities.

10. Fifteen quarts of peaches *(is, are)* what we canned last weekend.

Copyright © by Holt, Rinehart and Winston. All rights reserved.

NAME ______________________ CLASS ______________ DATE ______________

Special Problems in Subject-Verb Agreement D

5l. Some nouns that are plural in form take singular verbs.

Nouns such as *civics, electronics, genetics, linguistics, mathematics,* and *physics* are plural in form but take singular verbs. Nouns suggesting "a pair of" always take plural verbs.

EXAMPLES The **news** from the doctor **was** disturbing.

Measles was the diagnosis.

I didn't know that **mathematics is** your favorite subject.

Those **pliers have been missing** for months.

Where **are** the **scissors** I lent you?

5m. Even when plural in form, the titles of creative works (such as books, songs, movies, or paintings) and the names of countries, cities, and organizations generally take singular verbs.

EXAMPLES ***The Potato Eaters* is** a painting by Vincent van Gogh.

The **United States produces** large quantities of wheat.

Barnes Industries has been making office equipment for many years.

EXERCISE In each of the following sentences, underline the verb in parentheses that agrees in number with its subject.

Example 1. *(Aren't, Isn't) Green Eggs and Ham* one of your little brother's favorite books?

1. This year, physics *(is, are)* my most difficult course.
2. "The Outcasts of Poker Flat" *(are, is)* my favorite short story by Bret Harte.
3. *(Are, Is)* the binoculars in your backpack, Rachel?
4. Government statistics *(show, shows)* how the minimum wage has not kept up with inflation.
5. John's Discount Shoes *(have, has)* been in that same location for twenty years.
6. Molasses *(are, is)* what makes this gingerbread so moist.
7. Your new eyeglasses *(look, looks)* more attractive than your old ones.
8. "Hybrid Cars" *(explain, explains)* how these new vehicles run on both gasoline and electricity.
9. To prevent spreading plant diseases, be sure that the shears *(receive, receives)* a good cleaning and disinfecting after each use.
10. *(Are, Is)* the Philippines a large group of individual islands or a long island chain?

Copyright © by Holt, Rinehart and Winston. All rights reserved.

Special Problems in Subject-Verb Agreement E

USAGE

5n. A verb agrees with its subject but not necessarily with a predicate nominative.

EXAMPLES One cool-weather **crop** discussed in the article **is** peas.
Peas are one of the cool-weather crops discussed in the article.

5o. Subjects preceded by *every* or *many a(n)* take singular verbs.

EXAMPLES **Every student** and **teacher** at the assembly **was** awestruck.
Many a swimmer has dreamed of going to the Olympics.

EXERCISE In each of the following sentences, underline the subject of the verb in parentheses. Then, underline twice the verb in parentheses that agrees in number with its subject.

Example 1. *(Haven't, Hasn't)* the irises in the back yard been a success this year?

1. Our greatest concern *(is, are)* the orphaned puppies that were brought in last week.
2. My specialty in the kitchen *(is, are)* vegetable soups made from fresh produce.
3. Many a student in our calculus class *(have, has)* commented on Mr. Wright's ability to explain complex ideas simply.
4. The acrobats *(was, were)* the best part of the floor show.
5. Every pot and pan in the restaurant *(have, has)* been washed and put away.
6. Many an aspiring actor *(find, finds)* himself or herself waiting tables to pay the bills.
7. *(Is, Are)* sequined evening dresses the most becoming choice for your bridesmaids?
8. One thing I can never have enough of *(is, are)* colored pencils.
9. Not every high school athlete *(go, goes)* on to play his or her sport in college.
10. These days, many a computer enthusiast *(send, sends)* electronic greeting cards.
11. One of my chores *(is, are)* washing and drying the dishes after supper.
12. Strawberries and peaches *(were, was)* the dessert.
13. Every employee and volunteer *(look, looks)* forward to the technology fair.
14. Labrador retrievers *(is, are)* my favorite kind of dog.
15. One of the vegetables she has never eaten *(is, are)* rutabagas.
16. Kites and other flying objects *(was, were)* the main attraction at the fair.
17. Every parent and child *(is, are)* invited to attend the school picnic.
18. Peaches *(is, are)* my favorite fruit.
19. Many a young child *(has, have)* been thrilled by a sight of a small puppy.
20. One of the things I have to accomplish today *(is, are)* mowing and trimming the lawn.

Copyright © by Holt, Rinehart and Winston. All rights reserved.

Special Problems in Subject-Verb Agreement F

5p. When the relative pronoun *that, which,* or *who* is the subject of an adjective clause, the verb in the clause agrees with the word to which the relative pronoun refers.

EXAMPLES A citizen **who wants** to improve the government must vote. [*Who* refers to the singular noun *citizen.*]

We need reforms **that ease** the burdens of taxpayers. [*That* refers to the plural noun *reforms.*]

EXERCISE In each of the following sentences, underline the relative pronoun once and circle the word to which it refers. Then, underline twice the verb in parentheses that agrees in number with the word to which the relative pronoun refers.

Example 1. One of the subjects that *(have, has)* been hotly debated in the editorial pages of the newspaper is cost of the new highway.

1. The government needs census workers who *(are, is)* fluent in Spanish.
2. He suggested two different window treatments that *(seem, seems)* perfect for the room.
3. Janice has found an art program which *(are, is)* perfect for her interests and talent.
4. Ravi has used only two of the sick days that *(are, is)* allowed.
5. Ask the editor who *(coordinate, coordinates)* the yearbook schedules if it's too late to place an advertisement.
6. Jerome already has several good ideas for the history project that *(were, was)* assigned today.
7. Do you remember the names of the astronauts who *(was, were)* the first to land on the moon?
8. Zack found several Web sites that *(contain, contains)* useful information for our presentation.
9. Uncle Sean is my one relative who *(have, has)* an Irish first name.
10. This antique lacquer tray, which *(are, is)* very valuable, belonged to my great-great-grandmother.

Copyright © by Holt, Rinehart and Winston. All rights reserved.

USAGE

Agreement of Pronoun and Antecedent A

A pronoun usually refers to a noun or another pronoun, which is called the pronoun's *antecedent*.

5q. A pronoun should agree in number, gender, and person with its antecedent.

(1) Singular pronouns refer to singular antecedents. Plural pronouns refer to plural antecedents.

EXAMPLES **Theodore Roethke** won the Pulitzer Prize for one of **his** books of poetry. [singular]

The **trees** have shed **their** leaves. [plural]

(2) Some singular pronouns indicate gender.

EXAMPLES That morning **Mr. Itoh** took **his** dog for a long walk. [masculine]

Danielle was out of breath when **she** rushed into the room. [feminine]

The technician worked on the **computer** for hours but could not fix **it.** [neuter]

(3) ***Person*** indicates whether a pronoun refers to the one(s) speaking (***first person***), the one(s) spoken to (***second person***), or the one(s) spoken of (***third person***).

EXAMPLES **We** adopted **our** cat from the animal shelter. [first person]

Did **you** paint this beautiful landscape **yourself**? [second person]

They built **their** own adobe home in Taos, New Mexico. [third person]

EXERCISE In each of the following sentences, underline the correct pronoun in parentheses. Then, circle the antecedent with which the pronoun agrees.

Example 1. Did the principal announce when Josh will receive (*his, their*) award?

1. Please get the keys off the counter and bring (*it, them*) to me.
2. Tania has beaten (*her, their*) old record in the 200-meter freestyle.
3. If you see Dwayne, please tell (*him, them*) to pick up his uniform.
4. My brother and sister and I cleaned the house after school so that (*we, they*) could surprise Mom when she got home from work.
5. This bread is especially moist and delicious because (*it, them*) contains two tablespoons of toasted sesame oil.
6. In a few minutes, our veterinarian will tell us what (*she, they*) learned from Boots's X-ray.
7. Mara and Alana are accomplished gymnasts; therefore, (*she, they*) make even the most difficult flips look easy.
8. Frank is allergic to cats, so he tries to stay away from (*it, them*).
9. Because of extra piano practice, Ray has improved (*his, its*) performance of that Chopin nocturne.
10. The robin pulled bits of moss from the tree in order to make a nest for (*their, its*) eggs.

Copyright © by Holt, Rinehart and Winston. All rights reserved.

Agreement of Pronoun and Antecedent B

5r. Some indefinite pronouns are singular, some are plural, and some can be either singular or plural, depending on how they are used in the sentence.

(1) Use a singular pronoun to refer to any of the following antecedents: *anybody, anyone, anything, each, either, everybody, everyone, everything, neither, nobody, no one, nothing, one, somebody, someone,* or *something.*

EXAMPLES **One** of the planes was delayed because **it** had ice on **its** wings.

Each of the climbers brought **his or her** own equipment.

(2) Use a plural pronoun to refer to any of the following indefinite pronouns: *both, few, many,* or *several.*

EXAMPLE **Several** of my friends brought **their** parents to the ceremony.

(3) Use a singular or a plural pronoun, depending on the meaning of the sentence, to refer to any of the following indefinite pronouns: *all, any, more, most, none,* or *some.*

EXAMPLES Jolene spilled **some** of the rabbit food, but she cleaned **it** up.

Jolene spilled **some** of the pellets, but she cleaned **them** up.

EXERCISE Proofread the following sentences for errors in pronoun-antecedent agreement. Cross out each incorrect pronoun, and write the correct form in the space above it. If a sentence is already correct, write *C* at the end.

Example 1. Someone on the bus left ~~their~~ *his or her* briefcase on the seat.

1. One of the players on the boys' team hurt themselves badly.

2. Mrs. Jackson asked both of the boys to help, and she paid him well.

3. Several of the band members had forgotten their instruments.

4. One of the girls had left their ticket at home and had difficulty getting into the game.

5. None of the ladies had finished their salad.

6. Neither of my sisters has decided where they will work this summer.

7. Some of the club members haven't paid their dues.

8. Everybody in the boys' chorus has received his sheet music.

9. Anyone who works hard should achieve their goal.

10. Most of the salad has wilted, so you can throw them away.

Copyright © by Holt, Rinehart and Winston. All rights reserved.

NAME ______________ CLASS ______________ DATE ______________

USAGE

Agreement of Pronoun and Antecedent C

5s. Use a plural pronoun to refer to two or more antecedents joined by *and.*

Antecedents joined by *and* may name only one person or thing. Such a compound antecedent takes a singular pronoun.

EXAMPLES **Donnell, Martin,** and **Suki** worked hard on the project, and **they** received a good grade.

Do you know my best **friend** and business **partner**? **His** name is Max Connor.

5t. Use a singular pronoun to refer to two or more singular antecedents joined by *or* or *nor.*

EXAMPLES Neither **Rafael** nor **Dave** sang **his** part very well.

If you see **Maria** or **Bethany,** please ask **her** to call me.

EXERCISE On the line provided, complete each of the following sentences by adding a pronoun or pronoun group that agrees with its antecedent.

Example 1. The finches and chickadees seem to be enjoying *their* new feeders.

1. Have Mom and Dad said what ________ would like for their anniversary?
2. Bacon and eggs makes a hearty breakfast, but ________ is high in cholesterol.
3. The cat and her kittens meowed loudly, waiting for me to feed ________.
4. In a few days, the dogwoods, lilacs, and forsythias will be covered in ________ dazzling blossoms.
5. Either my sister Anita or Suzi will take ________ driving test tomorrow.
6. Has Dave or Rajiv offered to drive ________ car to the state park?
7. Both opera and jazz have ________ legions of devoted fans.
8. At income tax time, Mrs. Ramos or Ms. Tyndell offers ________ accounting services free to senior citizens.
9. Explain what either Brittany or Sheila meant by ________ comments.
10. If I have anything to say about it, the guest bedroom and bathroom will have ________ walls painted this weekend.

Copyright © by Holt, Rinehart and Winston. All rights reserved.

Special Problems in Pronoun-Antecedent Agreement A

5u. A collective noun may be either singular or plural, depending on how it is used.

A collective noun takes a singular pronoun when the noun refers to the group as a unit and a plural pronoun when the noun refers to the individual members or parts of the group.

SINGULAR Has the **band** raised enough money for **its** trip to the state competition?

PLURAL The **band** have loaded **their** instruments onto the bus.

USAGE

EXERCISE A In each of the following sentences, underline the collective noun once. Then, underline twice the pronoun in parentheses that agrees in number with the collective noun.

Example 1. The team can avoid making some of these mistakes again by following *(its, their)* coach's advice.

1. During the meeting, the committee reporting on the company's growth were enthusiastic about *(its, their)* data.
2. The bed of tulips that we planted was spectacular; *(it, they)* looked like a crimson carpet.
3. Please ask the staff to check *(its, their)* e-mail before coming to the meeting.
4. Our marching band complain that *(it, they)* need new white shoes to match the new uniforms.
5. This bushel of plums will last for many months once we make *(it, them)* into jam.
6. Has the pair of swans selected *(its, their)* nesting site yet?
7. The flock of sheep followed *(its, their)* leader into the pen.
8. Uncle Rob claims that the public do not always vote in ways that support *(its, their)* own best interests.
9. The crowd enjoyed the concert and tossed *(its, their)* hats on stage during the encore.
10. A colony of fire ants can protect *(itself, themselves)* quite effectively.

EXERCISE B Most of the sentences below contain errors in pronoun-antecedent agreement. If the pronoun in a sentence does not agree with its antecedent, cross it out and write the correct pronoun above it.

Example 1. The cast of the play invited all of ~~its~~ *their* families to the end-of-the-run party.

11. Surrounding the embassy, the mob shouted angrily and waved its fists in the air.
12. Did you disturb the swarm of bees or get too close to their hive?
13. That cluster of berries is poisonous, so don't eat anything from them.
14. Arriving in port, the crew looked forward to enjoying itself on leave.
15. Only a little nervous, the ensemble are tuning its instruments before the recital begins.

Copyright © by Holt, Rinehart and Winston. All rights reserved.

NAME CLASS DATE

for **CHAPTER 5: AGREEMENT** *pages 174–175*

USAGE

Special Problems in Pronoun-Antecedent Agreement B

5v. An expression of an amount (a measurement, a percentage, or a fraction, for example) may take a singular or a plural pronoun, depending on how it is used.

An expression of an amount is singular when the amount is thought of as a unit and plural when the amount is thought of as separate parts.

EXAMPLES I did have **eight dollars,** but I spent **it** on lunch.
She dropped the **eight dollars,** and a gust of wind promptly swept **them** away.

A fraction or a percentage is singular when it refers to a singular word and plural when it refers to a plural word.

EXAMPLES About **one quarter** of the pizza was left, and Tara put **it** in the refrigerator.
About **one quarter** of the enchiladas were left, and Tara put **them** in the refrigerator.

EXERCISE In each of the following sentences, underline the pronoun in parentheses that agrees with its antecedent.

Example 1. Four miles was how far we had hiked; *(it, they)* didn't take us very long.

1. He left thirty-five cents on the table; *(it, they)* didn't seem like much of a tip.
2. One half of the pie was missing; *(it, they)* must have been eaten by Dad.
3. The survey showed that sixty percent of the students favored taking *(his or her, their)* exams after 10:00 A.M.
4. If three cents is my change, just put *(it, them)* in the basket for others to use.
5. Three eighths of a cup was all the sugar the recipe called for, but *(it, they)* made the banana bread sweet enough.
6. Four quarts of fresh oil was all I used; *(it, they)* didn't cost much.
7. In the past year, seven percent of the employees have been promoted to *(his or her, their)* current positions.
8. Five dollars an hour for baby-sitting seems fair to me; *(it, they)* will help to pay for my car insurance.
9. Approximately one third of my classmates take care of *(his or her, their)* siblings after school.
10. Nearly five hundred pints of blood had been donated during the school's blood drive; *(it, they)* may have been the largest amount ever donated by a single institution in our city.

Copyright © by Holt, Rinehart and Winston. All rights reserved.

Special Problems in Pronoun-Antecedent Agreement C

5w. Some nouns that are plural in form take singular pronouns.

EXAMPLE **Economics** is a challenging subject, and I enjoy studying **it.**

However, a few nouns that refer to single items take plural pronouns.

EXAMPLE He tore those **shorts** when he fell off his bike, but he has patched **them.**

Even when plural in form, the titles of creative works (such as books, songs, movies, and paintings) and the names of countries, cities, and organizations generally take singular pronouns.

EXAMPLES Coretta liked ***The Waves*** so much that she read **it** a second time.
All I really know about **Colorado Springs** is that **it** is south of Denver.
Has **Wellington Plastics** opened **its** new plant yet?

EXERCISE In each of the following sentences, underline once the noun with a plural form. Then, underline twice the pronoun in parentheses that agrees in number with the noun.

Example 1. A good substitute for white sugar is molasses; *(it, they)* adds a richer, more complex flavor to many baked goods.

1. Physics with Mr. Dejani is such a popular class that students must get on a waiting list to take *(it, them).*

2. The binoculars are broken; *(it, they)* may need to be taken to the repair shop.

3. Blossoms is a local florist shop opening soon, and *(it, they)* will specialize in bouquets made from exotic, tropical flowers.

4. Aunt Sara brought us pajamas made of silk from Thailand, and *(it, they)* must be the most comfortable nightclothes I've ever worn.

5. Ted's older brother is studying economics because he says *(it, they)* will help him prepare for a career in politics.

6. My white shorts turned pale pink when I washed *(it, them)* with my red T-shirt.

7. Have you read "Beliefs and Truths"? *(It, They)* recently appeared in a collection of poems by young writers.

8. Danny watches the news first thing in the morning; he says *(it, they)* can oftentimes give him a pleasant start on the day.

9. *Dubliners* by James Joyce reflects the grim reality of Irish life; *(it, they)* can be difficult to read.

10. Mothers Against Drunk Drivers is holding *(its, their)* annual fund-raiser next Saturday.

Copyright © by Holt, Rinehart and Winston. All rights reserved.

Special Problems in Pronoun-Antecedent Agreement D

5x. The gender and number of the relative pronoun *that, which,* or *who* is determined by the number of the word to which it refers—its antecedent.

USAGE

EXAMPLES That pecan tree, **which** has already lost most of **its** leaves, does not seem very healthy. [*Which* refers to the singular, neuter noun *pecan tree*. Therefore, the singular, neuter pronoun *its* is used to agree with *which*.]

My little brother, **who** adores **his** Dr. Seuss books, tried to put a hat on our cat. [*Who* refers to the singular, masculine noun *brother*. Therefore, the singular, masculine pronoun *his* is used to agree with *who*.]

The players **who** had given **their** best efforts at practice got to play the most during the game. [*Who* refers to the plural noun *players*. Therefore, the plural pronoun *their* is used to agree with *who*.]

EXERCISE In each of the following sentences, underline the pronoun in parentheses that agrees with its antecedent.

Example 1. What can you do for someone who doesn't think *(he or she, they)* needs anyone's help?

1. The archaeologists, who announced *(their, its)* latest discovery, looked especially proud and happy.
2. Be quiet and move slowly around a mother cat that is protective of *(their, her)* new kittens.
3. Is that the woodpecker that keeps knocking *(its, his)* bill against your bedroom window?
4. We are taking the chair that needs *(their, its)* upholstery replaced to that shop on Miller Avenue.
5. Pablo is looking for a job with a company that offers *(its, his or her)* employees competitive starting salaries and good benefits.
6. All the shirts that are missing *(their, its)* price tags must be re-tagged before Monday.
7. Mr. Koichi, who works in *(his, their)* garden every weekend, grows the best-tasting eggplants.
8. The puppies that we fostered for a month have found *(themselves, itself)* good permanent homes.
9. Edie was the one who forgot to finish *(her, his or her)* history homework.
10. Sheep who wander away from *(their, his or her)* flock are in danger of being attacked by predators.

Copyright © by Holt, Rinehart and Winston. All rights reserved.

Review A: Subject-Verb Agreement

EXERCISE Proofread the following sentences for errors in subject-verb agreement. Cross out each incorrect verb form, and write the correct form in the space above it. If a sentence is already correct, write *C* at the end of the sentence.

Example **1.** Neither of those books ~~are~~ *is* available in the school library.

1. There's only three chapters left to finish.

2. Neither the principal nor the teachers favor this idea.

3. "The Lotus Eaters" is my favorite poem by W. B. Yeats.

4. Is these trousers washable?

5. There were four thousand people in the stadium.

6. Basic economics show that a balance of trade is necessary.

7. Every one of the streets need to be repaired.

8. The part of the concert that I most enjoyed was Elton John's songs.

9. Either the school committee members or the principal have the forms.

10. A squirrel and a chipmunk are both rodents.

11. Physics is the subject that I plan to major in at college.

12. The engine of one of the trucks were sputtering.

13. Many a candidate have spoken out eloquently on the issues.

14. Neither Felicia nor her brother were in the band.

15. He don't intend to debate the issues with you.

16. The store is looking for clerks who know about gardening.

17. Don't your father come from Hungary?

18. I need scissors that are very sharp.

19. We live on Oaks Avenue, which run north and south.

20. Ying is one of those ball players who do everything well.

21. Our baseball team are going to Dallas for a tournament this weekend.

22. Here's the pictures I had developed last week.

23. Jane thinks that linguistics are a fascinating field of study.

24. She don't know whether she should wash the car first or rake up the leaves in the yard.

25. Either Marguarita or Pilar are auditioning for the lead in the school play.

Copyright © by Holt, Rinehart and Winston. All rights reserved.

Review B: **Pronoun-Antecedent Agreement**

EXERCISE A Proofread the following sentences for errors in pronoun-antecedent agreement. Cross out each incorrect pronoun, and write the correct form in the space above it. If a sentence is already correct, write *C* at the end of the sentence.

Example 1. If anyone knows the answer, will ~~they~~ *he or she* please speak up?

1. Neither Mr. Syms nor Mr. Karras had worn their glasses.
2. Whether a candidate wins or not, they must submit a report about campaign expenditures.
3. Both Aola and Phoebe passed the driver's test and received their licenses.
4. That is a decision that everyone must make for themselves.
5. Krista and her brother asked me to go with them on a hiking trip.
6. No one on the city council has suggested that they will vote for the new ordinance.
7. Both Mr. Kelly and Mrs. Arcaro accepted their awards with gratitude.
8. Several local artists displayed their paintings during the festival.
9. Many of the Rotary Club members expressed his appreciation to the speaker.
10. Most of the hikers remembered to bring their own lunches.

EXERCISE B In each of the following sentences, underline the pronoun in parentheses that agrees with its antecedent.

Example 1. Neither Ted nor Michael changed *(their, his)* mind on the issue.

11. The flock of seagulls descended one by one into *(its, their)* nests.
12. The singer was given a standing ovation for *(her, their)* solo.
13. The dinner guests left one half of the fruit tart uneaten. I think I'll save *(them, it)* for tomorrow.
14. Dad said that fifty dollars seemed like a high price for a shirt. He said that in his day he could never have afforded to pay *(it, them)*.
15. Santana enjoys studying physics. She finds *(them, it)* very intriguing.
16. Either Barbara or Grace will attend the medical conference. *(She, They)* will also bring back materials to share with the group.
17. At school, each band member had been known for *(his or her, their)* dedication to music.
18. Did one of your cousins from Minnesota say that *(he or she, they)* loved the cold winters?
19. Each of the scientists will present *(their, his or her)* research at the conference in New York.
20. Neither Sandra nor Erin can go without eating *(their, her)* lunch later than noon.

Copyright © by Holt, Rinehart and Winston. All rights reserved.

NAME ______ CLASS ______ DATE ______

Review C: Agreement

EXERCISE Most of the following sentences contain errors in agreement. Cross out each incorrect verb or pronoun form, and write the correct form in the space above the error. If a sentence is already correct, write *C* at the end of the sentence.

Example 1. Often, a student fails a course because ~~they have~~ *he or she has* not worked hard enough.

1. Neither the secretary nor the treasurer have been paid.
2. There was still a few questions that had not been answered.
3. The price of diamonds vary from year to year.
4. Each of the girls paid for their own dinner.
5. No one will be excused from physical education classes unless they bring a note signed by a doctor.
6. She is one of those people who dream of changing the world.
7. When's the primary and the general elections?
8. Our team are playing the Eagles next Sunday on television.
9. Several of the members of last year's graduating class is enrolled at the University of Wisconsin.
10. One of the canaries had gotten their foot caught in the cage door.
11. Neither Tien nor her sister appear ready to leave for the concert yet.
12. My English teacher said that ethics might be very interesting for me to study in college. He said that they may be taught in the philosophy department.
13. Nearly one third of the band members carried its instruments in cases to the performance.
14. That bird in the trees don't look like the ones I have seen before.
15. Most of the recipes appeared to be original. I had never seen them before.
16. The class will go on a field trip to the Museum of Science to do research for its projects.
17. Several of the children ate his or her lunches outside because the weather was so beautiful.
18. Almost every book about insects that Sarah reads contribute to her ever-increasing knowledge of entomology.
19. Todd explained that the jury would probably take several hours to come to their collective decision.
20. Either her roommates or her sister are throwing a big surprise party for Samantha.

Copyright © by Holt, Rinehart and Winston. All rights reserved.

NAME CLASS DATE

for CHAPTER 5: AGREEMENT pages 152–176

Review D: Agreement

USAGE

EXERCISE In each of the following sentences, underline the correct word or group of words in parentheses

Example **1.** If any one of the girls tries hard, *(they, she)* will likely win a scholarship.

1. Neither Susan nor Tanya has finished *(their, her)* science project.

2. Every actor, musician, and stagehand *(is, are)* expected to be at the rehearsal tomorrow evening.

3. An accurate appraisal of valuable jewels *(require, requires)* an expert.

4. Both your English teacher and your guidance counselor *(has, have)* encouraged you.

5. The League of Women Voters *(have, has)* both male and female members.

6. Each of the boys should keep a record of the time *(he, they)* will spend on the project.

7. Three quarters *(have, has)* fallen under the turnstile gate.

8. Neither the groundskeeper nor her assistant *(remembers, remember)* where the tarpaulin was stored for the winter.

9. *Alice's Adventures in Wonderland (were, was)* first published in 1865.

10. Did any of the bakers create *(his or her, their)* own recipe for rye bread?

11. The museum that will display *(its, their)* new exhibits next week opens at 8 A.M.

12. All of the squirrels that live in our backyard come down from the tree at night to find *(its, their)* food.

13. When Jane gets home early from school, neither her mother nor her father *(have, has)* to cook dinner.

14. *(Has, Have)* Claire or Katie gone out to pick up the party supplies?

15. I think that at least 80 percent of the volunteers *(is, are)* going to show up for the food drive.

16. Most of the sugar from the two-pound bag *(are, is)* gone.

17. In the jazz quartet at school, everyone will have the chance to play *(their, his or her)* favorite song.

18. Darla plans to take several difficult courses at the university, but she thinks genetics *(are, is)* going to be the most interesting, if not the most challenging, course.

19. Despite their hard work, neither of the teams *(is, are)* ready for the tournament.

20. In this movie, there *(is, are)* a few characters who never seem to do anything interesting.

Copyright © by Holt, Rinehart and Winston. All rights reserved.

USAGE

Case Forms of Personal Pronouns

Case is the form that a noun or a pronoun takes to show its relationship to other words in a sentence. In English, there are three cases: ***nominative***, ***objective***, and ***possessive***. Most personal pronouns have three different forms, one for each case. Within each case, the forms of the personal pronoun also indicate number, person, and gender.

	NOMINATIVE	OBJECTIVE	POSSESSIVE
First Person Singular	I	me	my, mine
Second Person Singular	you	you	your, yours
Third Person Singular	he, she, it	him, her, it	his, her, hers, its
First Person Plural	we	us	our, ours
Second Person Plural	you	you	your, yours
Third Person Plural	they	them	their, theirs

EXERCISE A Classify each underlined personal pronoun in the following sentences. In the space above each pronoun, write *F* for *first person, S* for *second person,* or *T* for *third person.* Then, write *N* for *nominative case, O* for *objective case,* or *P* for *possessive case.*

Example 1. Denis and I (F—N) went to the Rose Bowl in Pasadena.

1. The clerk was very helpful to Ms. Ayala and me.

2. Was it he who called while I was at the recycling center?

3. I didn't know that their mother was a published poet.

4. I've decided that I thoroughly support your point of view.

5. Please provide them with your new address and phone number.

EXERCISE B On the blank in each of the following sentences, write an appropriate pronoun to correctly complete the sentence. A description of the pronoun appears in parentheses.

Example 1. Grandmother sent electronic greeting cards to both Jacob and ___me___ *(first person singular, objective).*

6. I gave Gino and ________ *(third person plural, objective)* copies of my speech.

7. The coach hasn't seen ________ *(first person singular, possessive)* best effort yet.

8. ________ *(First person plural, nominative)* have donated funds to the relief effort.

9. Do ________ *(second person singular, nominative)* understand this poem?

10. The riders have mounted ________ *(third person plural, possessive)* horses.

Copyright © by Holt, Rinehart and Winston. All rights reserved.

The Nominative Case A

The personal pronouns in the nominative case—*I, you, he, she, it, we,* and *they*—are used as subjects of verbs and as predicate nominatives.

USAGE

6a. The subject of a verb should be in the nominative case.

EXAMPLE **We** studied the poetry of Sylvia Plath.

6b. A predicate nominative should be in the nominative case.

EXAMPLE The candidate with the most votes is **she.**

EXERCISE A Each of the following sentences contains two personal pronouns in parentheses. Underline the pronoun that correctly completes the sentence. Then, on the line provided, write *S* if the pronoun is a subject or *PN* if it is a predicate nominative.

Example PN **1.** I believe the man you're looking for is *(him, he).*

_____ **1.** Vince and *(him, he)* are playing bridge tonight.

_____ **2.** Either Theo or *(I, me)* will be the punter for the football team.

_____ **3.** I'm sure that the woman who painted the portrait was *(her, she).*

_____ **4.** *(We, Us)* left the gate unlocked.

_____ **5.** Neither Han-Ling nor *(he, him)* has taken a course in calligraphy.

_____ **6.** The partners with the highest scores were *(us, we).*

_____ **7.** The people who requested my address were *(they, them).*

_____ **8.** Angelo knew that the people in the horse costume were *(them, they).*

_____ **9.** You and *(her, she)* deserve a lot of credit.

_____ **10.** *(He, Him)* and Marianne became finalists in the tennis tournament.

EXERCISE B Complete each of the following sentences by supplying a personal pronoun in the nominative case. Then, on the line provided before the sentence, write *S* if the pronoun is a subject or *PN* if it is a predicate nominative.

Example S **1.** Kim and I will go to the library this weekend.

_____ **11.** Do _____ and we have some research to do on Hopi culture?

_____ **12.** The leader of our study group is _____.

_____ **13.** Neither _____ nor we should use periodicals older than six months.

_____ **14.** Both she and _____ will write about contemporary art.

_____ **15.** The students who researched the bombing of Hiroshima were _____.

Copyright © by Holt, Rinehart and Winston. All rights reserved.

NAME ______________________ CLASS ______________________ DATE ______________________

The Nominative Case B

The personal pronouns in the nominative case—*I, you, he, she, it, we,* and *they*—are used as subjects of verbs and as predicate nominatives.

EXAMPLES Frank and Deanne said that **they** would help us clean up after dinner. [subject]
The only players left are Latasha and **she.** [predicate nominative]

EXERCISE A Complete each of the following sentences by supplying a personal pronoun in the nominative case. Then, on the line provided, write *S* if the pronoun is a subject or *PN* if it is a predicate nominative.

Example ___S___ **1.** ___She___ and they are going camping in New Mexico.

______ **1.** Have ________ or your friends ever been to the Chaco Canyon?

______ **2.** The tour guide for the senior class trip is ________.

______ **3.** Neither ________ nor I have ever been camping.

______ **4.** ________ and we are going to shop for sleeping bags this afternoon.

______ **5.** Mariana, he, and ________ also want to look at tents.

______ **6.** The students who hope to see the natural hot springs are ________.

______ **7.** Either Ms. Chavez or ________ will talk about the history of the rugged region.

______ **8.** The person who has toured the nearby reservation is ________.

______ **9.** Which campground did ________ and the student committee select?

______ **10.** After reviewing guidebooks, ________ and we narrowed it down to two locations.

EXERCISE B On the blank in each of the following sentences, write an appropriate pronoun to correctly complete the sentence. A description of the pronoun appears in parentheses.

Example **1.** The painter of the auditorium's panoramic mural is ___she___ *(third person singular, predicate nominative).*

11. ________ *(third person plural, subject)* played field hockey.

12. During the trip to Easter Island, ________ *(first person plural, subject)* and they took many photographs of carved stone relics.

13. Will ________ *(second person plural, subject)* and Mr. Douet take a look at my painting?

14. "The last in a long line of traditional woodcrafters is ________ *(first person singular, predicate nominative),"* my grandmother said.

15. Are ________ *(second person singular, subject)* the person to see about changing my schedule?

Copyright © by Holt, Rinehart and Winston. All rights reserved.

NAME ____________________ CLASS ____________ DATE ____________

for **CHAPTER 6: USING PRONOUNS** *pages 187–190*

USAGE

The Objective Case A

The personal pronouns in the objective case—*me, you, him, her, it, us,* and *them*—are used as direct objects, indirect objects, and objects of prepositions.

6c. A direct object should be in the objective case.

EXAMPLES Leta invited Mario and **me** to the new Japanese restaurant.

Did anyone see **her** and **them** at the recital?

6d. An indirect object should be in the objective case.

EXAMPLES Critics have awarded **them** many honors.

The director will give either Sonya or **her** the leading role.

6e. An object of a preposition should be in the objective case.

EXAMPLES Tyrone sat with **us** at the concert.

Estrella received an invitation from **him** and Rosa.

EXERCISE A Each of the following sentences contains two personal pronouns in parentheses. Underline the pronoun that correctly completes the sentence. Then, on the line provided, write *DO* if the pronoun is a direct object, *IO* if it is an indirect object, or *OP* if it is an object of a preposition.

Example __IO__ **1.** Mr. Graves offered Tranh and *(I, me)* endless encouragement and guidance.

______ **1.** Renee had lunch with *(we, us)* last Sunday.

______ **2.** The concert was sponsored by the record company and *(she, her).*

______ **3.** The company rewarded Sophie and *(him, he)* with raises.

______ **4.** The grocer sells *(they, them)* fresh fruit every day.

______ **5.** Norah saw *(they, them)* at the party for Darlene.

EXERCISE B On the line provided before each of the following sentences, write the personal pronoun that could be used in place of the underlined word or words.

Example __her__ **1.** I received a call from Ms. Kinoshi.

______ **6.** Have you read the biography about Carl Lewis?

______ **7.** Please notify Dr. and Mrs. Sanchez about the meeting.

______ **8.** After the presentation, the moderator gave a summation.

______ **9.** Most of the science and math classes have prerequisites.

______ **10.** Frank lent Joanna his guidebook of the Sierras.

Copyright © by Holt, Rinehart and Winston. All rights reserved.

The Objective Case B

The personal pronouns in the objective case—*me, you, him, her, it, us,* and *them*—are used as direct objects, indirect objects, and objects of prepositions.

EXERCISE A Complete the following sentences by supplying personal pronouns in the objective case. Then, on the line provided, write *DO* if the pronoun is used as a direct object or *IO* if it is used as an indirect object.

Example __DO__ **1.** Annamaria drove __us__ to the concert hall.

______ **1.** Have you given Ali and ________ the study guide?

______ **2.** Did Ben show ________ his collection of carved figurines from Thailand?

______ **3.** Dr. Guerra showed Daniel, Kelly, and ________ the model skeleton.

______ **4.** Our teacher has already graded Latisha and ________ on our presentation.

______ **5.** Ms. Chen complimented both ________ and ________ on the performance.

______ **6.** Would you please lend Sam and ________ the geography computer game?

______ **7.** During practice, the coach taught Penelope and ________ the proper stance.

______ **8.** The painting gave ________ some ideas for the contest.

______ **9.** My aunt is picking up both you and ________.

______ **10.** Please tell ________ the story about your trip.

EXERCISE B For each of the following sentences, choose the correct form of the object of the preposition in parentheses.

Example **1.** The Pomeranian belongs to (*he, him*).

11. Would you like to play soccer with Estella and (*me, I*)?

12. These slides were taken by David and (*she, her*).

13. We can rely on Terrence and (*he, him*) for their help.

14. Would you like to walk with Erica and (*me, I*)?

15. There has been much cooperation between the school board and (*we, us*).

16. On the tennis court, competitors like Dave and (*me, I*) really challenge each other.

17. The closing lines of the stage show will be spoken by you and (*she, her*).

18. We have been studying conversation and hope to practice with (*them, they*).

19. Most of the credit belongs to (*them, they*).

20. Please pick up the sheet music and hand it to (*us, we*).

Copyright © by Holt, Rinehart and Winston. All rights reserved.

Nominative and Objective Case Pronouns

Subjects and predicate nominatives should be in the nominative case.

EXAMPLES After the game Mom and **he** stopped at the sporting goods store. [subject]
The last ones to arrive at the meeting were Robert and **I.** [predicate nominative]

Direct objects, indirect objects, and objects of prepositions should be in the objective case.

EXAMPLES Mr. Asato helped Helen and **me** with our photography project. [direct object]
Justin lent **us** his camera for two weeks. [indirect object]
We are grateful to **them** for their help. [object of a preposition]

EXERCISE A For each of the following sentences, identify the underlined pronoun by writing *S* for *subject, PN* for *predicate nominative, DO* for *direct object, IO* for *indirect object,* or *OP* for *object of a preposition.*

Example 1. S Neither Caroline nor I could find the antique watch.

1. Both his uncle and he gave us excellent advice about our trip to Wyoming.
2. Alec hopes that the committee will give the scholarship to her.
3. Alejandra and she, the new exchange students from Guatemala, already speak some English.
4. The player with the best record for free throws in the district league is he.
5. Mrs. Soriano helped them with their speeches for the class election.

EXERCISE B On the lines provided, write complete sentences using the pronouns specified. Then, underline the pronouns.

Example 1. *(third person plural, indirect object)* Mr. Park gave them an excellent grade on the science project.

6. *(first person plural, predicate nominative)* ______
7. *(third person singular, direct object)* ______
8. *(second person plural, subject)* ______
9. *(first person singular, object of a preposition)* ______
10. *(third person singular, indirect object)* ______

Copyright © by Holt, Rinehart and Winston. All rights reserved.

NAME ____________________ CLASS ____________________ DATE ____________________

The Possessive Case

The personal pronouns in the possessive case—*my, mine, your, yours, his, her, hers, its, our, ours, their,* and *theirs*—are used to show ownership or possession.

6f. The possessive pronouns *mine, yours, his, hers, its, ours,* and *theirs* are used in the same ways that the pronouns in the nominative and objective cases are.

EXAMPLES **Hers** was the best performance of the night. [subject]

I got **mine** at a department store. [direct object]

6g. The possessive pronouns *my, our, your, his, her, its,* and *their* are used to modify nouns and pronouns.

EXAMPLES **Your** poem is beautiful. **Its** imagery is outstanding.

6h. A noun or a pronoun preceding a gerund should be in the possessive case.

EXAMPLE Mother objected to **his** calling at such a late hour.

EXERCISE A On the blank in each of the following sentences, write an appropriate possessive pronoun to correctly complete the sentence.

Example 1. Father had tired of ___our___ procrastinating.

1. My parents have become close friends with __________.
2. __________ winning the game came as no surprise to loyal fans.
3. Please tell the senator __________ views on the issue.
4. Ms. Pearson encouraged __________ studying in groups.
5. That old coat of __________ really needs a good cleaning.

EXERCISE B For each of the following sentences, underline the possessive pronoun. Then, above each pronoun, identify its function by writing *S* for *subject, PN* for *predicate nominative, O* for *object,* or *M* for *modifier.*

Example 1. We were all elated by <u>his</u> (M) scoring in the top 2 percent of the state.

6. Do you know his address or phone number?
7. This cardigan sweater is hers.
8. We ordered ours yesterday afternoon.
9. Mrs. Champion gave theirs a thorough review.
10. Your bicycle seat and mine are not the same height.

Copyright © by Holt, Rinehart and Winston. All rights reserved.

USAGE

Case Forms A

Subjects and predicate nominatives should be in the nominative case.

Direct objects, indirect objects, and objects of prepositions should be in the objective case.

Possessive personal pronouns are used to show ownership or possession.

EXERCISE A For each of the following sentences, underline the correct form of the pronoun in parentheses. Then, identify whether the pronoun functions as a subject *(S)*, a predicate nominative *(PN)*, a direct object *(DO)*, an indirect object *(IO)*, an object of a preposition *(OP)*, or a modifier *(M)*.

Example 1. Have you ever tasted (her, hers) appetizers? M

1. Because of the darkening sky, *(us, we)* decided to postpone our hike.
2. It is easy to write about someone as interesting as *(her, she)* is.
3. The most rewarding challenge remained for Lily and *(I, me)*.
4. The person who worked hardest on the homecoming parade was *(he, him)*.
5. Ms. Cruz advised Scott and *(I, me)* on our research papers.
6. Valerie and *(them, they)* have been classmates since middle school.
7. *(You, Your)* helping Ian in the kitchen made the dinner go smoothly.
8. To Sandra and *(I, me)*, attending the international festival is a must.
9. Did you see Alexander give Kim and *(him, he)* a pat on the back?
10. I am certain the film school scholarship winners will be *(us, we)*.

EXERCISE B For each of the following sentences, write the pronoun that most correctly completes the sentence. A description of the pronoun appears in parentheses.

Example 1. *(third person singular, objective)* Did you ask her or him who was at the front door?

11. *(first person singular, objective)* This afternoon the theater teacher will audition Teri and __________.
12. *(second person plural, nominative)* The best soccer players in the school are my sister Ariel and __________.
13. *(first person singular, possessive)* Your backpack and __________ are perfect for day hikes.
14. *(third person plural, possessive)* We have the same kind of plants in our garden as they do in __________.
15. *(third person singular, objective)* I helped Eric and __________ take down the tent and pack the car.

Copyright © by Holt, Rinehart and Winston. All rights reserved.

NAME ______________________ CLASS ______________ DATE ______________

Case Forms B

Subjects and predicate nominatives should be in the nominative case.
Direct objects, indirect objects, and objects of prepositions should be in the objective case.
Possessive personal pronouns are used to show ownership or possession.

EXERCISE Each of the following sentences contains incorrect pronoun usage. Cross out each incorrect pronoun and write the correct form above it. Some sentences may have more than one error.

Example 1. Neither Andrea nor ~~me~~ *I* lost the art projects.

1. Just between you and I, I think he should have studied a bit more.

2. Will Michelle and him post the fliers on campus today?

3. Principal Kostas encouraged the rest of we to volunteer for the project.

4. Mom lent Madeleine and I enough money to buy that book.

5. During the half-time show, them dancing got the most applause.

6. Jamie and her always finish their Spanish assignments.

7. I asked Eva and she to go to the art show with Julie and I.

8. Because Terrence and them have studied Russian, they were asked to translate for the exchange students.

9. Our chemistry teacher strongly objects to us staging experiments without supervision.

10. While training for the triathlon, make you exercising a top priority.

11. My grandfather taught we about life in South Korea after the Korean War.

12. Us should design a mural for the back wall of the cafeteria.

13. When we were children, Jeff and her could always run faster than Maya.

14. Josephine and they saw our standing on the corner, so they honked and waved.

15. He being late has ruined our chance to compete in the opening match.

16. Do you mind me telling Darla that you are coming for a visit?

17. We could barely see Alfred and they standing in the back of the theater.

18. His many overseas travels didn't interfere with him writing.

19. The schedule depended on me performing all of the research on time.

20. To Ali and she, it was the best graduation present anyone could give.

Copyright © by Holt, Rinehart and Winston. All rights reserved.

USAGE

Pronouns as Appositives

6i. A pronoun used as an appositive should be in the same case as the word to which it refers.

EXAMPLE The singers, Leonard and **she,** won the talent show. [*Leonard* and *she* identify the subject *singers.* Since a subject of a verb is in the nominative case, an appositive identifying the subject is also in the nominative case.]

EXAMPLE The judges chose the singers, Leonard and **her.** [*Leonard* and *her* identify the direct object *singers.* Since the direct object is in the objective case, an appositive identifying it is also in the objective case.]

The pronouns *we* and *us* are sometimes followed by noun appositives.

EXAMPLES **We actors** need a rehearsal. [subject, nominative case]
The director rehearsed **us actors.** [direct object, objective case]

EXERCISE A Underline the correct pronoun in parentheses in each of the following sentences.

Example 1. Several of (*we*, *us*) dancers have already learned the first routine.

1. Both poets, (*she, her*) and Gwendolyn Brooks, were extremely talented.
2. The newspaper chose two all-stars, Eubie and (*I, me*).
3. They gave (*we, us*) seniors instructions about the graduation ceremony.
4. (*We, Us*) artists have to learn to be confident about our work.
5. Wasn't it (*we, us*) Germans who introduced the pretzel to America?

EXERCISE B For each item, write a sentence using the given word group in the way specified in parentheses. Supply a pronoun in the correct case for each blank.

Example 1. my friends, ____ and Sal (*indirect object*) We told two of my friends, her and Sal, jokes.

6. the two star vocalists, ____ and Katie (*direct object*) ____
7. ____ and ____, the biggest fans (*subject*) ____
8. ____ performance artists (*object of a preposition*) ____
9. ____ seniors (*predicate nominative*) ____
10. the world's best teachers, ____ and Mrs. Leopold (*indirect object*) ____

Copyright © by Holt, Rinehart and Winston. All rights reserved.

NAME _______________ CLASS _______________ DATE _______________

USAGE

Pronouns in Elliptical Constructions

6j. A pronoun following *than* or *as* in an elliptical construction should be in the same case as it would be if the construction were completed.

ELLIPTICAL Is Eva really six months younger **than he?** [nominative case]
COMPLETED Is Eva really six months younger **than he is young?**

ELLIPTICAL He gives her more attention **than me.** [objective case]
COMPLETED He gives her more attention **than he gives me.**

ELLIPTICAL He gives her more attention **than I.** [nominative case]
COMPLETED He gives her more attention **than I give her.**

EXERCISE A On the line provided, write the completed form of the elliptical clause, using the correct form of the pronoun in parentheses. (Some items may have more than one possible answer, but you need to give only one.)

Example 1. He trusts you more than *(I, me).* than he trusts me or than I trust you

1. I gave him more dessert than *(she, her).* _______________
2. Mr. Moore paid her more money than *(I, me).* _______________
3. No one else I know is as brave as *(she, her).* _______________
4. They see him more often than *(we, us).* _______________
5. I have written as many pages as *(he, him).* _______________

EXERCISE B Underline the appropriate pronoun form to complete the elliptical construction in each of the following sentences. Then, above the pronoun write *N* if the pronoun is in the nominative case or *O* if the pronoun is in the objective case.

Example 1. Ellie studies longer hours than *(I, me).* [N above I, underlined]

6. No one else in my art class is as creative as *(I, me).*
7. The editors of our yearbook have written as much as *(they, them).*
8. Can you swim as fast as *(he, him)?*
9. If you want to beat Aaron's time, you need to run faster than *(he, him).*
10. My gym teacher told me that I had more agility than *(she, her).*
11. We were all more enthusiastic than *(he, him).*
12. Jeff is more interested in Fellini's films than *(she, her).*
13. Judges in the short-story contest presented Esperanza with a larger trophy than *(I, me).*
14. They sent Luisa as many flower arrangements as *(I, me).*
15. No one gave more time to volunteer work than *(she, her).*

Copyright © by Holt, Rinehart and Winston. All rights reserved.

USAGE

Reflexive and Intensive Pronouns

A *reflexive pronoun* ends in *–self* or *–selves* and refers to the subject of the sentence or clause. A reflexive pronoun may serve as a direct object, an indirect object, an object of a preposition, or a predicate nominative.

EXAMPLES Rick hurt **himself** at practice. [direct object]
All the team members can be proud of **themselves.** [object of a preposition]

An *intensive pronoun* emphasizes its antecedent and has no grammatical function in the sentence.

EXAMPLE I **myself** must take full responsibility. [*Myself* emphasizes *I.*]

6k. A pronoun ending in *–self* or *–selves* should not be used in place of a personal pronoun.

NONSTANDARD Sid and myself went to the art museum.
STANDARD Sid and **I** went to the art museum.

EXERCISE A Complete each of the following sentences by writing an appropriate reflexive or intensive pronoun in the blank. Then, classify the pronoun by writing, in the space above it, *REF* for *reflexive* or *INT* for *intensive.*

Example 1. Maria sanded and finished both bookshelves ~~INT~~ herself. (INT written above *herself*)

1. She made ________ a costume for the school play.

2. Felipe and Jed rebuilt the engine ________.

3. We should give ________ a lot of credit for a job well done.

4. Sit by ________ for a few minutes and collect your thoughts.

5. Billy Crystal ________ will give the graduation address.

EXERCISE B Most of the following sentences contain errors in pronoun usage. Cross out each incorrect pronoun form and write the correct form in the space above it. If a sentence is already correct, write *C* before the item number.

Example 1. Can we depend on Piper and ~~yourself~~ you to supply the cups, plates, and decorations?

6. My choices for the editors of the paper are Eula and yourself.

7. Thanks to ourselves, the publicity for the drama festival had great results.

8. Lilith introduced herself and myself to the visiting delegates.

9. Yoshi didn't want to walk to the concert all by himself.

10. Gerald and myself have set the agenda for the meeting.

Copyright © by Holt, Rinehart and Winston. All rights reserved.

NAME ______________________ CLASS ______________ DATE ______________

for **CHAPTER 6: USING PRONOUNS** *pages 198–200*

Who and *Whom*

In questions, *who* is used as a subject of a verb or as a predicate nominative. *Whom* is used as a direct object, an indirect object, or an object of a preposition.

EXAMPLES **Who** is speaking? [subject] **Who** was the winner? [predicate nominative]
Whom do you trust? [direct object] For **whom** is the gift? [object of preposition]

When choosing between *who* and *whom* in a subordinate clause, determine how the pronoun is used in the clause.

EXAMPLES The man **who** called was Dr. Tehrani. [*Who* is the subject of the verb *called*.]
The man **whom** I called was Dr. Tehrani. [*Whom* is the direct object of the verb *called*.]

USAGE

EXERCISE A Underline the subordinate clause in each of the following sentences. Then, on the line provided, indicate how *who* or *whom* is used in the clause. Write *S* if it is the subject in the clause, *PN* if it is the predicate nominative, *DO* if it is the direct object, or *OP* if it is the object of a preposition.

Example __S__ **1.** Ms. Kohari, who was released from the hospital yesterday, will recuperate at home for three more weeks.

______ **1.** Did you notice who the goalie was?

______ **2.** The woman who wrote that book is a reporter for *The New York Times.*

______ **3.** The boy with whom I was sitting is a student from Kenya.

______ **4.** Coco Chanel was a designer whom many others have imitated.

______ **5.** We enjoyed our visit with Mr. Cullen, whom we had not seen for months.

EXERCISE B Underline the correct pronoun in parentheses in each of the following sentences.

Example 1. I do not know *(who, whom)* the guest speaker will be.

6. I wondered *(who, whom)* the next volunteer would be.

7. We can't remember *(who, whom)* played the leading role.

8. *(Who, Whom)* has been selected as the team captain?

9. Dr. Brooks is a woman *(who, whom)* I greatly admire.

10. Do you know with *(who, whom)* Raskolnikov plotted?

11. Ms. Quarles, *(who, whom)* I met at the trial, is a reporter.

12. *(Who, Whom)* is your favorite poet?

13. Have you decided *(who, whom)* you will vote for on Tuesday?

14. *(Who, Whom)* can I rely upon to take care of my pets while I am on vacation?

15. Carol knows *(who, whom)* won the contest.

Copyright © by Holt, Rinehart and Winston. All rights reserved.

USAGE

Special Pronoun Problems

6i. A pronoun used as an appositive should be in the same case as the word to which it refers.

6j. A pronoun following *than* or *as* in an elliptical construction should be in the same case as it would be if the construction were completed.

A ***reflexive pronoun*** ends in *–self* or *–selves* and refers to the subject of the sentence or clause. An ***intensive pronoun*** emphasizes its antecedent and has no grammatical function in the sentence.

6k. A pronoun ending in *–self* or *–selves* should not be used in place of a personal pronoun.

Like most personal pronouns, the pronoun *who* (*whoever*) has three case forms.

NOMINATIVE	OBJECTIVE	POSSESSIVE
who, whoever	whom, whomever	whose, whosever

EXERCISE A Complete each of the following sentences by writing an appropriate reflexive or intensive pronoun in the blank. Then, classify the pronoun by writing above it, *R* for *reflexive* or *I* for *intensive*.

Example 1. Mimi made ~~R~~ herself a quesadilla for dinner.

1. Since no one else would do it, we cleaned the garage __________.

2. Michael gave __________ the day off.

3. You should allow __________ plenty of time to paint the fence.

4. Karen asked __________ if she really wanted the job.

5. The owner of the shop, Mr. Iwai, makes all the furniture __________.

EXERCISE B Underline the correct pronoun in parentheses in each of the following sentences.

Example 1. I'm not as well-read as (*her, she*).

6. Jenna and (*I, myself*) are responsible for the party decorations.

7. Philip Roth, (*who, whom*) wrote the book, will be speaking on campus tonight.

8. The two top-rated players, George and (*she, her*), will be playing again on Saturday.

9. I don't sing as well as (*he, him*).

10. The two representatives to the national congress will be the twins, Marla and (*him, he*).

11. I'll be expecting a response tomorrow from Nedra and (*yourself, you*).

12. In the end, we just played a better game than (*them, they*).

13. (*Who, Whom*) did the class select as homecoming queen this year?

14. Be sure to give (*whoever, whomever*) is going directions to the concert hall.

15. The president presented the activists, Tod and (*her, she*), with the pens he used to sign the bill.

Copyright © by Holt, Rinehart and Winston. All rights reserved.

Review A: Case Forms of Personal Pronouns

EXERCISE Underline the correct pronoun in parentheses in each of the following sentences.

Example 1. Mr. Epstein gave Shara and *(I, me)* commendations for our academic performance.

1. *(She, Her)* and the other members of the committee have prepared a financial report.
2. The article was signed by Bea Wightman and *(she, her).*
3. The remarks were aimed at you and *(I, me).*
4. It must have been either *(she, her)* or her sister.
5. Do you remember Ms. Fujimori and *(she, her)?*
6. The mayor and *(they, them)* have agreed to the suggestion.
7. After dinner the Martins and *(we, us)* played board games.
8. Ms. Kim has invited my family and *(I, me)* to the wedding.
9. Did I tell you that *(we, us)* and the Jacksons have rented a summer cottage for a month?
10. The woman sitting next to the principal is *(she, her).*
11. The driver asked Cesar and *(I, me)* about the best route to Buena Vista.
12. *(She, Her)* and the other council members are in favor of the amendment.
13. The winner of the grand prize could not have been *(she, her).*
14. These guidelines were prepared for you and *(they, them).*
15. No one except Joshua and *(I, me)* really understood the coach's instructions.
16. Neither Mr. Okumato nor *(he, him)* was on the bus.
17. The principal talked to Han-Ling and *(she, her)* about the trip to Austin.
18. It seemed to him that he and *(they, them)* could work well together.
19. Miss Takara praised Dwight and *(he, him)* for their campaign speeches.
20. Have you asked Carlota and *(she, her)* about it?

Copyright © by Holt, Rinehart and Winston. All rights reserved.

Review B: Using the Correct Forms of Pronouns

USAGE

EXERCISE Most of the following sentences contain errors in pronoun usage. Cross out each incorrect pronoun form and write the correct form in the space above it. If a sentence is already correct, write C before the item number.

Example 1. We listened to Ms. Kwan, ~~whom~~ *who*, everyone supposed, knew the answer.

1. Ms. Acosta and myself do not see eye to eye.

2. Two of the speakers, her and Senator Haskins, were strongly in favor of the project.

3. The captain did not approve of their taking unnecessary risks.

4. Abigail Adams, whom many people regard highly, was a fine letter writer.

5. We can count on him cooperating with us.

6. I invited Trulia and she to the play.

7. We must remember that there are many people in the world who are less fortunate than us.

8. They wondered who she favored as the next editor of the yearbook.

9. Some of we coin collectors wanted to see more commemorative coins.

10. I asked Ms. Savarino, whom has had experience with similar problems.

11. Us citizens have certain rights with which the government cannot interfere.

12. We had high hopes that him running in the track meet would give our team a chance at the title.

13. Jolanda Bradley, who we had not heard from since last year, finally contacted us.

14. No one objected to their raising the fare if they also improved the service.

15. You must keep in mind that your parents are much older than yourselves.

16. His cousin from Missouri is younger than him.

17. We met two old friends, Kenesha and her, at the party.

18. Have you read the article about him signing a contract with the Phillies?

19. Someone on the newspaper's staff, either Margarita or her, corrected the typo.

20. Three sophomores designed and built the set for *Our Town* themselves.

21 I am quite certain that she was talking to herself.

22. Please accept this gift from Ada and myself.

23. Neither of the other candidates is as well qualified as her.

24. Was Jiro the student whom had entered the mathematics competition?

25. I am grateful for you assisting me with my application.

Copyright © by Holt, Rinehart and Winston. All rights reserved.

Review C: **Using the Correct Forms of Pronouns**

EXERCISE A Underline the correct form of the pronoun in parentheses in each of the following sentences.

Example 1. I heard Mariel say into the phone, "Yes, this is (she, her)."

1. Last summer, my friend Mariel and *(I, me)* worked as counselors at a summer camp.

2. We made a pact that *(we, us)* teenagers would show the camp director that we were responsible role models.

3. Everything ran smoothly for the first month because our director, Ms. Flanagan, was a perso *(who, whom)* we admired for being fair and honest.

4. We were pleased by *(she, her)* giving us increased responsibility around the camp.

5. When Ms. Flanagan went into town to buy supplies, we doubted that her assistant, Mr. Cortez, would be as observant as *(she, her)*.

6. Our first error in judgment was in thinking that Ms. Flanagan and *(he, him)* would no iscuss our job performances.

7. We started giving *(us, ourselves)* extra breaks in the afternoon.

8. "Mariel and Lisa, I had thought you were employees *(who, whom)* took your posit ns very seriously," said Mr. Cortez one afternoon.

9. "If you continue to set a bad example for the younger campers," he said gently we, Ms. Flanagan and *(I, me)*, will have to reassign you to kitchen duty."

10. The experience has really taught *(we, us)* some valuable lessons.

EXERCISE B For each of the following sentences, underline the correct pronoun form in parentheses. Then, tell how it is used in the sentence—as a subject *(S)*, a predicate nominative *(PN)*, a direct object *(DO)*, an indirect object *(IO)*, or an object of a preposition *(OP)*.

Example 1. The person *(who, whom)* I admire most is Doreen. DO

11. A woman knocked on the door, but I didn't know *(who, whom)* she was.

12. Be sure to talk with *(whoever, whomever)* he introduces you to at the party.

13. Jules can't remember *(who, whom)* received the top award.

14. Eddie never saw *(who, whom)* the secret admirer was.

15. Was she the girl to *(who, whom)* the bicycle belongs?

Copyright © by Holt, Rinehart and Winston. All rights reserved.

Review D: **Using the Correct Forms of Pronouns**

EXERCISE A For each of the following sentences, underline the correct pronoun form in parentheses.

Example 1. Both Gail and (*I, myself*) signed up for the French Club.

1. Although the actor was talented and striking, what the audience admired most was (*him, his*) dancing.

2. The swim coach watched (*me, my*) diving and asked me to try out for the team.

3. The bus driver told Karen and (*I, me*) that the bus was full.

4. (*Who, Whom*) can describe the angles of the different geometric shapes?

5. "Does anyone sing better than (*them, they*)?" I wondered, as I listened to the musical number.

6. Elliot looked so much taller that I could hardly believe it was (*he, him*).

7. "If (*we, us*) residents don't organize a park patrol, how will we control the litter problem?" asked Mr. Potter at the weekly neighborhood meeting.

8. As we raced toward the finish line, I could see that the race was between Mickey and (*I, me*).

9. My grandmother, after (*who, whom*) I am named, came to the United States from Italy when she was a small child.

10. Maria is going to ask (*who, whom*) you and Daren are voting for in the next class election.

EXERCISE B For each of the following sentences, write a correct pronoun form on the line provided.

Example 1. Who do you think painted this portrait?

11. Alexa and I knew about _____ lending her a warm jacket.

12. Competing in a marathon is an experience from which you and _____ must have learned much.

13. My parents watched _____ and me playing a game of badminton.

14. I have already interviewed two of the women, _____ and Angela.

15. No one knew _____ the man in the tuxedo and top hat could be.

16. Mrs. Escobar asked that Carly and _____ consider going on the senior trip to Paris.

17. The top prize will be awarded to _____ writes the best short story.

18. The band director asked her and _____ to consider taking music lessons.

19. No one has worked harder than _____.

20. Was it Dr. Cross _____ they chose as president of the historical society?

Copyright © by Holt, Rinehart and Winston. All rights reserved.

NAME ______ CLASS ______ DATE ______

Pronouns and Their Antecedents

7a. A pronoun should refer clearly to its antecedent.

UNCLEAR Too many tourists visit the cave each year. It could possibly damage the rock formations.

CLEAR Too many tourists visit the cave each year. **They** could possibly damage the rock formations.

EXERCISE A For each sentence below, draw an arrow from each underlined pronoun to its antecedent.

Example 1. The divers found the sunken galleon, which to their amazement was mostly intact.

1. Donna found the keys in the refrigerator, but she cannot explain how they got there.

2. When Elena picks up the posters from the copy shop, ask her to have two more of them made.

3. Before he had read the book, Tyrone had listened to its sequel on tape.

4. Although the directions say this is the right street, it is not on the map.

5. Admirers of the mayor praise him as a reformer who is not afraid to take risks.

6. Do you like that table? David made it himself.

7. Those are the trees the farmers planted to keep the wind from blowing away their crops.

8. Pointing out a small cabin in one of the old photos, Grandma said, "That was my house."

9. The children thought the fountain, which featured a dragon spouting water from each nostril, was the funniest thing they had ever seen.

10. Fiona was delighted when the shopkeeper pointed to a pair of antique bookends and asked, "Are these what you had in mind?"

EXERCISE B Underline the pronoun in each of the following sentences. If the pronoun does not agree with its antecedent, write *U* for *unclear* over the pronoun. Otherwise, write *C* for *clear.*

Example 1. The queen-size sheets are on sale, but that (U) is too big for the bed.

11. Gina could not get back into the house because the door had locked behind her.

12. Gazing up at the stars, both girls were amazed by how immense it was.

13. My brother was exhausted after his first salsa class but is ready for next week's lesson.

14. The park ranger showed the tour group a figure etched into the rock. These are called petroglyphs.

15. Having never tried them, Maurice was eager to order a stuffed eggplant.

Copyright © by Holt, Rinehart and Winston. All rights reserved.

USAGE

Correcting Ambiguous References

7b. Avoid an ***ambiguous reference,*** which occurs when any one of two or more words could be a pronoun's antecedent.

AMBIGUOUS Mimi usually packs a lunch for Mrs. Chang before she goes to work. [To whom does *she* refer: *Mimi* or *Mrs. Chang*?]

CLEAR Before Mimi goes to work, she usually packs a lunch for Mrs. Chang.

CLEAR Before Mrs. Chang goes to work, Mimi usually packs a lunch for her.

EXERCISE On the line provided, revise each of the following sentences to correct the ambiguous pronoun reference.

Example 1. The dog was startled by the vacuum cleaner as it came around the corner.
As the dog came around the corner, it was startled by the vacuum cleaner.

1. When Paolo finally met my father, he had plenty to say.

2. Although this mountain bike costs more than that touring bike, it handles better.

3. The soldiers saluted the president and his family as they passed by.

4. Ariana will help Rachel pick up trash in the park so that she can complete her volunteer hours.

5. We should watch the movie after we read the book to see if it is any better.

6. The main difference between the TV programs aired last week and those from the week before is that they were mostly reruns.

7. Brent has sung with Peter before, so he should feel comfortable performing this duet.

8. Both the Parks and the Morrises drive minivans, but that one is theirs.

9. The baby brought the cup down on the edge of the bowl, spilling its contents on the floor.

10. Ever since Zora started working with Bridget, her writing has improved.

Copyright © by Holt, Rinehart and Winston. All rights reserved.

Correcting General References

7c. Avoid a ***general reference,*** which is the use of a pronoun that refers to a general idea rather than to a specific antecedent.

GENERAL On his second trip to Mexico, Daniel spoke Spanish well enough to make himself understood, which was encouraging. [*Which* has no specific antecedent.]

CLEAR On his second trip to Mexico, Daniel **felt encouraged that he** spoke Spanish well enough to make himself understood.

USAGE

EXERCISE Draw a line through each general pronoun reference below, and write an appropriate noun above it. For clarity, you may need to revise other words in the sentences as well.

Example 1. When the Berlin Wall came down in 1989, ~~this~~ *the spectacle* inspired the world.

1. My grandfather brought some games and coloring books to Tanya when she was in the hospital. It cheered her up considerably.
2. Trading in the new company's stocks should drop off after a few days, but this should come as no surprise.
3. The cookie sheet should be allowed to cool before putting the dough on it. That will make your cookies fluffier.
4. Jacob started exercising regularly, and he felt much better because of it.
5. The tomb was sealed by tons of rock, but that didn't keep thieves away.
6. Seconds before the time ran out, Rosario sank a shot from the three-point line, winning the game for our team. That made the crowd go wild.
7. In the past year Marshall has replaced the car's radiator and the coolant hoses, but it has not made any difference.
8. The cathedral took almost two hundred years to build, which comes as no surprise when one sees how magnificent it is.
9. Some people believe the old dam should be breached to allow salmon to swim upstream, but others in the community are opposed to that.
10. More students have been riding the bus to school recently, which may have been caused by a shortage of parking spaces.

Copyright © by Holt, Rinehart and Winston. All rights reserved.

USAGE

Correcting Ambiguous and General References

7b. Avoid an ***ambiguous reference,*** which occurs when any one of two or more words could be a pronoun's antecedent.

7c. Avoid a ***general reference,*** which is the use of a pronoun that refers to a general idea rather than to a specific antecedent.

AMBIGUOUS Rosa phoned Lois while she was in Miami. [To whom does *she* refer: *Rosa* or *Lois*?]

CLEAR While **Lois** was in Miami, Rosa phoned **her.**

GENERAL We sat down and talked for a while. It helped clear up the misunderstanding.

CLEAR **Sitting down and talking for a while** helped clear up the misunderstanding.

EXERCISE Revise each sentence to correct the ambiguous or general pronoun reference.

Example 1. The technician replaced the igniter. This fixed the furnace. *By replacing the igniter, the technician fixed the furnace.*

1. When the dog first met the cat, it was scared. ______

2. The clothing drive distributed coats to three thousand families. This was a success! ______

3. Last Saturday, Scott and his father washed his car. ______

4. Rain ruined our championship soccer game. It made us disappointed. ______

5. Diane told Ana her favorite joke. ______

6. The sun came out as soon as we woke up and looked outside our tent. That was a relief. ______

7. Calinda and Ethel wrote a play based on her grandmother's diary. ______

8. When the bottle hit the prow of the ship, it broke into a thousand pieces. ______

9. Before introducing the distinguished speaker, the professor briefly mentioned her latest book. ______

10. Global temperatures may be rising, which is frightening. ______

Copyright © by Holt, Rinehart and Winston. All rights reserved.

Correcting Weak References

7d. Avoid a ***weak reference,*** which occurs when a pronoun refers to an antecedent that has been suggested but not expressed.

WEAK Our whale-watching excursion lasted all afternoon, but we didn't actually see any.
CLEAR Our whale-watching excursion lasted all afternoon, but we didn't actually see any **whales.**
CLEAR **We spent all afternoon looking for whales,** but we didn't actually see any.

EXERCISE A Each of the following sentences contains at least one weak pronoun reference. Revise the sentences to correct each error.

Example 1. The car is certainly fast, but other performance features are more important than ~~that~~ *speed*.

1. I was surprised to see Marcus return from the bookstore without buying a single one.
2. Because Lorena grew up on a farm, she was naturally drawn to veterinary medicine, which she saw as a chance to help them.
3. After the artist visited an Alaskan village to paint an Inupiat ceremony, she was able to display several at a museum of American Indian art.
4. Bryce was not able to go ice-skating with us because he hadn't brought his.
5. Since employees commented that departments could communicate with each other more effectively, managers have made it their top priority.

EXERCISE B Revise each of the following sentences to correct the weak pronoun reference.

Example 1. We planted the garden in early March, and we've already harvested some.
We planted the vegetables in early March, and we've already harvested some.

6. Home from the fishing trip, Davida lifted an entire cooler full of them out of the truck. ______

______

7. Lionel has built a potter's wheel in his workroom but so far has not made any. ______

______

8. Our game has been rained out, and the weather forecast says to expect more of it this week.

______

9. The review of this strikingly designed computer says that many people buy it because of that.

______

10. The museum guide explained the ancient Egyptian practice of mummification and said that these were among the best preserved. ______

______

Copyright © by Holt, Rinehart and Winston. All rights reserved.

NAME ______ CLASS ______ DATE ______

for CHAPTER 7: CLEAR REFERENCE page 214

Correcting Indefinite References

7e. Avoid an ***indefinite reference***—the use of a pronoun that refers to no particular person or thing and that is unnecessary to the structure and meaning of a sentence.

INDEFINITE On this Web page they offer a wide variety of Ethiopian recipes.

CLEAR **This Web page offers** a wide variety of Ethiopian recipes.

USAGE

EXERCISE A For each sentence below, determine whether the underlined pronoun makes the sentence unclear because of an indefinite reference. If the sentence is unclear, write *U* over the pronoun. If it is clear, write C.

Example 1. In many places, you can see modern adaptations of Shakespeare plays. *U*

1. At a recent performance in our town, they set Shakespeare's *Othello* in South Africa.
2. Some critics argue that you should set Shakespeare's plays in their original locations.
3. We learned in our British literature class, however, that in Shakespeare's day, the stage was relatively bare and did not have elaborate backdrops or sets on it.
4. Instead of elaborate sets, they depended on spoken descriptions of the scene and elaborate costumes to indicate where and who characters were.
5. Costumes were not always historically accurate; on stage, they basically dressed in the fashions of the day.

EXERCISE B Revise each of the following sentences to correct the indefinite pronoun reference.

Example 1. During the Jewish festival of Sukkoth, you give thanks for the fruits of the harvest.
During the Jewish festival of Sukkoth, people give thanks for the fruits of the harvest.

6. At the bottom of the poster, it lists a toll-free number that runaways can call for help. ______
7. In the report that aired last night, they said that fewer asteroids orbit near the earth than had been previously estimated. ______
8. A sign at the pool warns that you should not bring food into the swimming area. ______
9. Beside the list of ingredients for this recipe, it lists metric equivalents for each measurement. ______
10. To celebrate the store's opening, they are giving out free groceries to the first fifty customers. ______

Copyright © by Holt, Rinehart and Winston. All rights reserved.

NAME ______________________ CLASS ______________ DATE ______________

for **CHAPTER 7: CLEAR REFERENCE** *pages 213–214*

Correcting Weak and Indefinite References

7d. Avoid a ***weak reference,*** which occurs when a pronoun refers to an antecedent that has been suggested but not expressed.

7e. Avoid an ***indefinite reference***—the use of a pronoun that refers to no particular person or thing and that is unnecessary to the structure and meaning of a sentence.

WEAK Greg went to the automotive show, intent on buying one.

CLEAR Greg went to the automotive show, intent on buying **a car.**

INDEFINITE I can't believe that on this box of toothpicks it actually includes instructions.

CLEAR I can't believe that **this box of toothpicks** actually includes instructions.

USAGE

EXERCISE Revise each sentence below to correct the weak or indefinite pronoun reference.

Example 1. Seeing Maurizio on the dance floor, no one was sure where he had learned those.
Seeing Maurizio on the dance floor, no one was sure where he had learned those steps.

1. In this new atlas, it shows the recent changes in the countries of Europe and Asia. ______

2. As the parade passed by, people on several threw candy to the spectators. ______

3. Jesse Jackson is an eloquent speaker, and that was one of his best. ______

4. At that amusement park, they've got one of the biggest roller coasters in Texas. ______

5. We found tiny footprints all over the snowdrifts, but didn't actually see it. ______

6. Before 1970, you had to be twenty-one to vote. ______

7. After talking to Mary about the charity event, I decided I wanted to contribute to one. ______

8. We weeded the garden and gave them some water. ______

9. In the article they said that this year has had the worst hurricane season in recorded history. ______

10. They wore gorilla masks to the meeting, which made everyone laugh. ______

Copyright © by Holt, Rinehart and Winston. All rights reserved.

USAGE

Review A: Clear Reference

EXERCISE A For each sentence below, draw an arrow from each underlined pronoun to its antecedent.

Example 1. Ken didn't mind doing yardwork in his old shoes, which were already dirty.

1. People write to that columnist because he offers easy solutions for their computer problems.
2. When Ashley peered through the microscope, she was amazed to see the little creatures propel themselves with hundreds of tiny hairs.
3. Entering the subway station, Diane pressed a token into her son's hand and said, "Don't lose this."
4. Amid the docks is a tower that served as a jail before it became an apartment building.
5. Leading Ryan to the display case, Katie said, "These are the watches I described to you earlier."

EXERCISE B Revise each item to correct the error in pronoun reference.

Example 1. The corporation may be sold, which the executives hope to avoid.
The executives hope to avoid selling the corporation.

6. The officer told Pete that his car had been stolen. ____________
7. In this computer-virus warning, they say to update antivirus software regularly. ____________
8. If only the sun would shine a little; that would make the winter seem less bleak. ____________
9. After seeing the news report about high-definition television, Grandmother commented that she could remember watching it in black and white. ____________
10. The engineers have gone over every inch of wiring in the space shuttle, which should ensure the safety of the next flight. ____________

Copyright © by Holt, Rinehart and Winston. All rights reserved.

NAME ____________ CLASS ____________ DATE ____________

Review B: Clear Reference

EXERCISE A Each of these items contains an error in clear pronoun reference. On the line provided, revise each item to make the sentence clear and correct.

Example 1. Our relay team just broke its all-time record, which gives us confidence about the next track meet. *Because our relay team just broke its all-time record, we are confident about the next track meet.*

1. We wanted to buy our movie tickets, but it was closed. ____________

2. The receptionist told the patient that she had laryngitis. ____________

3. When Karl admitted that he could not swim, this came as a surprise. ____________

4. They said on the radio that Monday will be sunny and warm. ____________

5. The game was canceled because of rain. That was annoying. ____________

EXERCISE B Each sentence in the following paragraph contains at least one weak or indefinite pronoun reference. Draw a line through each unclear reference, and write a correction above it. You may need to change other words in the sentence for clarity and sense.

Example **[1]** I enjoy listening to a variety of singers other than Hanah Dahan, but ~~hers~~ *her songs* are among my favorite ones.

[6] In this interview, it explains that Hanah Dahan is an acclaimed popular singer from Israel. **[7]** She has said that when singing, you feel as if you are in heaven. **[8]** Her love for her family, her roots, and her home come across in each one. **[9]** Its striking, pure tone gets the message of her words across, even to audiences who do not understand Hebrew and Aramaic. **[10]** In critical reviews, they compare Ms. Dahan's voice to those of both America's Mariah Carey and France's legendary cabaret singer, Edith Piaf.

Copyright © by Holt, Rinehart and Winston. All rights reserved.

NAME ______ CLASS ______ DATE ______

for **CHAPTER 7: CLEAR REFERENCE** pages 208–214

Review C: Clear Reference

USAGE

EXERCISE Each of these items contains an error in clear pronoun reference. On the line provided, revise each item to make the sentence clear and correct.

Example 1. We arrived late for the first act of the play, which really annoyed us.
Arriving late for the first act of the play really annoyed us.

1. Dad told Juan that he needed to wash the car. ______

2. This recipe is new. Would you like to try them? ______

3. In the American League, they have designated hitters. ______

4. When he put the pan in the water, it was still hot. ______

5. When I told Mom my essay had won the contest, she said this was cause for celebration. ______

6. Even though drivers, not roads, cause accidents, they should still be improved. ______

7. Do the boating regulations allow you to use sailboats on the reservoir? ______

8. In the dictionary it says that the word *maverick* was originally someone's name. ______

9. When the astronaut radioed back, the control room erupted in applause. This forced the communications officer to shout in order to be heard. ______

10. The commercial showed a man pushing a shopping cart through a maze of grocery store aisles, which was very amusing. ______

Copyright © by Holt, Rinehart and Winston. All rights reserved.

USAGE

The Principal Parts of Verbs

8a. The ***principal parts*** of a verb are the *base form,* the *present participle,* the *past,* and the *past participle.* All other verb forms are derived from these principal parts.

BASE FORM	PRESENT PARTICIPLE	PAST	PAST PARTICIPLE
save	[is] saving	saved	[have] saved
think	[is] thinking	thought	[have] thought
begin	[is] beginning	began	[have] begun

EXERCISE On the line provided, write the correct present participle, past, or past participle verb form of the verb in parentheses.

Example 1. All the pecans have ___fallen___ from our tree because of last night's strong winds. *(fall)*

1. I think he has been __________ on the telephone long enough. *(talk)*

2. The new space telescope will be __________ the earth by this time tomorrow. *(orbit)*

3. Amanda is __________ the ball better than anyone else on her softball team. *(hit)*

4. Roberto __________ me a seat at this morning's assembly. *(save)*

5. The movie previews had already __________ when we entered the theater. *(begin)*

6. I turned out the lights because I __________ you had already left. *(think)*

7. Leo's mom, who is a professional chef, __________ the last awards banquet. *(cater)*

8. The graph for our research paper was __________ last week. *(draw)*

9. The cost of gasoline is __________ again next week. *(rise)*

10. My sister is __________ for class president. *(run)*

11. If no candidate receives a majority, a run-off election will be __________. *(hold)*

12. The bicyclist should have __________ at the intersection. *(stop)*

13. I __________ the telephone number on a scrap of paper. *(write)*

14. Sharon __________ the director and some of the actors in a local restaurant. *(see)*

15. Malcolm had __________ by the building many times on his way to work. *(walk)*

16. As hard as we __________, we could not win a game all season. *(try)*

17. The dog had __________ patiently outside the store for an hour. *(sit)*

18. The class __________ to sponsor a car wash to raise money for the trip. *(decide)*

19. She had __________ all her grandfather's letters in a shoebox in the closet. *(keep)*

20. Please be quiet while the baby is __________. *(sleep)*

Copyright © by Holt, Rinehart and Winston. All rights reserved.

USAGE

Regular Verbs

8b. A ***regular verb*** forms its past and past participle by adding *–d* or *–ed* to its base form.

BASE FORM	PRESENT PARTICIPLE	PAST	PAST PARTICIPLE
work	[is] working	worked	[have] worked
imagine	[is] imagining	imagined	[have] imagined
use	[is] using	used	[have] used
collect	[is] collecting	collected	[have] collected

EXERCISE A In the blank in each of the following sentences, write the past or past participle of the verb shown in parentheses after the sentence.

Example 1. Joseph has often ___envisioned___ that he will one day become a master chef. *(envision)*

1. Last weekend Fatima, Joseph, and I ____________ breaded chicken rolls. *(cook)*

2. First, we ____________ all the recipe ingredients. *(purchase)*

3. We were ____________ to mince the garlic and parsley. *(suppose)*

4. Then we ____________ the bread crumbs, garlic, parsley, and cheese. *(combine)*

5. I ____________ the chicken with a mallet to make it easy to roll. *(pound)*

6. Joseph had ____________ lemon juice and oil into the crumb mixture. *(pour)*

7. Each piece of chicken was ____________ with the moistened crumbs. *(coat)*

8. Then, we rolled each piece and ____________ it with a toothpick. *(secure)*

9. After we had ____________ the rolls in a pan, we baked them. *(arrange)*

10. I ____________ to think cooking was hard, but our cooking experience was fun and easy. *(use)*

EXERCISE B In the blank in each of the following sentences, write the past or past participle of the verb shown in parentheses after the sentence.

Example 1. My best friend ___used___ to live in the house across from mine. *(use)*

11. Carla's family ____________ in a hotel while their plumbing was being repaired. *(stay)*

12. I never ____________ that our team, made up entirely of sophomores, would be playing for the state championship. *(imagine)*

13. The mechanic ____________ my car's oil leak before my trip. *(fix)*

14. I think we were ____________ to take that last exit. *(suppose)*

15. The answers she gave on the test ____________ those on the answer key. *(match)*

Copyright © by Holt, Rinehart and Winston. All rights reserved.

NAME ______________________ CLASS ______________ DATE ______________

Irregular Verbs A

8c. An ***irregular verb*** forms its past and past participle in some way other than by adding *–d* or *–ed* to its base form.

BASE FORM	PRESENT PARTICIPLE	PAST	PAST PARTICIPLE
teach	[is] teaching	taught	[have] taught
choose	[is] choosing	chose	[have] chosen
run	[is] running	ran	[have] run
tear	[is] tearing	tore	[have] torn
hurt	[is] hurting	hurt	[have] hurt

EXERCISE In the blank in each of the following sentences, write the past or past participle of the verb shown in parentheses after the sentence.

Example 1. By 1949, Indonesia had ___become___ an independent nation. *(become)*

1. The *slendang,* a batik cloth that is __________ by Javanese women, is wrapped around the head or used to carry babies. *(wear)*
2. When the Javanese want to celebrate an important event, a *selametan,* or ceremonial feast, is __________. *(hold)*
3. There are close to sixty active volcanoes in Indonesia, and the ash from the volcanic eruptions has __________ the soil fertile. *(make)*
4. Although Indonesians speak more than two hundred different languages, since the 1940s, the use of Indonesian, the country's official language, has __________. *(spread)*
5. Since many Indonesians are followers of the Muslim religion, they are __________ to eat pork. *(forbid)*
6. Most houses in Indonesia have been __________ on stilts. *(build)*
7. Puppet dramas have always __________ popular on the island of Java. *(be)*
8. I __________ that a puppet drama can last all night. *(read)*
9. Many babies born on Java are __________ a single name. *(give)*
10. Indonesia's chief food crop is rice, which is __________ on many small farms. *(grow)*

Copyright © by Holt, Rinehart and Winston. All rights reserved.

USAGE

Irregular Verbs B

8c. An ***irregular verb*** forms its past and past participle in some way other than by adding *–d* or *–ed* to its base form.

BASE FORM	PRESENT PARTICIPLE	PAST	PAST PARTICIPLE
fly	[is] flying	flew	[have] flown
read	[is] reading	read	[have] read

EXERCISE On the line provided, write the correct past or past participle verb form of the verb in parentheses.

Example 1. Has Greta ___brought___ her notes from the meeting? *(bring)*

1. Unfortunately, Julie ______________ a cold during her vacation. *(catch)*
2. None of us ______________ before the end of our band's concert. *(leave)*
3. Anita's mom had ______________ sandwiches for us to eat during the hike. *(send)*
4. "That exercise wasn't as hard as I ______________ it would be," he said after class. *(think)*
5. The major difficulty has been overcome, but two smaller ones have ______________. *(arise)*
6. My grandparents have never owned or ______________ a car. *(drive)*
7. I have ______________ the scavenger-hunt items in the backyard. *(hide)*
8. Sherry waited until the plaster had ______________ before removing the mold. *(set)*
9. Yesterday my father ______________ to the neighbors who have just moved in next door. *(speak)*
10. My dog, who is scared of thunder, ______________ me during the storm. *(wake)*
11. We stacked the newspapers and ______________ them with string. *(bind)*
12. He was exhausted, but he ______________ hard to stay awake through dinner. *(fight)*
13. Late last night, she remembered that she had ______________ her book to Sarah. *(lend)*
14. Our team ______________ in the final few seconds of the game. *(lose)*
15. By this time tomorrow, we will have ______________ all the tickets to the play. *(sell)*
16. I would go with you, but I have already ______________ all of my money. *(spend)*
17. Nathan woke up, ______________ dressed, and went downstairs to fix breakfast. *(get)*
18. The student body ______________ blue and gold as the school colors. *(choose)*
19. Either you've grown an inch this week, or those pants have ______________! *(shrink)*
20. The cat ______________ stealthily toward the bird. *(creep)*

Copyright © by Holt, Rinehart and Winston. All rights reserved.

NAME ______________________ CLASS ______________ DATE ______________

for **CHAPTER 8: USING VERBS CORRECTLY** *pages 224–234*

Irregular Verbs C

8c. An ***irregular verb*** forms its past and past participle in some way other than by adding *–d* or *–ed* to its base form.

BASE FORM	PRESENT PARTICIPLE	PAST	PAST PARTICIPLE
shake	[is] shaking	shook	[have] shaken
burst	[is] bursting	burst	[have] burst

USAGE

EXERCISE On the line provided, write the correct past or past participle verb form of the verb in parentheses.

Example 1. After you have ___beaten___ the eggs, pour them into this bowl. *(beat)*

1. The superintendent ________________ the ribbon at the construction site. *(cut)*

2. Have you ________________ to the museum to see the new exhibit? *(come)*

3. Dimitri had ________________ the rest of the pizza by the time we arrived. *(eat)*

4. The warm breeze ________________ invigorating after the long winter. *(feel)*

5. Have you ________________ about the changes to the team's uniforms? *(hear)*

6. Ernie was the only person in our class who ________________ the new student. *(know)*

7. The people who work at that company get ________________ every two weeks. *(pay)*

8. The bell ________________ just after Ms. Alvarez finished her lecture. *(ring)*

9. The squirrel had ________________ up the tree before the dog could bark twice. *(spring)*

10. Tracy knew she had ________________ the election when Paula, who had counted the votes, smiled at her. *(win)*

11. The old clock in the hallway ________________ one. *(strike)*

12. I wish James hadn't ________________ my sister about the incident in the cafeteria. *(tell)*

13. The little boy picked up the stick and ________________ it as far as he could. *(fling)*

14. The tour guide ________________ us down some steep stairs into a dungeon. *(lead)*

15. I'm sure that I ________________ the cats out this morning before I left for school. *(let)*

16. The rain started a few minutes after the game ________________. *(begin)*

17. Neither of my grandmothers has ever ________________ in an airplane. *(fly)*

18. The branches must have ________________ from the tree during the storm. *(fall)*

19. Could you have ________________ anything to avoid the accident? *(do)*

20. Elaine should have ________________ help with her math homework long before now. *(seek)*

Copyright © by Holt, Rinehart and Winston. All rights reserved.

Irregular Verbs D

USAGE

8c. An ***irregular verb*** forms its past and past participle in some way other than by adding *–d* or *–ed* to its base form.

BASE FORM	PRESENT PARTICIPLE	PAST	PAST PARTICIPLE
break	[is] breaking	broke	[have] broken
cost	[is] costing	cost	[have] cost

EXERCISE In the sentences below, draw a line through any incorrect verb form and write above it the correct past or past participle. If a sentence is already correct, write *C* after it.

Example 1. Who ~~letted~~ *let* the neighbor's cat into the house?

1. The wind from the storm blowed all night and howled in the rafters.

2. The cat creeped into my bed after I turned off the light.

3. My younger sister done that puzzle in less than two minutes.

4. After an all-night bus trip, we fighted to stay awake during the opening ceremonies.

5. Have you gotten your test scores back yet?

6. Cecil has lain down his keys and forgotten where he left them.

7. The curator carefully putted the antique toy back into the glass case.

8. The skater spinned numerous times, making the feat look effortless.

9. Somebody has stealed the picture I taped to the outside of my locker!

10. The coach telled us we might see this sort of defense in our next game.

11. If I hadn't bumped into the hive, the bees wouldn't have stinged me.

12. Cecily grabbed the rope, took a deep breath, and swang out over the water.

13. Without a map, we couldn't have founded the convention center.

14. After the match, my parents buyed lunch for the whole team.

15. Marilyn knew that Judith had not yet forgive her for the unkind comment.

16. The window must have broke when you slammed it shut.

17. Erin forgot where she had put the information about the tournament.

18. I simply could not have bear one more minute of that awful music!

19. If you had explained the situation, I'm sure he would have understanded.

20. Before the dinner party, my brother and I shone the silver candlesticks.

Copyright © by Holt, Rinehart and Winston. All rights reserved.

Irregular Verbs E

8c. An ***irregular verb*** forms its past and past participle in some way other than by adding *–d* or *–ed* to its base form.

BASE FORM	PRESENT PARTICIPLE	PAST	PAST PARTICIPLE
lose	[is] losing	lost	[have] lost
sting	[is] stinging	stung	[have] stung

EXERCISE A On the line in each of the following sentences, write the past or past participle of a verb listed below to complete the sentence correctly and sensibly.

find lend seek swim have lie
sell write hurt ride sing

Example 1. The mayor announced that she had *found* a way to satisfy both groups.

1. The sprinter ____________ his ankle a second time by trying to rush his recovery.
2. While saving his money, Carl called every day to see if the car had been ____________ yet.
3. For many months, the investigator ____________ the person who had written the note.
4. I have already ____________ dinner, so I won't be eating again tonight.
5. Is this the book that you ____________ to me last year?
6. Ruth has ____________ in the school choir since she was a sophomore.
7. My grandfather doesn't leave the gym until he has ____________ ten laps.
8. According to the postmark, this letter was ____________ nearly a century ago.
9. Michelle had just ____________ down for a nap when the phone rang.
10. Is that the horse that has never been ____________?

EXERCISE B In each of the following sentences, draw a line through any incorrect verb form and write above it the correct past or past participle.

Example 1. That winter, the river ~~freezed~~ *froze* solid.

11. After I win the race, I must have drank a gallon of water.
12. She has already pay the store for the dishes that she accidentally broke.
13. Mike taked a deep breath, looked down at the water, and dived straight in.
14. I'm sorry, but we have already ate the whole pie.
15. LaSandra has chose a difficult topic for her final paper.

Copyright © by Holt, Rinehart and Winston. All rights reserved.

USAGE

Lie and *Lay*

The verb *lie* means "to rest," "to recline," or "to be in a certain place." *Lie* does not take a direct object. The verb *lay* means "to put [something] in a place." *Lay* generally takes a direct object.

BASE FORM	PRESENT PARTICIPLE	PAST	PAST PARTICIPLE
lie	[is] lying	lay	[have] lain
lay	[is] laying	laid	[have] laid

EXAMPLES The evidence **lay** on the table. [no direct object]

The attorney **laid** the evidence on the table. [*Evidence* is the direct object of *laid*.]

EXERCISE In the sentences below, underline the correct verb form in parentheses.

Example 1. After a morning swim, the crocodile has (*lain*, *laid*) in the sun all afternoon.

1. My grandfather's hens are known for (*lying, laying*) the largest eggs at the farmers' market.
2. In winter, my cat (*lies, lays*) on top of the wool blanket in the closet.
3. After she finished the marathon, Millicent (*lay, laid*) down right on the sidewalk.
4. For the next six months, the street department will be (*lying, laying*) new asphalt on the streets.
5. My sister and my father carefully (*lain, laid*) the shelf on its side before attaching the back panel.
6. Believe it or not, I (*lay, laid*) these kitchen tiles by myself.
7. The dog was patiently (*laying, lying*) by its bag of food when I got home.
8. The dirty laundry (*lay, laid*) in a heap next to the washer.
9. Lee (*lay, laid*) the map to the meeting on the passenger's seat.
10. Mom says she hopes we don't plan to (*lie, lay*) around the house all weekend.
11. She (*lay, laid*) her baby daughter in the crib and quietly shut the door.
12. Who knows what adventures (*lay, lie*) ahead of us?
13. Hidden in the tall grass, the cat (*lay, laid*) in wait for an unsuspecting bird.
14. I would like to (*lie, lay*) down for an hour, but I don't want to take a nap.
15. After (*lying, laying*) the clean sheets and towels on the bed, he left the room.
16. These shoes must have (*laid, lain*) out all night in the rain.
17. How long ago was this section of the railroad track (*laid, lain*)?
18. When the cease-fire was announced, the soldiers (*laid, lay*) down their weapons.
19. My keys must have been (*laying, lying*) under this newspaper the whole time.
20. The cornerstone of the new capitol was (*lain, laid*) sometime in the 1930s.

Copyright © by Holt, Rinehart and Winston. All rights reserved.

NAME ______________________ CLASS ______________ DATE ______________

Sit and *Set*

The verb *sit* means "to be in a seated, upright position" or "to be in a place." *Sit* seldom takes a direct object. The verb *set* means "to put [something] in a place." *Set* generally takes a direct object.

BASE FORM	PRESENT PARTICIPLE	PAST	PAST PARTICIPLE
sit	[is] sitting	sat	[have] sat
set	[is] setting	set	[have] set

EXAMPLES Aaron **is sitting** at his desk. [no direct object]
Aaron **is setting** the computer on his desk. [*Computer* is the direct object of *is setting*.]

EXERCISE On the line in each sentence below, write the form of *sit* or *set* that correctly and sensibly completes the sentence.

Example 1. Should Robert be ___sitting___ this close to the television?

1. Albert will be ______________ up our booth for the schoolwide food fair.
2. My brother always ______________ the table for dinner.
3. Jerrel ______________ the fossil to one side.
4. I had been ______________ for almost an hour when my name was finally called.
5. She ______________ between her two best friends at the awards ceremony.
6. This package from my aunt was ______________ on the front porch when I got home.
7. That old house, the first in the area, ______________ on the bluff overlooking the river.
8. Robert ______________ out the books he would need for tomorrow's classes.
9. Should I ______________ the groceries on the counter or the table?
10. The substitute teacher asked us to ______________ in our assigned seats.
11. Please ______________ the box of decorations near the door.
12. ______________ at a desk for hours at a time is also tiring.
13. When you visit Key West, be sure to watch the sun ______________ over the ocean.
14. We need to arrive early so that we can ______________ up the chairs.
15. Geoff's new setter quickly learned to stay, ______________, and fetch.
16. Who ______________ next to you during the dance performance?
17. She asked the children to ______________ in a circle on the floor.
18. In the first part of the story, the author ______________ the scene.
19. During the banquet, the school board members ______________ at the head table.
20. Has your sister ______________ a date for the wedding yet?

Copyright © by Holt, Rinehart and Winston. All rights reserved.

USAGE

Rise and *Raise*

The verb *rise* means "to go up" or "to get up." *Rise* does not take a direct object. The verb *raise* means "to lift up" or "to cause [something] to rise." *Raise* generally takes a direct object.

BASE FORM	PRESENT PARTICIPLE	PAST	PAST PARTICIPLE
rise	[is] rising	rose	[have] risen
raise	[is] raising	raised	[have] raised

EXAMPLES Most of the employees' salaries **have risen** steadily. [no direct object]
The company **has raised** salaries on a regular basis. [*Salaries* is the direct object of *has raised.*]

EXERCISE A In the sentences below, underline the correct verb form in parentheses.

Example 1. The temperature began to (*rise, raise*) as soon as the sun appeared above the horizon.

1. Student council members were (*rising, raising*) a banner in the hall this morning.
2. The popularity of that restaurant (*rises, raises*) every week.
3. Gerardo (*rose, raised*) all the money for his trip in record time.
4. By morning, floodwaters had (*risen, raised*) another foot.
5. Dora (*rises, raises*) many different types of vegetables in her garden.
6. The bread was (*rising, raising*) as we walked past the bakery window.
7. Cynthia will (*rise, raise*) the blinds in your office to give your plants some light.
8. Grant had (*risen, raised*) from his chair to introduce me to his parents.
9. Sailors across the bay have (*rose, raised*) the bad-weather signal flags.
10. Everyone will now (*rise, raise*) and join in the Pledge of Allegiance.

EXERCISE B On the line in each sentence below, write a form of *rise* or *raise* that correctly and sensibly completes the sentence.

Example 1. When the moon ___rose___, we could see the path.

11. My grandparents __________ seven children in that small house.
12. As the battered ship approached the island, the sailors' spirits __________ .
13. This is a difficult exam, but I know the class will __________ to the challenge.
14. Crystal has been __________ before dawn every day to train for the marathon.
15. The ranchers in this region __________ several breeds of wool-bearing goats.

Copyright © by Holt, Rinehart and Winston. All rights reserved.

NAME _______________ CLASS _______________ DATE _______________

Six Troublesome Verbs

The verb *lie* means "to rest," "to recline," or "to be in a certain place." *Lie* does not take a direct object. The verb *lay* means "to put [something] in a place." *Lay* generally takes a direct object.

The verb *sit* means "to be in a seated, upright position" or "to be in a place." *Sit* seldom takes a direct object. The verb *set* means "to put [something] in a place." *Set* generally takes a direct object.

The verb *rise* means "to go up" or "to get up." *Rise* does not take a direct object. The verb *raise* means "to lift up" or "to cause [something] to rise." *Raise* generally takes a direct object.

EXERCISE A Underline the correct verb in parentheses in each of the following sentences.

Example 1. Chad (lay, laid) quietly on the couch all afternoon, but his headache would not subside.

1. Pang had (*sat, set*) his tennis bag against the wall while he paused to tie his shoe.
2. How long has Elmo been (*laying, lying*) in the sun?
3. Sally had (*laid, lain*) down to take a brief nap, but an hour passed before she awoke.
4. My soufflé (*raised, rose*) elegantly but collapsed before I brought it to the table.
5. (*Lie, Lay*) on the bed until you feel better.
6. We (*sat, set*) at the counter because all the booths were occupied.
7. It was time to (*raise, rise*) the issue of funding for education.
8. The river has been (*raising, rising*) for two days because of the torrential rains.
9. When will Chandra (*lay, lie*) the tiles in the bathroom?
10. Three raucous mockingbirds were (*sitting, setting*) on a branch near the fence.

EXERCISE B Proofread the following sentences for correct verb usage. Cross out each incorrect verb form, and write the correct form in the space above it. If a sentence is already correct, write *C* before the item number.

Example 1. The cost of oil had ~~raised~~ *risen* considerably, and everyone was trying to conserve.

11. The paint set had been laying in the corner the whole time.
12. After they laid their books down on the steps, the boys started a game of baseball.
13. Please do not set in the chair with the carved legs.
14. The patient was so exhausted she could scarcely rise her head from the pillow.
15. Luther set his cap on the back of his head and swaggered off toward the ball field.

Copyright © by Holt, Rinehart and Winston. All rights reserved.

Tense and Form

8d. The ***tense*** of a verb indicates the time of the action or of the state of being expressed by the verb.

THE SIX TENSES

PRESENT	PAST	FUTURE	PRESENT PERFECT	PAST PERFECT	FUTURE PERFECT
sings	sang	will sing	has sung	had sung	will have sung

Each tense has an additional form called the *progressive form,* which expresses continuing action or state of being.

EXAMPLES is singing, was singing, has been singing, will be singing

The present and past tenses also have an *emphatic form,* which consists of *do, does,* or *did* plus the base form of a verb.

EXAMPLE Although the sky was gray, we **did go** on our picnic.

EXERCISE On the line provided before each sentence, write the tense of the underlined verb. If the verb is in the progressive or emphatic form, also indicate the form by writing *progressive* or *emphatic.*

Example present perfect, progressive **1.** Mr. Diaz has been teaching poetry at the community college for almost fifteen years.

_______ **1.** I have read the poem "Dusting" by Julia Alvarez.

_______ **2.** The poem does reveal something about the speaker's feelings.

_______ **3.** The poem's speaker was feeling neglected and anonymous within her family.

_______ **4.** There are times, I think, when all children feel that way.

_______ **5.** Julia Alvarez had grown up in the Dominican Republic.

_______ **6.** She was only ten when she moved to the United States with her family.

_______ **7.** Ms. Alvarez has studied creative writing at the university level.

_______ **8.** She did base her poetry and short stories on her childhood experiences.

_______ **9.** By the end of the term, we will have discussed several poems from her book *Homecoming.*

_______ **10.** Next term, we will be reading selections from her first book of fiction, *How the García Girls Lost Their Accents.*

Copyright © by Holt, Rinehart and Winston. All rights reserved.

Correct Use of Verb Tenses A

8e. Each of the six tenses has its own uses.

PRESENT TENSE Dwayne **makes** the batter for the shrimp tempura. [The action is occurring now.]

PAST TENSE Last weekend he **made** pork lo mein. [The action occurred in the past and did not continue into the present.]

FUTURE TENSE Tomorrow he **will make** his specialty, chicken teriyaki. [The action will occur in the future.]

PRESENT PERFECT TENSE Conchita **has sent** her application to the University of Virginia. [The action occurred at some indefinite time in the past.]

PAST PERFECT TENSE She already **had sent** applications to two other universities. [The action occurred in the past and ended before some other past action.]

FUTURE PERFECT TENSE By next week, Conchita **will have sent** at least five applications. [The action will end before some other action takes place.]

EXERCISE In each sentence below, underline the verb form in parentheses that correctly completes the sentence.

Example **1.** We *(have been working, will have been working)* in the yard all morning.

1. Be sure you *(have put, will have put)* the lid on the trash can before leaving it at the curb.

2. By next Thursday, Monica *(has been finishing, will have finished)* all the exams for her first semester of college.

3. Tired of waiting, the impatient couple *(leaves, had left)* by the time the clerk called their number.

4. Without telling their coach, the tennis team *(will be training, trained)* harder than usual for the meet they won yesterday.

5. Because the starting guard picked up three fouls in the first ten minutes of the game, my sister *(played, will play)* at that position until the second half.

6. Do you know that Jennifer Moddes still *(has been, is)* the tallest of the four sisters?

7. Because Bryan had outgrown his favorite pair of pants, he *(gave, gives)* them to his younger brother.

8. My cousin *(collects, has been collecting)* photographs of the desert ever since his trip to the Grand Canyon.

9. What *(will have been, was)* your favorite chapter in that book?

10. Sometimes I accidentally *(do call, will call)* the twins by the wrong name.

Copyright © by Holt, Rinehart and Winston. All rights reserved.

USAGE

Correct Use of Verb Tenses B

8e. Each of the six tenses has its own uses.

PRESENT TENSE	Angel **buys** bread at that bakery. [The action is occurring now or is customary or habitual.]
PAST TENSE	Angel **bought** bread at that bakery yesterday. [The action occurred in the past and did not continue into the present.]
FUTURE TENSE	Tomorrow, Angel **will buy** bread for the picnic. [The action will occur in the future.]
PRESENT PERFECT TENSE	Angel **has bought** bread at that bakery before. [The action occurred at some indefinite time in the past.]
PAST PERFECT TENSE	Angel **had** already **bought** turkey and cheese. [The action occurred in the past and ended before some other action in the past.]
FUTURE PERFECT TENSE	By tomorrow afternoon, Angel **will have bought** all the supplies. [The action will end before some other action takes place.]

EXERCISE In each of the following sentences, identify the tense of the underlined verb by writing above it the tense of the verb.

Example 1. By the time we graduate, most of us will have been (*future perfect*) in school for twelve or thirteen years.

1. Nicole walked to school every day last year.
2. Next fall, when she goes to college, she will live at home for a semester.
3. By then, she will have saved enough to buy a small car.
4. She thought she had saved enough, but then she remembered the additional cost of insurance.
5. Textbooks and other supplies are usually very expensive.
6. She has registered for classes and will meet the professors during orientation week.
7. Some of her friends will be going to the same college.
8. Others plan to work in a community volunteer program for a year.
9. Nicole's sister joined the Navy after she graduated.
10. Nicole had considered military service but decided to go to college first.

Copyright © by Holt, Rinehart and Winston. All rights reserved.

USAGE

Sequence of Tenses

8f. Use tense forms correctly to show relationships between verbs in a sentence.

(1) When describing events that occur at the same time, use verbs in the same tense.

The telephone **rang,** and I **answered** it. [past tense]

(2) When describing events that occur at different times, use verbs in different tenses to show the order of events.

Peter **told** me that he **had studied** all evening for the history test. [The studying occurred before Peter made the statement.]

8g. Do not use *would have* in an *"if"* clause that expresses the earlier of two past actions. Use the past perfect tense.

NONSTANDARD If she would have practiced, the coach would have let her play.

STANDARD If she **had practiced,** the coach would have let her play.

EXERCISE Most of the following sentences contain errors in the use of tenses. Cross out each incorrect verb form, and write the correct form above it. If a sentence is already correct, write *C* before the item number.

Example 1. On February 12, Mom will ~~be~~ *have been* working for the museum for exactly five years.

1. After blowing her whistle, the official explained that the player's right foot has touched the sideline.
2. She delivered the mail when the regular letter carrier is sick.
3. My cousin and I quarreled earlier, but we were friends again by the end of the day.
4. We would have eaten outdoors if the rain would have stopped.
5. I was surprised to learn that modern-day birds may be related to dinosaurs.
6. By next summer, my family will be living in this house for five decades.
7. I wish that you hadn't been telling her that secret.
8. I had written two pages of the essay before I remembered that we had been asked to use a blue or black pen.
9. I have just learned that Jimmy Carter will have spoken at our commencement ceremony.
10. By the time you returned, we will have been waiting for half an hour.

Copyright © by Holt, Rinehart and Winston. All rights reserved.

NAME _______________ CLASS _______________ DATE _______________

Infinitives and Participles

8h. The ***present infinitive*** expresses an action or a state of being that follows another action or state of being.

EXAMPLE The boys hoped **to win** the tennis match.

8i. The ***present perfect infinitive*** expresses an action or a state of being that precedes another action or state of being.

EXAMPLE Paula would like **to have received** an invitation.

8j. When used as a verbal, the ***present participle*** or ***past participle*** expresses an action or a state of being that occurs at the same time as another action or state of being.

EXAMPLE **Walking** onstage, I heard the applause.

8k. When used as a verbal, the ***present perfect participle*** expresses an action or a state of being that precedes another action or state of being.

EXAMPLE **Having been notified,** I wrote a speech.

EXERCISE In the sentences below, cross out any errors in the use of infinitives or participles and write the correct forms above them. (*Note:* There is more than one way to revise some sentences.)

Example 1. I would like to ~~have gone~~ *go* to the play with you when it opens next week.

1. Leaving my book at home, I had borrowed another copy from the teacher.
2. My ten-year-old brother hopes to have become an architect.
3. Ten minutes ago, Ms. Shane said, "You should choose a classmate to have worked with on this project."
4. The little girl stood on the curb, having looked both ways for cars before she crossed the street.
5. Excited to be elected class president, Carlotta outlined her ideas for the year.
6. Cole would like to take physics with us this semester, but he had to take another math class instead.
7. Having waited for the light to change, I gazed out the windshield.
8. Not wanting to have waked the sleeping baby, Emma tapped on the window.
9. I hope to have read all of Shakespeare's tragedies this summer.
10. Having shaken his head and muttered to himself, the team captain walked off the field.

Copyright © by Holt, Rinehart and Winston. All rights reserved.

Active and Passive Voice

8l. ***Voice*** is the form a transitive verb takes to indicate whether the subject of the verb performs or receives the action.

When the subject of a verb performs the action, the verb is in the ***active voice***. When the subject receives the action, the verb is in the ***passive voice***. Verbs in the active voice take direct objects; verbs in the passive voice do not.

ACTIVE VOICE A group of ecologists **visited** the Amazon rain forest. [The subject, *group*, performs the action. *Rain forest* is the direct object.]

PASSIVE VOICE The Amazon rain forest **was visited** by a group of ecologists. [The subject, *rain forest*, receives the action. There is no direct object.]

EXERCISE A Indicate the voice of each of the following sentences by writing, on the line provided, *AV* for *active voice* or *PV* for *passive voice.*

Example AV **1.** Alex Shoumatoff wrote a book about Chico Mendes's fight to save the rain forest.

______ **1.** Chico Mendes was raised in Brazil, deep in the Amazon rain forest.

______ **2.** Mendes and his fellow rubber tappers were angered by the devastation of the Amazon rain forest by ranchers.

______ **3.** Their voices were heard by environmentalists and ecologists all over the world.

______ **4.** The Brazilian government eventually declared millions of acres in the Amazon protected.

______ **5.** Mendes's murder by two local ranchers in 1988 overshadowed his victory.

EXERCISE B Indicate the voice of the verb in the following sentences by writing *AV* for *active voice* or *PV* for *passive voice* on the line provided. Then, underline the performer or agent of the action. If no performer is stated, write *none* after the sentence.

Example PV **1.** The bonds were approved by a majority of the voters.

______ **6.** Hundreds of bags of trash had been collected by nightfall.

______ **7.** By discussing and debating the problem openly, the group reached a consensus.

______ **8.** More data will be gathered by the research team during the expedition.

______ **9.** The local newspaper publishes letters and articles by student reporters.

______ **10.** Two award-winning features were written by students from our school.

Copyright © by Holt, Rinehart and Winston. All rights reserved.

Uses of the Passive Voice

8m. Use the passive voice sparingly.

In general, the passive voice is less direct, less forceful, and less concise than the active voice. In fact, the passive voice may produce an awkward effect.

AWKWARD PASSIVE As soon as the book was found by Timothy, the chapter on robotics was carefully read by him.

ACTIVE As soon as Timothy found the book, he carefully read the chapter on robotics.

Use the passive voice when you do not know or do not want to reveal the performer of an action, or when you want to emphasize the receiver of an action.

EXAMPLES In recent years specific areas of the ocean floor **have been studied.**

Their home **was** severely **damaged** by the tornado.

EXERCISE On the lines provided, revise each sentence that would be better in the active voice. Write *Correct* if the sentence is already in the active voice or if the performer of an action is not known and no change seems necessary.

Example 1. We were given an informative tour of the historical district by her.

She gave us an informative tour of the historical district.

1. Items in the antique store have been collected from all over the country by the owners.

2. The fire station on the town square was built in 1889.

3. My mother's interest in woodworking was encouraged by my grandfather, who built many pieces of furniture for the family.

4. Woodworking books, in addition to the tools themselves, have been collected by her.

5. Cans and bottles of all sizes, colors, and shapes were found along the highway by us.

Copyright © by Holt, Rinehart and Winston. All rights reserved.

Mood

8n. The ***indicative mood*** expresses a fact, an opinion, or a question.

EXAMPLE Sweden **claims** one of the world's highest per capita incomes.

8o. The ***imperative mood*** expresses a direct command or a request.

EXAMPLE **Tell** me where you learned that information.

8p. The ***subjunctive mood*** expresses a suggestion, a necessity, a condition contrary to fact, or a wish.

EXAMPLES Herbert asked that he **be allowed** to participate in the debate.
Canditha wishes that her computer skills **were** stronger.

EXERCISE A Identify the mood of the underlined verb in each of the following sentences. On the line provided, write *IND* for *indicative*, *IMP* for *imperative*, or *SUB* for *subjunctive*.

Example SUB **1.** Council member Yates recommended that the new recycling facility be built as soon as possible.

______ **1.** I do wish it were summer.

______ **2.** The carpenters and the bricklayers worked together to finish the project on time.

______ **3.** If I were speaking, I'd have phrased that question differently.

______ **4.** Save me a seat in the auditorium.

______ **5.** Blanche wished that her literary background were more comprehensive.

______ **6.** Natalia Makarova dances as if she were born dancing.

______ **7.** They were sitting around the seminar table discussing the question.

______ **8.** They were students together and remained lifelong friends.

______ **9.** Please explain the answer to the last question one more time.

______ **10.** I'd be preparing for the exam if I weren't playing my match right now.

EXERCISE B Most of the following sentences contain verbs that are awkward or incorrect. Cross out each incorrect or awkward verb form, and write the correct form above it. If a sentence is already correct, write *C* before the item number.

Example 1. It is critical that she ~~sees~~ *see* a doctor immediately.

11. If I was the coach, I would make a different play call.

12. It is essential that all the actors be at the theater by five o'clock.

13. The room would seem larger if that wall was a lighter color.

14. I wish that my television set wasn't broken so that I could watch the game.

15. The veterinarian has recommended that Tucker is vaccinated.

Copyright © by Holt, Rinehart and Winston. All rights reserved.

NAME ________________ CLASS ________________ DATE ________________

Modals A

8q. A ***modal*** is a helping (auxiliary) verb that is joined with a main verb to express an attitude toward the action or state of being of the main verb.

EXAMPLES Koko **can perform** the dance routine perfectly.
No, you **may** not **borrow** my notes.
Mr. Malone **might have forgotten** to put a stamp on the envelope.
To train your dog effectively, you **must establish** a trusting bond with him.

USAGE

EXERCISE Complete the sentences below sensibly by filling in each blank with one of the following modals: *can, could, might, may,* or *must.*

Example 1. ____May____ we have the last two pieces of pie?

1. We ______________ not have found that restaurant if you had not pointed out that sign.

2. I ______________ only hope that we have time to rehearse before we go onstage tonight.

3. Please let me know when I ______________ have a few minutes to tell you my good news.

4. You or I ______________ renew our membership before the expiration date.

5. ______________ you find the happiness and success you seek.

6. John ______________ graduate with a perfect 4.0 grade-point average.

7. Charlotte ______________ have cleaned out this closet last night.

8. I don't see any cars, so the other guests ______________ not have arrived yet.

9. ______________ all of you help me at the youth center today after school?

10. If Mark doesn't tell this joke just right, you ______________ guess the punch line.

11. I really ______________ remember to call the restaurant for reservations.

12. The picture ______________ have fallen off the wall when you slammed the door.

13. I suppose we ______________ leave a few minutes early to pick you up.

14. She has a rehearsal after school today, so she doesn't know if she ______________ join us at the rink.

15. He ______________ have had permission to leave school early today.

16. Jerome ______________ carry the suitcases to the ticket counter while Raymond parks the car.

17. If she expects to pass this course, she really ______________ study more.

18. Christina ______________ not remember all her lines, but she ______________ certainly dance!

19. ______________ you kids always make so much noise?

20. Well, we ______________ have lost this game, but we're still in the play-offs.

Copyright © by Holt, Rinehart and Winston. All rights reserved.

Modals B

8q. A ***modal*** is a helping (auxiliary) verb that is joined with a main verb to express an attitude toward the action or state of being of the main verb.

EXAMPLES You **ought to tidy** up your work area before you leave for the day.

As soon as I have all the addresses, I **will** [or **shall**] **mail** the invitations.

If you are going to be late, you **should call** to let them know.

If Judith had explained the problem, I gladly **would have helped** her.

EXERCISE Complete the sentences below sensibly by filling in each blank with one of the following modals: *ought, shall, will, should,* or *would.*

Example 1. ___Would___ your cousin care to join us for lunch?

1. Moira ______________ to do quite well on her driving test.
2. We wondered what Michael ______________ do to prepare for the student-exchange program.
3. No one ______________ forget that reminder to study for the final exam.
4. ______________ you mind bringing me my book from the dining room table?
5. We ______________ appreciate having you attend our next meeting.
6. ______________ any of you change your minds, please let me know.
7. If you had been able to finish your chores, I ______________ not have done them myself.
8. You ______________ always have your doctor check even a minor injury.
9. We ______________ be happy to help you pack for the senior science trip.
10. I think you ______________ have let us know you had changed your plans.
11. We ______________ have called Grandmother before we left the house.
12. They ______________ have arrived much earlier, but their plane was delayed.
13. Carolyn really ______________ to have included that information in her report.
14. Nan and her brother ______________ be going to the same college next year.
15. ______________ we plan on meeting at the same time next week?
16. I believe I ______________ close the windows in case of rain.
17. Reginald thinks that we ______________ be home before the storm starts.
18. You ______________ not to have taken her friendship for granted.
19. If Kim had waited for us, we ______________ have given her a ride.
20. I don't know what I ______________ have done in that situation.

Copyright © by Holt, Rinehart and Winston. All rights reserved.

Review A: Principal Parts of Verbs

EXERCISE A Most of the following sentences contain errors in the use of verbs. Cross out each incorrect verb, and write the correct form above it. If the sentence is already correct, write *C* before the item number.

Example 1. Before I left for California, my friends ~~given~~ *gave* me a farewell party.

1. I had did most of my packing the previous evening.
2. My two best friends had drove across town to attend the party.
3. Each of us had already chose a college to attend, and we spent much of the evening debating the merits of our respective schools.
4. My dog Molly slept peacefully at my feet during most of this discussion.
5. I guess old Molly had hear it all before.
6. When silence at last come, she woke up suddenly.
7. Then the doorbell rung, and Molly started barking furiously.
8. At the door were my friends Fritz and Melanie, whom Molly had meet several times before.
9. Fritz and Melanie joined in the party, and before long we had putted aside our debate and had began a game of charades.
10. I have never had a more memorable party.

EXERCISE B On the line in each sentence below, write the correct present participle, past, or past participle of the verb provided in parentheses.

Example 1. (past form of *run*) To prepare for the marathon, Kathryn *ran* six miles every day.

11. (past participle of *see*) The players have ______ the coach's signal.
12. (present participle of *take*) As we speak, my cousin Stacy is ______ her driver's test.
13. (past form of *ring*) The bell ______ just as Mr. Ruark finished his lecture.
14. (past participle of *speak*) Ramona ______ not ______ to me about her family trip until the day before she left.
15. (present participle of *sing*) The ensemble ______ at several local hospitals during the holidays.

Copyright © by Holt, Rinehart and Winston. All rights reserved.

Review B: Tense, Voice, Mood, and Modals

EXERCISE A Many of the following sentences contain errors in the use of verbs. Cross out each incorrect verb form, and write the correct form above it. If a sentence is already correct, write *C* before the item number.

were
Example **1.** If I ~~was~~ a poet, I would want to destroy my first poems.

1. Having been a poet in an age of prose often makes life difficult for a sensitive person.

2. Many poets start writing early in life.

3. Alexander Pope's childhood writings could not have brought him lasting fame.

4. Whoever expects to find great poetry among Pope's childhood writings undoubtedly will have been disappointed.

5. On the other hand, Mozart is writing brilliant works when he was fifteen.

6. Subsequent generations have been delighted to have listened to these compositions.

7. If he would have written nothing in his youth, would he have become a composer later?

8. Mozart's father began to teach his son composition when Mozart is only five years old.

9. By the time he was ten, Mozart composed dozens of lovely works.

10. In the case of most writers and musicians, however, talent needs time to grow.

EXERCISE B Most of the following sentences contain errors in the use of verbs. Cross out each incorrect verb form, and write the correct form above it. If a sentence is already correct, write *C* before the item number.

Having decided
Example **1.** ~~Deciding~~ to do a thorough job, Soledad spent many hours on the assignment.

11. Soledad reviewed all the notes she took the week before.

12. If she would have taken more notes, she would have been better prepared.

13. She had hoped to have written a good report on U.S. presidents.

14. If I was a harder worker, she thought, I'd get higher grades.

15. In her notes, she had written that the first six presidents come from Virginia and Massachusetts.

16. Then Andrew Jackson is elected in 1828.

17. If Jackson came from Virginia, he would have carried on the tradition.

18. Jackson, however, was born in South Carolina.

19. If Soledad's report would have been nothing more than a chronology, it would have lacked interest.

20. She managed to have included all kinds of interesting facts, though.

Copyright © by Holt, Rinehart and Winston. All rights reserved.

Review C: Six Troublesome Verbs

EXERCISE In the sentences below, draw a line through any incorrect verb form and write the correct present participle, past form, or past participle above it. If a sentence is already correct, write *C* before the item number.

Example **1.** The branches had ~~laid~~ *lain* by the curb all week.

1. The letter from my older sister, who is in college, laid on my computer desk.

2. He has never once risen his voice in anger.

3. My dog was laying peacefully by the front window, when suddenly a squirrel ran across the lawn.

4. We set up the telescope as soon as the sun had set and the moon had risen.

5. The pen has laid on the floor all day.

6. We lain the folded clothes on top of the dresser.

7. Where was Julia setting when you saw her last?

8. Had the newspaper lain out in the yard all weekend?

9. The temperature raised another twenty degrees before the rain started.

10. As soon as he laid down, the telephone rang.

11. The cost of gasoline has rose sharply because of cuts in production.

12. We had sat in the stadium for more than two hours before the game started.

13. Frank rose the lid off the terrarium and added a little water.

14. Melting icebergs rumbled and cracked as the temperature raised.

15. My bicycle was laying on the garage floor in pieces.

16. How many people do you know who have rose their grade-point average so much?

17. Heavy rains have rose the water level of the lake more than a foot.

18. Please sit the groceries on the kitchen counter.

19. The crane lifted the steel girder and sat it on top of the structure.

20. Strong winds raised from the valley and whistled through the trees.

Copyright © by Holt, Rinehart and Winston. All rights reserved.

Review D: Correct Use of Verb Forms

EXERCISE A Most of the following sentences contain errors in the use of verbs. Cross out each incorrect verb form, and write the correct form above it. If the sentence is already correct, write *C* before the item number.

Example 1. "The plumber ~~has done~~ *did* this job last time," my father said doubtfully.

1. "Anybody can fix a leaky faucet," I says to him.

2. Dad brang me the tools from the basement, and I creeped under the sink to turn off the water.

3. I knowed how to begin, and soon I was hard at work.

4. Tools and faucet parts laid strewn about.

5. I seen right away that a new washer would do the job, and I swang into action with complete self-assurance.

6. My father come into the room just as I was finishing.

7. With the water back on, I raised in triumph, flinged the wrench aside, and turned on the faucet.

8. To my amazement, water flew everywhere.

9. I sank back down and turned off the water.

10. "I've never swam in the kitchen before," Dad said softly.

EXERCISE B In the paragraph below, draw a line through any incorrect verb usage and write a correction above it. (*Hint:* There is more than one way to correct the sentences, but your revised paragraph must make sense as a whole.)

Example **[1]** If you ~~were~~ *had been* on a job interview several years ago, ~~skills learned on previous jobs would have been reviewed by a personnel director or manager.~~ *a personnel director or manager would have reviewed skills you learned on previous jobs.*

[11] In the current job market, your abilities have been examined on a questionnaire as well as during one or more face-to-face interviews. **[12]** Some interviewers will have asked you questions about your qualities as a leader. **[13]** Other interviewers may be requesting information about your skill as a team player. **[14]** Knowing your own strengths and weaknesses would prevent your being taken by surprise. **[15]** Keep these hints in mind the next time you set down for an interview.

Copyright © by Holt, Rinehart and Winston. All rights reserved.

USAGE

Adjective or Adverb?

9a. An ***adjective*** makes the meaning of a noun or a pronoun more specific.

9b. An ***adverb*** makes the meaning of a verb, an adjective, or another adverb more specific.

EXERCISE For each underlined modifier in the sentences below, circle the word or word group it modifies. Then, identify the modifier by writing above it *ADJ* for *adjective* or *ADV* for *adverb*.

Example 1. Shadow puppetry is a fascinating art. (ADJ)

1. All a shadow puppet show requires is a translucent screen, a light source, and some opaque, two-dimensional figures to cast the shadows.
2. Traditionally, shadow puppets have been made of leather.
3. The puppeteer skillfully manipulates the puppet using thin rods.
4. The audience usually sits on the other side of the screen to watch the shadows.
5. Shadow puppetry is an extremely ancient art.
6. Experts believe that in India shadow puppets performed onstage long before human actors.
7. Pretending to be someone else was strictly forbidden in ancient Indian culture.
8. However, puppets were not bound by such restrictions.
9. A Chinese legend dates shadow puppetry in China to 120 B.C.
10. The legend says that a man named Chiao-meng cleverly devised a plan to trick the emperor.
11. The empress had recently died, and the emperor mourned for her.
12. Chiao-meng placed an elaborate silhouette of the empress between a light and a cotton screen.
13. The emperor apparently thought the shadow was his deceased wife.
14. He listened attentively to "her" advice on state matters.
15. Chiao-meng's great influence ended, as did his life, when the emperor discovered the trick.
16. However, Chiao-meng is duly remembered as the original shadow puppeteer of China.
17. In Bali today, shadow puppetry survives in an ancient form.
18. There, the puppeteer plays a spiritual and ceremonial role.
19. In fact, a priest must ordain the puppeteer and write a mystic symbol on his tongue before he may perform.
20. An important part of traditional events such as weddings, the puppet play, or *wayang*, often lasts all night.

Copyright © by Holt, Rinehart and Winston. All rights reserved.

USAGE

Phrases Used as Modifiers

Like one-word modifiers, phrases can also be used as adjectives and adverbs.

EXAMPLES **Hiding behind the tree,** my nephew waited for us to approach. [The participial phrase *Hiding behind the tree* acts as an adjective that modifies *nephew*.]

I just put the bowl of cherries **on the table.** [The prepositional phrase *on the table* acts as an adverb that modifies *put*.]

EXERCISE In the following sentences, decide whether each underlined phrase acts as an adjective or an adverb. Above each phrase, write *ADJ* for *adjective* or *ADV* for *adverb.* Then, circle the word or words each phrase modifies.

Example 1. Ray volunteered at the shelter, which was having a crisis. (ADV)

1. The man with the intelligent dog won the contest.
2. After class, Penelope and Cary Ann shared a granola bar.
3. Because of the mud stains, Tom took his suit to the dry cleaner.
4. To me, summer seemed a long, long time away.
5. The boat in the harbor was searched for illegal goods.
6. With all of his belongings on his back, he crossed the river.
7. Because of the new job, my life has improved.
8. My friend in the band plays both the saxophone and the clarinet.
9. Come inside the building to avoid the heavy rain.
10. The seal with the insignia belongs to the governor of the state.
11. Walk to the store and take your little brother with you.
12. Hanging inside the coliseum, there is a photograph of all of the players on the team.
13. The speaker talked about crime prevention.
14. Of all the singers in the world, I like Neil Young best.
15. The box inside the trunk rattled the whole way to Cleveland.
16. She took a picture of the bird sitting on the fence.
17. Articles about his astounding discovery were in all the papers.
18. Finishing the text first, Jim appeared happy with himself.
19. In case of fire, move quickly and calmly to the nearest exit.
20. Light from the bedroom window indicated someone was awake.

Copyright © by Holt, Rinehart and Winston. All rights reserved.

USAGE

Clauses Used as Modifiers

Like words and phrases, clauses can also be used as modifiers.

EXAMPLE **After we land in New York,** we will take a taxi to the hotel. [The adverb clause *After we land in New York* modifies the verb *will take*.]

EXERCISE In the following sentences, decide whether each underlined clause functions as an adjective or an adverb. Above each, write *ADJ* for *adjective* or *ADV* for *adverb*.

Example 1. ADV When I woke up this morning, I knew I was going to have a nice day.

1. Because my sister was in the shower, I had to wait fifteen minutes to get into the bathroom.
2. I was a bit late for breakfast, which was cereal and low-fat milk.
3. I had to run all the way to the bus stop since I was behind schedule.
4. The bus, which was early, had left without me.
5. I had to walk to school, which is only a few blocks from my house.
6. I arrived at school just as the bell was ringing.
7. I was happy about that until I found out that we were having a pop quiz in my first class.
8. Fortunately, I was well prepared for the quiz because I had studied the night before.
9. In biology class my lab partner, who is great at dissections, was absent.
10. The lab project that we did today didn't involve dissections.
11. After I finished the project, I was ready for a nice quiet hour in study hall.
12. However, the workers who were repairing the roof created a lot of noise.
13. At 3:30 P.M., I went to the gym that is in my school to get some exercise.
14. When I walked in the door, I saw my two best friends, Lisa and Peter.
15. Although we are not great players, we still decided to play a few games of basketball.
16. This afternoon I had a piano lesson with Ms. Lufler, who has won many competitions as a pianist.
17. For dinner Mom, who is an excellent cook, prepared grilled chicken and mashed potatoes.
18. After we ate, my sister and I offered to wash the dishes.
19. Mom was very happy that we were helping out because she needed to do some other chores around the house.
20. Before I went to bed, I read several chapters in my history book.

Copyright © by Holt, Rinehart and Winston. All rights reserved.

Uses of Modifiers

9c. Use a predicate adjective to modify the subject of a linking verb.

EXAMPLE Wool feels **scratchy** to me. [*Scratchy* is a predicate adjective modifying *Wool*, which is the subject of the linking verb *feels*.]

9d. Use an adverb to modify an action verb.

EXAMPLE The rain stopped **suddenly.** [*Suddenly* is an adverb modifying the action verb *stopped*.]

EXERCISE For each of the following sentences, identify the underlined word by writing above it *ADJ* for *predicate adjective* or *ADV* for *adverb*.

Example 1. When you think about it, the human brain is amazing. (ADJ)

1. The brain processes information very rapidly.
2. Think of all the numbers, names, and other information you remember easily.
3. The memory-enhancing system called mnemonics is fascinating.
4. Let me explain it quickly.
5. The system is simple: Imagine you meet someone named Art Baker.
6. What if you forget the person's name immediately?
7. Making a mental image to help you remember the name is important.
8. Try simply imagining a painting.
9. It could be a painting of a man who is skillfully baking pastries.
10. Now, associate that image consistently with the person you met named Art Baker.
11. See how easy it can be?
12. The process just described may seem silly, but you will be surprised at how well it works.
13. For names that are less visual than "Art Baker," you have to think more creatively.
14. Forming mental pictures moves information more reliably from short-term to long-term memory.
15. In order to succeed, you must think associatively.
16. Of course, memory becomes crucial when taking tests.
17. Stress can sometimes interfere substantially with memory.
18. The results can be terrible (a bad grade, for example).
19. Memory is complex and occasionally frustrating.
20. Don't forget to make mental pictures regularly if you want to improve your ability to recall.

Copyright © by Holt, Rinehart and Winston. All rights reserved.

USAGE

Bad and *Badly*; *Good* and *Well*

Bad is an adjective. *Badly* is an adverb. The expression *feel badly* is common in informal situations, but you should use *feel bad* in formal speaking and writing.

EXAMPLES Do you think this bean soup tastes **bad**? [adjective modifying *soup*]

They hung the wallpaper **badly**. [adverb modifying the verb *hung*]

Good is an adjective. *Well* may be used as an adjective or an adverb. Avoid using good to modify an action verb.

EXAMPLES This is a **good** place to fish. [adjective modifying *place*]

She plays the violin **well.** [adverb modifying *plays*]

Feel good means "to feel happy or pleased." *Feel well* means "to feel healthy."

EXERCISE Underline the correct modifier from the pair given in parentheses.

Example 1. He feels (*bad, badly*) about stealing her seat.

1. I think you all did (*good, well*) on yesterday's pop quiz.

2. This finger painting of an apple is particularly (*good, well*).

3. Ozzie performed (*bad, badly*) during band tryout.

4. The boy who takes care of our lawn did (*good, well*) trimming the hedges.

5. Wow! This book is (*good, well*)!

6. After eight years of lessons, he plays the piano extremely (*good, well*).

7. The defense for our football team is playing (*bad, badly*).

8. He seems (*bad, badly*) at remembering to bring his lunch on Fridays.

9. I feel (*good, well*) about our chances for finishing the yearbook.

10. The airplane pilot landed the plane (*good, well*).

11. I think we've done (*good, well*) as a group.

12. It's too (*bad, badly*) about the injured antelope.

13. The roof of the house was constructed (*bad, badly*).

14. When it's all over, I think the results will be (*good, well*).

15. Tomorrow we'll try not to paint the barn quite so (*bad, badly*).

16. The patient's prognosis looks (*good, well*), but he should stay in the hospital for several more days.

17. I'm disappointed that the car we purchased drives so (*bad, badly*).

18. JoAnne definitely did (*good, well*) in the marathon.

19. The forecast appears (*bad, badly*); tornadoes are expected.

20. Jane said she felt (*good, well*) after her surgery.

Copyright © by Holt, Rinehart and Winston. All rights reserved.

Real and *Really*; *Slow* and *Slowly*

Real is an adjective. *Really* is an adverb meaning "actually" or "truly."

EXAMPLES This is a **real** diamond. [adjective modifying *diamond*]
I am **really** glad to be home. [adverb modifying the adjective *glad*]

Slow is used both as an adjective and an adverb. *Slowly* is used as an adverb. In most adverb uses, *slowly* is preferred.

EXAMPLES Why do I always pick the **slow** line? [adjective modifying *line*]
He walked **slowly** to the front of the room. [adverb modifying *walked*]

EXERCISE In each of the following sentences, underline the correct modifier from the pair given in parentheses.

Example **1.** He is *(real, really)* talented at fixing cars.

1. He moved *(slow, slowly)* after his knee operation.

2. Are turtles as *(slow, slowly)* as everyone says they are?

3. Does Juan Pablo ride his mountain bike *(real, really)* well?

4. She is *(real, really)* cool!

5. I need to polish my shoes *(real, really)* carefully.

6. The bus driver turned *(slow, slowly)* on the icy freeway.

7. Photography has been my favorite hobby for a *(real, really)* long time.

8. I'm *(slow, slowly)* to understand geometrical concepts.

9. We had a *(real, really)* great time at your uncle's house.

10. This is a *(real, really)* important project.

11. If we go *(slow, slowly)* through each problem, then we're less likely to make mistakes.

12. The doctor said that I need to have a *(real, really)* thorough checkup.

13. I slept *(real, really)* well in the water bed.

14. My brother ate each piece of broccoli *(slow, slowly)*.

15. I thought the meeting was at four o'clock, but it did not start until *(real, really)* late.

16. Your new cat is *(real, really)* beautiful.

17. This particular ant crawls around *(slow, slowly)*.

18. The cars left very *(slow, slowly)* from the parking lot.

19. I wish *(real, really)* strongly that Christmas break started tomorrow.

20. Everyone moved *(slow, slowly)* toward the exits.

Copyright © by Holt, Rinehart and Winston. All rights reserved.

NAME CLASS DATE

Eight Troublesome Modifiers

Bad and _Badly_ *Bad* is an adjective. *Badly* is an adverb.

Good and _Well_ *Good* is an adjective. *Well* may be used as an adjective or an adverb. Avoid using *good* to modify an action verb.

Real and _Really_ *Real* is an adjective. *Really* is an adverb meaning "actually" or "truly."

Slow and _Slowly_ *Slow* is used both as an adjective and an adverb. *Slowly* is used as an adverb. In most adverb uses, *slowly* is preferred.

EXERCISE In each of the following sentences, underline the correct modifier from the pair given in parentheses.

Example 1. Last weekend we had a *(real, really)* good time.

1. Doug and Kristen, two friends of mine, and I get along very *(good, well).*
2. All of a sudden, I noticed that our train was moving very *(slow, slowly).*
3. Last weekend was a *(real, really)* big challenge for the team.
4. My tennis partner and I played extremely *(good, well)* today.
5. I need to wash my car *(bad, badly).*
6. Gardening is *(real, really)* important to my dad; it relaxes him.
7. Sometimes, Dad seems to be working very *(slow, slowly)*, but he enjoys it.
8. That TV program is coming in *(bad, badly)* because of the storm.
9. Tim and Jack decided to do something *(real, really)* different.
10. Doug thought the building of the new school was going too *(slow, slowly).*
11. He wanted to help haul in the materials and keep the site organized *(good, well).*
12. My sister and I are *(slow, slowly)* becoming very excited about our vacation next summer.
13. After jogging, I realized I needed a *(real, really)* big glass of water to quench my thirst.
14. When we work together, things never turn out *(bad, badly).*
15. Tom was *(slow, slowly)* in coming up with the answer, but suddenly he thought of a great one.
16. Cecile and Sarah paint very *(good, well).*
17. The dancers in the troupe don't perform as *(bad, badly)* as they did a year ago.
18. We approached the timid bird *(slow, slowly)* in order not to scare it away.
19. My watch seems to be working less *(good, well)* than it was yesterday.
20. Last summer we had a lot of fun at the beach, and everything turned out *(good, well).*

Copyright © by Holt, Rinehart and Winston. All rights reserved.

Regular Comparison

9e. Modifiers change form to show comparison.

POSITIVE	COMPARATIVE	SUPERLATIVE
cold	colder	coldest
happy	happier	happiest
serious	more serious	most serious

EXERCISE The modifiers in the following exercise all form their comparative and superlative forms according to the usual methods. Fill in the blank spaces in the following chart. One form of each modifier is provided.

	positive	comparative	superlative
Example	**1.** sincere	*more sincere*	*most sincere*

	positive	comparative	superlative
1.			longest
2.	silly		
3.			most comical
4.			most absorbent
5.		prettier	
6.		less boring	
7.	wild		
8.			least troublesome
9.		more unsettling	
10.		flimsier	
11.			most carefully
12.		more interesting	
13.			most curious
14.		heavier	
15.		younger	
16.			funniest
17.		less honest	
18.			most ridiculous
19.	large		
20.		more grown-up	

Copyright © by Holt, Rinehart and Winston. All rights reserved.

NAME CLASS DATE

Irregular Comparison

9e. Modifiers change form to show comparison.

The comparative and superlative degrees of some modifiers are not formed by the usual methods.

POSITIVE	COMPARATIVE	SUPERLATIVE
good	better	best

EXERCISE In each of the following sentences, underline the correct form of the modifier in parentheses.

Example 1. This is the *(baddest, worst)* story I've ever read!

1. I prefer stories with fantastic scenarios *(more, mucher)* than I prefer any other type of story.
2. For instance, I think Franz Kafka's stories are some of the *(goodest, best).*
3. In my opinion, no novel is *(gooder, better)* than Kafka's *The Castle.*
4. Kafka's ideas and plots push reality *(further, farrer)* than everyday pulp fiction does.
5. His short story "The Metamorphosis" is one of his *(goodest, best).*
6. The plight of the narrator could not get much *(badder, worse)* after he turns into an insect.
7. The writings published posthumously were often *(better, gooder)* than what was published while Kafka was alive.
8. Kafka's father's temper was *(iller, worse)* than most men's.
9. Do Kafka's writings include a cruel, authoritarian power *(more, morer)* often than not?
10. During his life, Kafka spent *(much, mucher)* time in Prague.
11. Kafka was trained as a lawyer, but he devoted himself *(more, mucher)* to writing fiction.
12. He also kept a diary and made entries *(more, mucher)* often than one might think.
13. Diaries can offer some of the *(goodest, best)* insights into a person's life.
14. Of course, people with less creative minds than Kafka's might have *(little, littler)* to write.
15. It might be encouraging to see how someone like Kafka felt on his *(baddest, worst)* days.
16. Discovering how other people overcome their problems makes me feel *(better, gooder).*
17. When I write in my diary, I write *(more, mucher)* on difficult days.
18. Writing out my concerns helps me get a *(better, gooder)* perspective on my life.
19. I often feel *(worse, badder)* if I don't write my feelings.
20. I wonder if Kafka's writing caused him to understand himself *(weller, better).*

Copyright © by Holt, Rinehart and Winston. All rights reserved.

NAME ____________________ CLASS ____________ DATE ____________

for **CHAPTER 9: USING MODIFIERS CORRECTLY** *pages 282–283*

Regular and Irregular Comparison

9e. Modifiers change form to show comparison.

POSITIVE	COMPARATIVE	SUPERLATIVE
fast	faster	fastest
good	better	best

USAGE

EXERCISE A On the lines provided, write the comparative and superlative forms of each of the following modifiers.

	positive	comparative	superlative
Example	**1.** slowly	*more slowly*	*most slowly*

positive	comparative	superlative
1. good	________	________
2. many	________	________
3. thick	________	________
4. soft	________	________
5. much	________	________
6. smoothly	________	________
7. useful	________	________
8. little (size)	________	________
9. little (amount)	________	________
10. selective	________	________

EXERCISE B For each of the following modifiers, give the comparative and superlative forms that show a decrease in the qualities they express.

	positive	comparative	superlative
Example	**1.** well	*less well*	*least well*

positive	comparative	superlative
11. angry	________	________
12. ill	________	________
13. difficult	________	________
14. clear	________	________
15. tolerant	________	________

Copyright © by Holt, Rinehart and Winston. All rights reserved.

NAME ______________________ CLASS ______________ DATE ______________

Uses of Comparative and Superlative Forms A

9f. Use the comparative degree when comparing two things. Use the superlative degree when comparing more than two things.

COMPARATIVE He is the **luckier** of the two brothers.

SUPERLATIVE You are the **luckiest** girl in the group.

EXERCISE In the following sentences, underline the correct modifier given in parentheses.

Example **1.** Coach Leonard is the *(louder, loudest)* person I've ever met.

1. Summer is the *(hotter, hottest)* time of year.

2. Slappy is a *(smarter, smartest)* monkey than his brother, Mr. Tippo.

3. Would you agree that this diamond is the *(brighter, brightest)* of the two?

4. This is the *(more infuriating, most infuriating)* word problem we have to solve.

5. Is it *(warmer, warmest)* in here than it was ten minutes ago?

6. The radio tower is the *(taller, tallest)* structure in my hometown.

7. Water is *(less effective, least effective)* in removing the dirt than water and soap combined.

8. Which of the two options is *(more dangerous, most dangerous)*?

9. I think tea is the *(tastier, tastiest)* beverage in the world!

10. North Dakota is usually *(colder, coldest)* than Oklahoma.

11. It's *(more difficult, most difficult)* to catch than it is to throw.

12. The puzzle with the mountain scene is *(trickier, trickiest)* than the one with the ocean scene.

13. The airplane ride was *(more comfortable, most comfortable)* when the storm was over.

14. I worked *(less rapidly, least rapidly)* than Glen.

15. This has to be the *(worse, worst)* football game in school history!

16. Backpackers usually bathe *(less frequently, least frequently)* than other travelers.

17. The comic book character I enjoy *(more, most)* is the funny rat with the sunglasses.

18. Thomas is *(more skilled, most skilled)* at drawing trees than anyone else in our class is.

19. It would be *(better, best)* to meet on Monday than on Wednesday.

20. Who is the *(funnier, funniest)* person in the class?

Copyright © by Holt, Rinehart and Winston. All rights reserved.

Uses of Comparative and Superlative Forms B

9f. Use the comparative degree when comparing two things. Use the superlative degree when comparing more than two things.

9g. Include the word *other* or *else* when you are comparing one member of a group with the rest of the group.

9h. Avoid using double comparisons.

EXERCISE In each of the following sentences, correct the comparative or superlative forms. Cross out any unnecessary words. Insert any missing word by inserting a caret (^) and writing the word above it. If the sentence is already correct, write *C* at the end.

Example 1. Ed is taller than any ^*other* person in the class.

1. Dorrie is happier than anyone I know.
2. Ted can skateboard better than any other kid on our block.
3. This is the most juiciest orange!
4. Our team won more games than any team in the league.
5. You received more votes than anyone who was running.
6. She chose the most difficult exercise of the three.
7. My sister is better at skiing than any member of my family.
8. Which is the most hardest material in the world?
9. That egg is smaller than any egg in its nest.
10. The train is less likelier to be on time than the plane is.
11. I am more better at grammar now than I was last year.
12. He was less friendlier to me than he was to her.
13. I'm sure Susan can outrun any girl on her track team.
14. That coffeepot is more fuller than this one.
15. Ed is the least excitable person I have ever met.
16. Can you think of anyone else in our club who would want to go?
17. Our puppy was the most cutest one in the litter.
18. You are just as important as every member of your team.
19. Gloria sold more boxes of cookies than anyone in the troop.
20. You are more luckier than I am.

Copyright © by Holt, Rinehart and Winston. All rights reserved.

USAGE

Uses of Comparative and Superlative Forms C

9f. Use the comparative degree when comparing two things. Use the superlative degree when comparing more than two things.

9g. Include the word *other* or *else* when you are comparing one member of a group with the rest of the group.

9h. Avoid using double comparisons.

EXERCISE In each of the following sentences, correct the comparative or superlative forms. Cross out any unnecessary words. Insert any missing word by inserting a caret (^) and writing the word above it. If the sentence is already correct, write *C* at the end.

Example 1. Our drama group has some of the most ~~interestingest~~ ^*interesting* people in it.

1. This semester I joined the better group in the whole school—the drama team.

2. I wanted to join it more than any team.

3. I was the happier kid around when I found out that I had been selected.

4. I was even most excited than that when I heard we were doing a play soon.

5. The play was *Macbeth,* by Shakespeare, who may be the more revered British writer.

6. The choice of play was great because I like *Macbeth* better than any Shakespeare play.

7. I was worried that I wouldn't get a part because I was the least experienced one in the group.

8. However, I got to do the more fun thing of all—I was the understudy for everyone.

9. I got to play more roles in rehearsal than anyone in the group.

10. Fortunately, I have a greater knack for memorizing lines than anyone.

11. It was the more challenging thing ever to play a different part at each rehearsal.

12. The director had the most silliest superstitions about the play, though.

13. We couldn't say "Macbeth" backstage, even though it is the most important character's name.

14. Even more weirder than that, we had to call the play "The Scottish Play."

15. I think our director is more superstitious than any team sponsor at school.

16. However, it did make the rehearsals most exciting after he told us about the "curse."

17. He thought that if anyone said "Macbeth," the show would be the worse performance ever.

18. Of course, we would rather have had any other fate than that.

19. We were having a lot of fun, and our enjoyment seemed to make the time go by fastest.

20. Soon it was opening night, and I think we put on the better show ever, if I do say so myself!

Copyright © by Holt, Rinehart and Winston. All rights reserved.

USAGE

Clear Comparisons and Absolute Adjectives A

9i. Be sure comparisons are clear.

When making comparisons, clearly indicate what items you are comparing.

UNCLEAR These brakes are better than any other car.

CLEAR These brakes are better than **those on any other car.**

Be sure to include all words necessary to complete a ***compound comparison.***

INCOMPLETE I'm at least as qualified, if not more than, the other candidate.

COMPLETE I'm at least **as qualified as,** if not more than, the other candidate.

Absolute adjectives have no comparative or superlative forms, so they should not be used in comparative constructions in formal writing.

INFORMAL My answer is more correct than your answer.

FORMAL My answer is **correct.**

EXERCISE In each of the following sentences, correct any unclear comparisons, incomplete comparisons, or incorrect absolute adjective forms. Cross out any unnecessary words. Insert any missing word by inserting a caret (∧) and writing the word above it.

Example 1. Their house is as old ∧as if not older than, our house.

1. Howard told me more about ice fishing than you.

2. I have heard more about the new class than Dr. Taylor.

3. It seems as if my uncle's collection of books is larger than the library.

4. This book is as long, if not longer than, *A Tale of Two Cities*.

5. Our coaching staff has the most unique training techniques.

6. Dad gave me a longer speech than you.

7. Copernicus thought it was more true that the earth orbited the sun than the other way around.

8. This essay is as good, if not better than, any I have written thus far.

9. My hero, Stephen Hawking, has used mathematics to try to develop a more complete model of how the universe works.

10. Do hawks eat more small animals than eagles?

Copyright © by Holt, Rinehart and Winston. All rights reserved.

Clear Comparisons and Absolute Adjectives B

USAGE

9i. Be sure comparisons are clear.

When making comparisons, clearly indicate what items you are comparing.

UNCLEAR I have known Jane longer than Tom.

CLEAR I have known Jane longer **than Tom has.**

CLEAR I have known Jane longer **than I have known Tom.**

Be sure to include all words necessary to complete a ***compound comparison***.

INCOMPLETE Juan is as happy, if not happier than, any other person.

COMPLETE Juan is **as happy as,** if not happier than, any other person.

Absolute adjectives have no comparative or superlative forms, so they should not be used in comparative constructions in formal writing.

INFORMAL That is the most perfect place to go on vacation.

FORMAL That is the **perfect** place to go on vacation.

EXERCISE In each of the following sentences, correct any unclear comparisons, incomplete comparisons, or incorrect absolute adjective forms. Cross out any unnecessary words. Insert any missing word by inserting a caret (^) and writing the word above it.

Example 1. Ms. Chong volunteers to drive the neighborhood kids to events more often than Ms. Battaglia ^*does*.

1. The panelists decided that Dan's research proposal was more interesting than Phil, so they gave Dan the grant.
2. Of all the ice skaters, Joan was the most perfect because of her style and grace.
3. Betsy talks to her plants more often than Patricia.
4. Those injured birds need as much care, if not more care than, the healthy ones.
5. Theo and Susan enjoy Renaissance writers more than Catherine.
6. Rafael speaks as many different languages, if not more than, Beverly.
7. The very unique properties of this element have intrigued scientists.
8. Exaggerating somewhat, Jane said that the coming weekend offered a more infinite number of possibilities.
9. Temika likes to challenge her sister to a game of chess more often than Bill.
10. Kim reads as much Russian literature, if not more than, her roommate Sandra does.

Copyright © by Holt, Rinehart and Winston. All rights reserved.

NAME CLASS DATE

Comparisons Review

USAGE

EXERCISE In each of the following sentences, correct any errors in the use of comparisons. Cross out any unnecessary words. Insert any missing word by inserting a caret (∧) and writing the word above it. If the sentence is already correct, write *C* at the end.

Example **1.** Of my many hobbies, I enjoy assembling jigsaw puzzles ∧most ~~more.~~

1. I am much gooder at doing jigsaw puzzles now than I used to be.

2. When I was more younger, I used to feel frustrated when I worked on puzzles.

3. Finally, though, I realized that it was less impossible than I had thought.

4. I watched my neighbor Sarah, who was more better at puzzles than I was.

5. I noticed that I was not as patient with puzzles as Sarah.

6. Once I learned to go slowly and be patient, I was better at doing jigsaw puzzles than anyone on our block.

7. I like jigsaw puzzles more than my dad, but he helps me put them together sometimes.

8. Last year, my dad and I put together a puzzle that was more challenging than any one we have ever done.

9. The picture on the box was more harder to model than any other I had seen.

10. It was a perfect circle, and it was solid silver on both sides!

11. After we solved that puzzle, which was more difficult than any puzzle you could buy, I became interested in making my own puzzles.

12. I like making jigsaw puzzles as much, if not more than, putting them together.

13. First I draw a design on thick cardboard—the more thicker the better.

14. Then I carefully cut out the pieces with my dad's jigsaw, which is the most perfect tool for the job.

15. With the jigsaw, I can make the pieces most easily than I could by using scissors or a knife.

16. Now that I know how to make my own puzzles, I can make my friends the better gifts ever.

17. Sometimes I have photographs enlarged, and I make puzzles out of them that are very unique.

18. I think I like making puzzles for my friends even better than myself.

19. Recently, I made the most unique one—a picture of us doing a jigsaw puzzle.

20. Isn't that the most coolest thing?

Copyright © by Holt, Rinehart and Winston. All rights reserved.

NAME CLASS DATE

Review A: Forms of Modifiers

EXERCISE In the following sentences, each of the underlined words or word groups functions as either an adjective or an adverb. Identify each by writing above it *ADJ* for *adjective* or *ADV* for *adverb.*

Example 1. Plato was born in 428 or 427 B.C., a year after the death of Pericles, the great statesman. (ADV)

1. Socrates, Plato, and Aristotle share the honor of molding the Western philosophical tradition.
2. Socrates gained a reputation for wisdom early in his life.
3. In fact, he was declared the wisest of men by the revered oracle at Delphi.
4. Socrates lived very humbly and focused his energies on other people and on Athens.
5. During the Peloponnesian War, he was a foot soldier and reportedly a good fighter.
6. Socrates' extreme patriotism even contributed to his death.
7. After he was convicted on charges that he considered false, Socrates would not let his friends help him escape.
8. He said that the verdict, even though unfair, must be obeyed because the court was a legitimate institution.
9. Socrates' execution in 399 B.C. had a large impact on Plato's life.
10. Plato had probably met Socrates when Plato was a boy.
11. Plato's family, which was one of the most distinguished families in ancient Athens, was well acquainted with Socrates.
12. After Socrates was forced to drink hemlock, a poison, Plato and several other friends and followers of Socrates left Athens for some time.
13. Plato made Socrates the subject of many of his greatest written works.
14. That he did so is fortunate as Socrates himself did not write anything.
15. Plato eventually returned to Athens and founded his Academy there.
16. Although it was not the only such center for learning, Plato's Academy is sometimes considered to have been the first university.
17. Plato's Academy also played an important role in the life of Aristotle.
18. Aristotle went to the Academy as a youth and studied there for twenty years.
19. He later founded his own school called the Lyceum, and he is also well-known for tutoring the young Alexander the Great.
20. Aristotle's influence dominated Western thought until the end of the seventeenth century.

Copyright © by Holt, Rinehart and Winston. All rights reserved.

NAME CLASS DATE

Review B: Eight Troublesome Modifiers

EXERCISE In the following sentences, underline the correct modifier of the pair given in parentheses.

Example 1. Is it a *(real, really)* good idea to call ahead for a reservation at that restaurant?

1. When I had the flu and wasn't feeling *(good, well)*, my mom told me stories.

2. Ever since the tune-up, my car doesn't run *(bad, badly)* anymore.

3. Randy feels pretty *(good, well)* about his scores on the college entrance exams.

4. The mime began to walk *(slow, slowly)* toward the audience.

5. During the second match the tennis player who was expected to win was faring *(bad, badly)*.

6. A mysterious man known only as Jim entered wearing a *(real, really)* long cape.

7. We are happy to be doing so *(good, well)* in the chess competition.

8. The train seemed to be moving *(slow, slowly)* around the side of the mountain.

9. The quality of that recording sounds *(bad, badly)*.

10. Suzi rested *(good, well)* after the long hike in the woods.

11. Devorah's speech at the conference was *(real, really)* interesting.

12. Annie thought that the fresh fruit salad tasted *(good, well)*.

13. Kevin was dressed so *(good, well)* because he was going to a wedding in the afternoon.

14. That fake gem looks *(real, really)*, but I know it isn't.

15. Carla couldn't hide her joy about her travel plans; she was *(real, really)* excited.

16. Eric didn't look too *(bad, badly)* after his haircut.

17. Marcia suggested that we all take things a little more *(slow, slowly)* so we don't get too stressed.

18. After the storm a rainbow emerged and stretched *(slow, slowly)* across the sky.

19. Kathryn's new procedures were working out quite *(good, well)*.

20. They were *(real, really)* sad to see Jane go, but they knew they would see her again soon.

Copyright © by Holt, Rinehart and Winston. All rights reserved.

NAME ______ CLASS ______ DATE ______

Review C: Comparison

EXERCISE In each of the following sentence, correct any errors in comparisons. Cross out any unnecessary words. Insert any missing word by inserting a caret (^) and writing the word above it. If a sentence is already correct, write C before the item number.

Example 1. Considering Harold's experience in journalism, I think we should give him the ~~best~~ *better* assignment of the two.

1. This is the worse casserole I have ever tasted.
2. I am as tall, if not taller than, John.
3. That was the most perfect double play.
4. This spider is more bigger than that one.
5. That was the less usefull suggestion of all.
6. I think the African gray parrot is a better talker than any bird.
7. He is getting more stronger every day.
8. I like your plan better than Lisa.
9. The water is as cold, if not colder than, the air above it.
10. I built my bicycle myself, so it is more unique.
11. Until you joined, I was the stronger swimmer in our club.
12. This is the most fastest car on the market.
13. I think Aunt Colleen chose the most elegant of the two gowns.
14. This trip to the dentist was less painful than the last one.
15. Cousin Nora sent me more postcards than you.
16. The pizza crust is least crispy than it usually is.
17. Darren prefers his mom's cooking to any professional chef.
18. Their dog is more better at fetching than our dog.
19. I am as upset, if not more upset than, you are.
20. Our treasurer is more responsible than anyone in the club.

Copyright © by Holt, Rinehart and Winston. All rights reserved.

Review D: All Types of Problems

EXERCISE A In the sentences below, identify each underlined word or word group by writing above it *ADJ* for *adjective* or *ADV* for *adverb*.

Example 1. The helicopter landed <u>slowly</u> on the landing strip. (ADV)

1. Elephants reputedly have <u>better</u> memories than other animals have.
2. My <u>old</u> shoes are very comfortable.
3. We will <u>definitely</u> consult more experts the next time.
4. I think your <u>first</u> answer was correct.
5. Watch closely, everyone, <u>because we are now entering the lions' habitat</u>.
6. That <u>smoking</u> volcano is the most active one on the island.
7. <u>When we go swimming</u>, I usually get hungry around eleven in the morning.
8. In a can of <u>mixed</u> nuts, which kind of nut do you prefer?
9. Edgar and I wished <u>fervently</u> for snow, so we could ride our sleds.
10. I don't think I have ever been more sleepy than I was <u>after we stayed up all night</u>.

EXERCISE B In each of the following sentences, correct any errors in comparisons. Cross out any unnecessary words. Insert any missing word by inserting a caret (∧) and writing the word above it.

Example 1. That was a ~~real~~ ∧really good idea you had!

11. Training to run a full marathon can seem slowly.
12. Of the three violinists who performed, Ms. Buchanan played better.
13. I was the worse player on our rugby team, but I had a wonderful time.
14. I have always thought that our dog Samson is braver than any animal.
15. The narrow pass through the ravine is most treacherous than the longer road around the mountains.
16. I think we will have a more equal amount of work if you handle the most recent account.
17. The meeting will probably run as late, if not later than, four o'clock.
18. I believe Joe's account of events more than Ana.
19. Sonja doesn't feel good; she has a high fever.
20. Our new dog is no longer acting bad.

Copyright © by Holt, Rinehart and Winston. All rights reserved.

NAME CLASS DATE

USAGE

Misplaced Modifiers A

10a. Avoid using misplaced modifiers.

A modifying word, phrase, or clause that seems to modify the wrong word or word group in a sentence is a ***misplaced modifier.*** To correct a misplaced modifier, place the modifying word, phrase, or clause as close as possible to the word or words you intend to modify.

MISPLACED High up in the air, we watched the trapeze artist do a triple somersault. [Was the writer high up in the air or was the trapeze artist?]

CLEAR We watched the trapeze artist, **high up in the air,** do a triple somersault.

EXERCISE A Most of the sentences below contain a misplaced modifier. In each of those sentences, underline the misplaced modifier. If a sentence is already clear, write *C* on the line provided.

Example ______ **1.** I attended a powwow featuring many fine craft items made by American Indian artists <u>with my family.</u>

______ **1.** A woman showed us how to bead necklaces near the judges' stand.

______ **2.** The woman giving the demonstration in her hair wore beaded jewelry.

______ **3.** A Blackfoot artist on one dress had sewn numerous shells.

______ **4.** The powwow's main event was a costume competition, which featured a dazzling array of different styles.

______ **5.** The contestant earned a cash prize whose costume was chosen.

EXERCISE B Revise the following sentences to correct misplaced modifiers. Write your revised sentences on the lines provided. Some sentences can be correctly revised in more than one way.

Example **1.** Located on an important strait, many battles were fought for control of the fortress.

Many battles were fought for control of the fortress, located on an important strait.

6. Michelle had wanted to attend the college where her mother taught ever since she was young.

____

7. The man and woman caught several fish using fancy lures.

____

8. After sitting in the cold for hours, a single Canada goose was all the bird-watchers spotted.

____

9. Could you ask Joshua what he plans to sing for everyone when you pick him up at school?

____

10. Startled by the noise, the slamming door sent the kitten dashing headlong from the room.

____

Copyright © by Holt, Rinehart and Winston. All rights reserved.

NAME ______________________ CLASS ______________ DATE ______________

Misplaced Modifiers B

10a. Avoid using misplaced modifiers.

MISPLACED Shining through the fog, the sailors could barely see the lighthouse's beam.

CLEAR The sailors could barely see the lighthouse's beam **shining through the fog.**

EXERCISE Revise the following sentences to correct misplaced modifiers. Write your revised sentences on the lines provided. Some sentences can be correctly revised in more than one way.

Example 1. Lying lazily under the truck, even the passing traffic didn't wake the old hound.
Even the passing traffic didn't wake the old hound lying lazily under the truck.

1. The losing candidate gave a gracious speech in which he thanked all voters for taking part in the democratic process after the election results were announced.

2. Tricia proudly displayed a picture of her three children on her desk.

3. Stranded on the mountain, the climber's family were glad that their son had learned survival skills.

4. The new community centers will be paid for with city funding and corporate contributions that are being built downtown.

5. The astronomer explained how a telltale wobble could indicate that one or more planets are in orbit around a star at the end of her presentation.

6. Safety Guide listed children's toys in its newsletter that could cause injury.

7. We will see the ballet that caused such a stir when it was first performed next season.

8. Thanks to the firefighters' efforts, the house missed being burned fortunately by the brush fire.

9. Please sing me the song Nana taught you when you have the time.

10. Visiting an American supermarket for the first time, the size of the store overwhelmed Ty.

Copyright © by Holt, Rinehart and Winston. All rights reserved.

NAME ______________________ CLASS ______________ DATE ______________

for **CHAPTER 10: PLACEMENT OF MODIFIERS** *pages 296–297*

USAGE

Squinting Modifiers A

10b. Avoid misplacing a modifying word, phrase, or clause so that it seems to modify either of two words.

Such a misplaced modifier is often called a *squinting,* or *two-way,* modifier.

MISPLACED Remind Michelle before lunch we have a meeting.

CLEAR **Before lunch,** remind Michelle we have a meeting.

CLEAR Remind Michelle we have a meeting **before lunch.**

EXERCISE A Read each sentence below, and decide whether it is clear or it contains a squinting modifier. On the line provided, write C for *clear* or S for *squinting modifier.*

Example __S__ **1.** Eliot said when school was over he would find that book for me.

______ **1.** The accused denied in his previous statement he had lied about the car's whereabouts.

______ **2.** I told Viet during the play he should relax and enjoy performing.

______ **3.** Charla discovered by some chance her lens was lying just at the mouth of the drain.

______ **4.** The shopkeeper hinted when we returned to the shop he could lower the price.

______ **5.** As the ticket agent announced "Can I have your attention please," the stranded passengers bet their bus had been delayed yet again.

EXERCISE B Revise the following sentences to correct squinting modifiers. Write your revised sentences on the lines provided. Each sentence can be correctly revised in more than one way.

Example 1. Tell whoever calls next week I will return the call as soon as I can.

Tell whoever calls I will return the call as soon as I can next week.

6. The scientists explained throughout the week the oil slick should continue to break up.

____

7. Dad promised after he ran some errands I could use the car.

____

8. Many visitors to the historic mosque say during their stay in Istanbul they have never seen a building of such beauty.

____

9. Ms. Singh requested when we were finished with the test we read quietly.

____

10. The pilot told the passengers before the plane took off they should turn off any personal electronic devices.

____

Copyright © by Holt, Rinehart and Winston. All rights reserved.

Squinting Modifiers B

10b. Avoid misplacing a modifying word, phrase, or clause so that it seems to modify either of two words.

Such a misplaced modifier is often called a *squinting,* or *two-way,* modifier.

MISPLACED The ushers were told after the overture they should seat latecomers.

CLEAR **After the overture,** the ushers were told they should seat latecomers.

CLEAR The ushers were told they should seat latecomers **after the overture.**

USAGE

EXERCISE A Most of the sentences below contain a squinting modifier. In each of those sentences, underline the squinting modifier. If a sentence is already clear, write *C* on the line provided.

Example ______ **1.** Lloyd bragged before the contest was over he would sell the most tickets.

______ **1.** Having weathered the drought, the farmers hoped in the fall more rain would come.

______ **2.** Four of the doctors were convinced because of the positive test results their patients would want to undergo the treatment.

______ **3.** Please reassure Anita driving on the highway will not be so frightening once she has finished her driving lessons.

______ **4.** The company's spokesperson said during a press conference investors were getting nervous about the company's future.

______ **5.** Paul assured us after an hour of hiking the trail would become less rugged.

EXERCISE B Each of the following sentences has a squinting modifier. Underline each squinting modifier, and draw an arrow from the modifier to where it belongs. Each sentence can be correctly revised in more than one way.

Example 1. Our school's Community Service Committee decided for the coming year to involve more students in community service.

6. The committee agreed over the holidays we should sponsor some kind of service project.

7. Daniel had suggested throughout the semester we encourage more students to volunteer regularly.

8. Jeanette argued on one occasion we could get more students to work at smaller projects, thus helping more people.

9. Jeanette explained afterwards some volunteers would be inspired to volunteer more regularly.

10. Kahlil said by the end of the meeting we should generate a list of agencies for which students could volunteer.

Copyright © by Holt, Rinehart and Winston. All rights reserved.

NAME ________________ CLASS ________________ DATE ________________

Dangling Modifiers A

10c. Avoid using dangling modifiers.

A modifying word, phrase, or clause that does not clearly and sensibly modify any word or word group in a sentence is a ***dangling modifier.*** To correct a dangling modifier, add or replace words to make the meaning of the sentence clear.

DANGLING Tired from studying, the chapter seemed endless.

CLEAR Tired from studying, **I thought** the chapter seemed endless.

CLEAR **Because I was tired from studying,** the chapter seemed endless.

EXERCISE A Read each sentence below, and decide whether it is clear or it contains a dangling modifier. On the line provided, write *C* for *clear* or *D* for *dangling modifier.*

Example __D__ **1.** Finally finding the old book, Gordon's quest was over.

______ **1.** Coming into the hall, the bouquet on the table looked beautiful.

______ **2.** To solve the problem, patience is necessary.

______ **3.** Exhausted by all the hard work, it felt good to sit down.

______ **4.** Watching the clock, the speaker summed up her last two points.

______ **5.** In search of a quarter under the seat, his car bumped into the tollbooth.

EXERCISE B Revise the sentences below to correct dangling modifiers. Write your revised sentences on the lines provided. Each sentence can be correctly revised in more than one way.

Example **1.** Poised and elegant, the singer's new dress made quite an impression.

Poised and elegant, the singer made quite an impression in her new dress.

6. After spending all day Saturday reading, my eyes ached. ________________

____

7. To give ourselves enough time, the taxi picked us up an hour and a half before our train left.

____

8. While working in New York, Sora's family lived in California. ________________

____

9. Peering at my map, the streets looked completely unfamiliar. ________________

____

10. Not usually shy, public speaking upset his stomach. ________________

____

Copyright © by Holt, Rinehart and Winston. All rights reserved.

NAME ______________________ CLASS ______________ DATE ______________

USAGE

Dangling Modifiers B

10c. Avoid using dangling modifiers.

A modifying word, phrase, or clause that does not clearly and sensibly modify any word or word group in a sentence is a ***dangling modifier.*** To correct a dangling modifier, add or replace words to make the meaning of the sentence clear.

DANGLING After raising the car, the cracked axle was inspected.

CLEAR After raising the car, **the mechanic inspected** the cracked axle.

CLEAR **After the mechanic raised the car,** he inspected the cracked axle.

EXERCISE A Read each sentence below, and decide whether it is clear or it contains a dangling modifier. On the line provided, write *C* for *clear* or *D* for *dangling modifier.*

Example __D__ **1.** To learn more about the subject, my plan was to take an online course.

______ **1.** While reading the newspaper, the cat jumped on the table and sat on the front page.

______ **2.** To increase sales, the company's customer service must improve.

______ **3.** Having discussed the chapter thoroughly, it was time for the quiz.

______ **4.** Beside herself with joy, her first impulse was to share the news with everyone.

______ **5.** Written in advance, the ambassador's statement was clear and direct.

EXERCISE B Revise the sentences below to correct dangling modifiers. Write your revised sentences on the lines provided. Each sentence can be correctly revised in more than one way.

Example **1.** Shouting to be heard above the noise, there was no reason for Matt's sister to play her stereo so loud. *Shouting to be heard above the stereo, Matt thought his sister had no reason to play her stereo so loud.*

6. For returning the movie early, the next rental is free. ______________________

7. While on her backpacking trip, the compass proved essential. ______________________

8. To set the clock, the "mode" button must be pressed first. ______________________

9. Not one to give up easily, the second attempt to climb the mountain would be a success. ______

10. Cartwheeling head over foot, the spectators gasped at the acrobatic spectacle. ______________________

Copyright © by Holt, Rinehart and Winston. All rights reserved.

NAME ______________________ CLASS ______________ DATE ______________

Review A: Placement of Modifiers

EXERCISE A Identify the faulty modifier in each sentence below by writing *M* for *misplaced modifier*, *S* for *squinting modifier*, or *D* for *dangling modifier* on the line provided.

Example __M__ 1. Lying in bed with eyes wide open, the night light reassured little Akira.

_____ **1.** Towering high above the rooftops, most of downtown lies in the building's shadow.

_____ **2.** To hear the information again, the red button may be pushed.

_____ **3.** Remind Pat before our trip to Scotland she must get her passport renewed.

_____ **4.** Arranged in neat rows, Scott surveyed his newly grafted grapevines.

_____ **5.** The article explained that to regain control of a skidding car the steering wheel should be turned in the direction of the skid.

EXERCISE B The following sentences contain misplaced, squinting, or dangling modifiers. On the lines provided, revise each sentence so that its meaning is clear and correct. Most sentences can be correctly revised in more than one way.

Example **1.** After dumping planeload after planeload of water on the blaze, nothing could stop the forest fire. *After dumping planeload after planeload of water on the blaze, the firefighters thought nothing could stop the forest fire.*

6. Holding hands to keep from being separated, the museum seemed huge to the preschoolers.

____

7. Carla assured me once we had entered the national park she would stop more often to take pictures. ____

____

8. Stunned by the news of the earthquake, donations of food and money poured in from everywhere. ____

____

9. Tina showed the goldfish to her parents which had grown since she put it in a larger bowl.

____

10. Having won first place in the obedience contest, Mr. Sawyer won a year's supply of dog food for his schnauzer, Wolfy. ____

____

Copyright © by Holt, Rinehart and Winston. All rights reserved.

Review B: Placement of Modifiers

EXERCISE The following sentences contain misplaced, squinting, or dangling modifiers. On the lines provided, revise each sentence so that its meaning is clear and correct. Most sentences can be correctly revised in more than one way.

Example 1. Beautifully soaring, it was breathtaking to hear the choir.
Beautifully soaring, the song the choir sang was breathtaking to hear.

1. She stared at the poster Elias was tacking up with open amazement.

2. Arriving in class without any books, the teacher sent the students to the office.

3. Remind Dr. Scoffield at three o'clock her appointment has been canceled.

4. In this medieval book, the artist used a brush to paint this tiny angel with only a few hairs.

5. Sung Li has determined with considerable effort we can finish the job.

6. While crossing the street, the red light caught me halfway across.

7. No one is allowed to drive a car whose driver's license has been revoked.

8. Maya had thought before the movie her friends would meet her by the ticket counter.

9. Having learned to cook in home economics, my culinary skills surprised Dad.

10. To find out how the contraption works, it is not a good idea to push buttons at random.

Copyright © by Holt, Rinehart and Winston. All rights reserved.

NAME CLASS DATE

Review C: Placement of Modifiers

EXERCISE The following sentences contain misplaced, squinting, or dangling modifiers. On the lines provided, revise each sentence so that its meaning is clear and correct. Most sentences can be correctly revised in more than one way.

Example 1. To organize our data for the experiment, our decision was to use a computer spreadsheet program. *To organize our data for the experiment, we decided to use a computer spreadsheet program.*

1. Luke saw a bird through the binoculars with a long bill.

2. Tell the dance instructor when this song is over I need to review the steps.

3. To recognize a talented player, the game must be understood.

4. We're sponsoring a dance to raise money for famine victims in the gym.

5. Having finally made the honor roll, my parents congratulated me.

6. The man wore a ring on his little finger with a large red ruby.

7. Bruno saw a deer riding on the school bus this morning.

8. A mysterious woman warned the king before he had reigned a year he would regret his rash decision.

9. Leaving the store, the icy sidewalk caused me to slip.

10. Finding the diary, Jodi's first inclination was to read it.

Copyright © by Holt, Rinehart and Winston. All rights reserved.

Glossary of Usage A

Review the glossary entries on pages 308–311 of your textbook for information on the correct usage of the following terms:

a, an
accept, except
adapt, adopt
affect, effect
ain't
all right
all the farther, all the faster
allusion, illusion
a lot
alumni, alumnae
amount, number
and, etc.
anyways, anywheres
assure, ensure, insure
at
a while, awhile

EXERCISE In each of the following sentences, underline the correct word or words in parentheses.

Example 1. We *(insured, assured)* them that we would raise enough money for the trip.

1. Every year, our class takes a field trip to *(a, an)* historic site.
2. Before the trip, though, we have to raise *(alot, a lot)* of money.
3. This year, we had a large *(amount, number)* of fund-raising ideas.
4. We thought of all sorts of things, such as selling T-shirts, washing cars, *(etc., and etc.)*
5. Finally, we asked if having a carnival would be *(allright, all right)* with the teachers.
6. They *(accepted, excepted)* our idea with enthusiasm.
7. Our teachers Mrs. Hurst and Ms. Connor are *(alumni, alumnae)* of the school themselves.
8. They used to have carnivals to raise money *(awhile, a while)* ago, when they were students.
9. Now where were we going to *(have it, have it at)*?
10. We knew that we could not have a carnival just *(anywhere, anywheres)*.
11. We had gone *(all the farther, as far as)* we could go in our plans without a location.
12. The principal said it would be *(allright, all right)* to have the carnival in the gym.
13. There *(ain't, isn't)* a better place on campus for a carnival!
14. The good news had an energizing *(affect, effect)* on us.
15. With such a large *(amount, number)* of support, we knew we could have a great carnival.
16. We started *(adapting, adopting)* booths from folding tables and large boxes.
17. In one booth, the principal stood behind a pane of glass so that people could have the *(allusion, illusion)* that they were drawing a moustache on her.
18. The Another booth, we had baloons with cat and dog faces on them, which you could *(adapt, adopt)* for a dollar.
19. The carnival was *(a, an)* huge success.
20. It *(assured, ensured)* that we would have enough money for the class trip—now where will we go?

Copyright © by Holt, Rinehart and Winston. All rights reserved.

Glossary of Usage B

Review the glossary entries on pages 314–317 of your textbook for information on the correct usage of the following terms:

because	**bring, take**	**done**
being as, being that	**bust, busted**	**don't, doesn't**
beside, besides	**credible, creditable, credulous**	**emigrate, immigrate**
between, among	**data**	**famous, notorious**
borrow, lend	**discover, invent**	**fewer, less**

EXERCISE Each of the following sentences has one underlined word. If that word is used incorrectly, make the appropriate correction. If the sentence is already correct, write *C* next to the sentence number.

Example 1. His story seemed ~~creditable~~ *credible*, so we believed him.

1. My teacher invented a popular math trivia game; now he's notorious!
2. The performer sang two ballads besides the ones listed in the program.
3. Being as my father received a promotion, our family moved to Chicago.
4. Less teenagers were able to find jobs this summer.
5. Owen and Chad split the meal among themselves.
6. When I eat meals, my dog lies on the floor beside my chair.
7. Odessa don't know where the microscope should go.
8. How did you bust your arm?
9. After lunch, Hisako and I done the dishes while the others picked berries.
10. The reason I was late for class is because my dad's car wouldn't start.
11. Who discovered the electron microscope?
12. How many people had to immigrate from Ireland during the potato famine?
13. The data was carefully reviewed by our panel of experts.
14. Their efforts to prevent the fire from spreading were credible.
15. Sure, I would be happy to borrow you my lawnmower.
16. Young people today have fewer cavities than children in past generations.
17. Did the police bust anyone for trespassing?
18. When you leave tonight, bring this umbrella with you.
19. He's so creditable; he believed that the moon was really made of green cheese.
20. We doesn't care how far it is—we're going!

Copyright © by Holt, Rinehart and Winston. All rights reserved.

Glossary of Usage C

Review the glossary entries on pages 320–321 of your textbook for information on the correct usage of the following terms:

had ought, hadn't ought **hopefully** **kind(s), sort(s), type(s)**
he, she, it, they **imply, infer** **kind of, sort of**
hisself, theirself, theirselves **in, into**

EXERCISE Revise each of the following sentences to correct any errors in the usage of the above glossary terms. If a sentence is already correct, write *C* next to the sentence number.

Example 1. My brother, who is very athletic, ~~he~~ introduced me to cyclo-cross racing.

1. If you have never heard of cyclo-cross racing, I had ought to tell you about it.

2. The race, which takes place in open country, it is usually about ten to fifteen miles long.

3. The obstacles, of which there are plenty, they can include ditches, or even flights of stairs.

4. The bikers often have to pick up their bikes theirselves and carry them over obstacles.

5. These kinds of challenges may not appeal to all bicycle enthusiasts.

6. From the large crowd at the last race I attended, I can imply that the sport has some real fans.

7. My brother, the great athlete, he took me to my first cyclo-cross race.

8. These sort of event was not my usual Saturday afternoon fare.

9. I went, though, because my brother had helped set up the event hisself.

10. When we got there, we walked right in the registration tent.

11. My brother had not told me that I would actually be helping with the race, but I guess he had inferred it.

12. It was kind of exciting to be a part of the event staff.

13. We even got to wear these type of badge that looked really snappy.

14. But what would I have to do—what kind of job had I gotten myself in?

15. Hopefully, it wouldn't be anything too boring.

16. I hadn't ought to have worried about that.

17. A girl named Jen, who had worked at several races, she explained what I had to do.

18. During a race, each helper had ought to stand on the course with a spare bike.

19. This was in case any rider's bike, which can get damaged or bogged down with mud, it was unfit to finish the race.

20. Being that close to the action was sort of intimidating, but it was fun!

Copyright © by Holt, Rinehart and Winston. All rights reserved.

USAGE

Glossary of Usage D

Review the glossary entries on pages 321–322 of your textbook for information on the correct usage of the following terms:

kind of a(n), sort of a(n)	**like, as**	**literally, figuratively**
learn, teach	**like, as if, as though**	**myself, ourselves**
leave, let	**likely, liable**	

EXERCISE Revise each of the following sentences to correct any errors in the usage of the above glossary terms. If a sentence is already correct, write *C* next to the sentence number.

Example 1. Did the community develop ~~like~~ *as* the planners intended?

1. I saw a design for a kind of a clock that wakes you by dropping corks on your face.

2. I won't see that film, because I am likely to have nightmares.

3. I know that Layla and myself can paint the backdrop this afternoon.

4. My uncle is the man who learned me how to play the guitar.

5. Do you think Dad will leave me go to the concert?

6. Jerold will call for Evelyn and ourselves at eight o'clock.

7. When we shook hands, Arthur was literally shocked; static electricity had built up as I crossed the carpet.

8. I feel like I will never finish my homework.

9. The day is not going like I had planned.

10. Betsy has promised to learn me about my new computer this weekend.

11. This is a kind of a problem we don't encounter very often.

12. If we don't leave soon, we are liable to arrive late.

13. Do you mean he figuratively spilled the beans—he dumped a bag of dry beans onto the table?

14. It seems like it was only yesterday that we were at the beach.

15. I'm sorry, but I cannot leave you have the car this weekend.

16. Can you teach me to sing the harmony to that tune?

17. Karen and myself are going out for ice cream tonight.

18. Unfortunately, this is not the right sort of a wrench for the job.

19. Literally speaking, we were out of business, having only sold a few snow cones a day.

20. Bill is liable to show up any time now.

Copyright © by Holt, Rinehart and Winston. All rights reserved.

Glossary of Usage E

Review the glossary entries on pages 325–326 of your textbook for information on the correct usage of the following terms:

nauseated, nauseous
number of
of
off, off of
or, nor
persecute, prosecute
phenomena

EXERCISE Revise each of the following sentences to correct any errors in the usage of the above glossary terms. If a sentence is already correct, write C next to the sentence number.

Example 1. I copied the address ~~off of~~ *from* this business card.

1. That particular phenomena has never been explained.

2. The dumpster behind the cafeteria is a nauseous sight.

3. My aunt is a lawyer—she persecutes people.

4. You ought to of seen how deep the snow was in my backyard.

5. I will neither resign or apologize.

6. We should of made reservations for dinner.

7. Does the old regime have a history of prosecuting minorities?

8. I got this pitcher's rookie card off my cousin.

9. Either you have the item, nor you don't.

10. The number of people who signed up were surprising.

11. I need to sit down; I'm feeling nauseous.

12. Did you get any good debate tips off of that guy?

13. I could of brought an extra plate if I had known we needed one.

14. This store persecutes all shoplifters.

15. I have neither approved or disapproved her proposal.

16. He might have gone ahead without us when he heard of our delay.

17. A number of applications was waiting for me on my desk.

18. Someone must of told them about the secret meeting.

19. I can't believe they didn't win either first nor second place.

20. A number of strange phenomenon have been reported in this area recently.

Copyright © by Holt, Rinehart and Winston. All rights reserved.

Glossary of Usage F

Review the glossary entries on pages 327–329 of your textbook for information on the correct usage of the following terms:

Reverend, Honorable	**them**	**what**
say	**this here, that there**	**when, where**
some, somewhat	**try and, try to**	**where**
supposed to, used to	**type, type of**	**who, which, that**
than, then	**ways**	

EXERCISE Revise each of the following sentences to correct any errors in the usage of the above glossary terms. If a sentence is already correct, write C next to the sentence number.

Example 1. Mr. Allan is the speaker ~~which~~ *who* came to talk to our class.

1. The Reverend Allan spoke to our class on Monday.

2. The topic that he spoke about was communication.

3. Mr. Allan use to be a family counselor.

4. He looked at us seriously and says that communication was always a big issue.

5. He said that family members which communicate well have happier home lives.

6. Good communication is where each person talks and listens in a caring and constructive way.

7. Mr. Allan had us try an interesting type of communication game.

8. We were each suppose to choose a partner.

9. He gave each pair of us a hypothetical situation, and than we had to act it out.

10. First, we acted out that there situation in an angry way.

11. Than, we talked about the words most of us had used to express ourselves.

12. We had been saying "you always do this" and that type thing.

13. When we used them accusing words, our partners felt defensive.

14. We realized where we had not been focused on solving the problem.

15. Next, we tried the same discussion, except it was some different.

16. This time we had to try and keep the other person's feelings in mind.

17. Immediately after deciding on this new approach, we began to feel as if tensions had eased some.

18. Before we even started the discussion, my partner turned to me and says that our friendship is more important than our problems.

19. After that there statement, I felt much more inclined to listen and compromise.

20. Mr. Allan said we had come a long ways toward having better relationships.

Copyright © by Holt, Rinehart and Winston. All rights reserved.

NAME ______________________ CLASS ______________ DATE ______________

for **CHAPTER 11: A GLOSSARY OF USAGE** *pages 332–335*

The Double Negative and Nonsexist Language

Review pages 332–335 of your textbook for information on:

The Double Negative

Nonsexist Language

USAGE

EXERCISE Revise any of the following sentences that contain a double negative or sexist language. If a sentence is already correct, write *C* next to the sentence number.

Example 1. Right now I ~~can't~~ *can* hardly imagine what career I would like most.

1. Last week a number of businessmen came to the city convention center.

2. They were looking for more manpower for their businesses.

3. I hadn't never been to a career fair before, so I decided to attend.

4. The recruiters seemed like salesmen trying to sell their companies.

5. At first, I didn't think they had nothing that would interest me.

6. There weren't any representatives there from theater or dance companies.

7. I couldn't hardly find any booths there that weren't for computer companies.

8. There weren't but a few tables for more old-fashioned professions.

9. One company was looking for seamstresses to do complicated alterations.

10. I wasn't nowhere close to being qualified for that job, but it sounded interesting.

11. I think the most interesting booth was the one the firemen had set up—it had real firefighting equipment and uniforms.

12. I bet I wouldn't hardly look bad in one of those outfits.

13. The officers who were there had neat uniforms, too.

14. I can't never imagine myself carrying a gun, though.

15. I have a cousin who is a stewardess, so I looked at the airlines' booths.

16. I wouldn't be good at that, because I already know I'm a lousy waiter.

17. I did well as a deliveryman for a pizza chain last summer, though.

18. I noticed that there weren't no booths for some of the jobs I respect most.

19. My mother is a housewife, and I think that's a very worthwhile profession.

20. I'm sure that once I find the right career, there won't be nobody else better at it than I am!

Copyright © by Holt, Rinehart and Winston. All rights reserved.

Review A: Glossary of Usage

EXERCISE Revise any of the following sentences that contain sexist language or an error in usage. If a sentence is already correct, write *C* next to the sentence number. Refer to a dictionary as necessary.

Example 1. Ed is the gardener ~~which~~ *who* is in charge of the topiaries.

1. Nan and Jo were the two policemen which were in charge of patrolling the carnival.

2. I read in the paper where the team lost again yesterday.

3. Her remarks inferred that she was not happy in her new school.

4. Next year there will be fewer students in each class.

5. Some illnesses may effect the brain.

6. French, history, and mathematics are taught by Mrs. Vigne, Mr. Wolfe, and Ms. Poston, respectively.

7. She borrowed five dollars off of her sister.

8. According to the chairman, the plan was kind of complicated.

9. The children built the treehouse theirselves, without any help from their parents.

10. There were less people in the audience than there were on the stage.

11. The mailman said that the package required a large amount of postage stamps.

12. We noticed that there weren't hardly enough test booklets for everyone in the class.

13. Belle Starr, born Myra Belle Shirley, was a notorious outlaw.

14. Shall we except the Smiths' invitation to dinner?

15. I read where Bethune-Cookman College in Florida is named after Mary McLeod Bethune.

16. Gwendolyn Brooks was a poet which won a Pulitzer Prize in 1950.

17. Being as the lake was frozen, we decided to ice-skate.

18. The judge had few illusions about the accuracy of people's memories.

19. They found less wild strawberries than they had expected.

20. The students had to explain the differences among nouns, verbs, and adjectives.

Copyright © by Holt, Rinehart and Winston. All rights reserved.

Review B: Glossary of Usage

EXERCISE Each of the following sentences contains a line for which two or three different completions are given. Choose the correct completion, and write it on the line provided. Base your answers on standard, formal English usage.

Example 1. Her reason for quitting the restaurant job was ___that___ she needed more time to study. *(that, because)*

1. The first speaker will be ______. *(Reverend Jackson, the Reverend Jackson, the Reverend Edward Jackson)*

2. The lifeguard dived ______ the water to rescue the struggling child. *(into, in)*

3. My great-grandparents ______ from Sicily in the '30s. *(immigrated, emigrated)*

4. ______ he was a good actor, he got the lead role in the school's one act play. *(Being as, Being that, Because)*

5. You are ______ to hurt yourself if you try to climb over those rocks. *(likely, liable)*

6. We hiked a long ______ before we found a suitable campsite. *(way, ways)*

7. The rescue workers looked ______ they had not slept for days. *(like, as if, as)*

8. This year there are ______ students in the senior class than there were last year. *(less, fewer)*

9. ______ dog is usually hard to train. *(Those kinds of, That kind of a, This kind of)*

10. Jim ______ Amy that the library would be open late. *(insured, assured, ensured)*

11. The store no longer carries ______ shoes. *(those kinds of, that kind of, these sort of)*

12. Please ______ this report to Mr. Benson when you go to his office. *(bring, take)*

13. The audience was deeply ______ by her speech. *(affected, effected)*

14. We ______ done a better job if we had had more time. *(could have, could of, should of)*

15. Kim's letter ______ that she would be paying us a visit soon. *(implied, inferred)*

16. An unusually large ______ of applications have been received. *(amount, number)*

17. I think that Ana has done a very ______ job as class president. *(credible, creditable, credulous)*

18. Gloria acted ______ she had never seen him before. *(as if, like)*

19. Do you remember that you borrowed a dollar ______ me last week? *(off, off of, from)*

20. We cannot help ______ proud of our new yearbook. *(but feel, feeling)*

Copyright © by Holt, Rinehart and Winston. All rights reserved.

NAME ______ CLASS ______ DATE ______

Review C: Glossary of Usage

EXERCISE Revise any of the following sentences that contain sexist language or an error in usage. If a sentence is already correct, write *C* next to the sentence number.

Example 1. I read ~~where~~ *that* the Taj Mahal was built as a monument to true love.

1. In 1612, Shah Jahan of India married a woman which would become the love of his life.

2. They were literally inseparable—she went almost everywhere with him, even to war.

3. Shah Jahan, who loved his wife very much, he gave her a special name: "Mumtaz Mahal."

4. That there name means "Chosen One of the Palace."

5. Queen Mumtaz was notorious in India for her kindness.

6. She inspired Shah Jahan to commit many credible acts of charity.

7. They also had a large amount of children together.

8. It must of been a terrible shock, then, when she died suddenly.

9. Being as Shah Jahan was so grief-stricken, he mourned for eight days in a locked room.

10. I read where his black hair had turned almost completely white by the time he came out of the room.

11. He decided to build the world's finest mausoleum to assure that Mumtaz's memory would be preserved.

12. No one isn't certain about the origin of the name "Taj Mahal" for the mausoleum, but it is thought to be an abbreviation of Mumtaz Mahal's name.

13. Twenty thousand workmen were used in the colossal building effort.

14. No less than 1,000 elephants hauled the building materials from all over the Far East.

15. Artisans decorated the inside of the building with gold, turquoise, precious gems, and etc.

16. It took a while to build the monument—about twenty-two years.

17. Legend says that Shah Jahan intended to build a second mausoleum for himself, but his son, who seized the throne and imprisoned his father, would not leave him do it.

18. I think that the Taj Mahal has the most beautiful architecture of any building anywheres.

19. According to the original design, the interior had ought to be perfectly symmetrical.

20. The reason it is not is because, after Shah Jahan's death, his cenotaph was placed beside that of his beloved wife, upsetting the perfect balance of the room.

Copyright © by Holt, Rinehart and Winston. All rights reserved.

First Words, *O*, and the Pronoun *I*

12a. Capitalize the first word of every sentence.

(1) Capitalize the first word of a sentence following a colon.
(2) Capitalize the first word of a resolution following the word *Resolved.*
(3) Capitalize the first word of a quoted sentence.
(4) Capitalize the first word of a statement or question inserted without quotation marks into a sentence.

EXAMPLES **T**he city's streets were crowded with people on the day of the big parade.
Every club meeting begins with this statement: **T**he meeting will now come to order.
Resolved: **T**hat the development of new sources of energy should be promoted.
In a speech in 1856, Abraham Lincoln said, "**T**he ballot is stronger than the bullet."
This essay attempts to answer the question **W**hat is the meaning of life?

12b. Capitalize the pronoun *I* and the interjection *O.*

EXAMPLES My brother and **I** spent the afternoon looking at old family photographs.
Shade me with your branches, **O** majestic tree.

12c. Capitalize the first word in both the salutation and the closing of a letter.

EXAMPLES **D**ear Ms. Yuan, **S**incerely yours,

MECHANICS

EXERCISE In each of the following sentences, strike through each error in capitalization and write the correct form above it.

Example 1. ~~as~~ [A] students, you should often ask yourselves, ~~am~~ [A] ~~i~~ [I] working to the best of my ability?

1. When asked his favorite sport, Lloyd said, "basketball to watch and tennis to play."
2. The resolution began with "Resolved: that support for day care be increased by 15 percent."
3. for breakfast, i had two bowls of cereal and two bananas because, Oh, was I hungry.
4. Claire, I have one thing to say: college admission requirements are more stringent than you think.
5. Measure my humble self against your vastness, o majestic sky.
6. Butler wrote, "an expert is one who knows more and more about less and less."
7. I believe that Dr. Kimura's point is, exercise is essential for good health.
8. The epitaph that my grandfather Tomás wrote for himself is an enigma: "he always strove to look beyond harmony."
9. Luisa closed her letter to her aunt with "yours truly."
10. My question to you is, do you think it is worth your time to finish this project?

Copyright © by Holt, Rinehart and Winston. All rights reserved.

Proper Nouns A

12d. Capitalize proper nouns and proper adjectives.

(1) Capitalize the names of persons and animals. Capitalize initials in names and abbreviations that either precede or follow names.

EXAMPLES **S**t. **J**oan | **D**r. **A**ntonia **N**ovello | **W**hiskers
Martin **L**uther **K**ing, **J**r. | **E. E. C**ummings | **F**ido

EXERCISE In each of the following sentences, strike through each letter that should be capitalized but is not and write the correct form above it. If the sentence contains no error in capitalization, write *C* after it.

Example 1. Have you read ~~a~~. ~~e~~. ~~h~~ousman's poem "When I Was One and Twenty"? (A E H written above)

1. adela rogers st. johns was a famous journalist.
2. I've had my parakeet tweety for two years.
3. Have you heard of George s. Patton, an important military figure in World War II?
4. Sabrina's uncle, dr. Ray Hinojosa, jr., is a well-known surgeon in Boston.
5. Did your parents use to watch the television program about lassie, the dog?
6. Our guest speaker is heidi v. martenson, president of the Chamber of Commerce.
7. My cousin ambrosio is named for st. ambrose, patron saint of Milan, Italy.
8. Can you recommend Dr. C. R. Baugh as a neurologist?
9. The First Baptist Church minister, the rev. Carlton H. Colson, has announced his retirement.
10. It gives me great pleasure to introduce Lt. taneesha wilson of the United States Army.
11. Berta's dog Ranger is the best watchdog in town.
12. My sister just became engaged to a man named john doe.
13. Joan of Arc became St. Joan of Arc when she was canonized by the Catholic Church.
14. "Auntie Louise" is mrs. Burnside's nickname.
15. Roy Higginbotham, sr.—not his son morgan—wants to buy our farm.
16. The course in twentieth-century philosophy will be taught by dr. Jean Marchand.
17. Your cat Tomboy isn't a very good mouser.
18. Do you think I should send the letter today, mr. Goldblatt?
19. The Broadway musical *Cats* is based on t. s. Eliot's humorous poems about cats.
20. Peter the great made great efforts to modernize Russia in the late 1600s and early 1700s.

Copyright © by Holt, Rinehart and Winston. All rights reserved.

Proper Nouns B

12d. Capitalize proper nouns and proper adjectives.

(2) Capitalize geographical names.

TOWNS, CITIES	**B**eeville	**A**lexandria
COUNTIES, TOWNSHIPS, PARISHES	**O**range **C**ounty	**A**cadia **P**arish
STATES, PROVINCES, REGIONS	**S**askatchewan	the **P**acific **N**orthwest
COUNTRIES, CONTINENTS	**E**cuador	**A**ustralia
ISLANDS, MOUNTAINS	**G**overnors **I**sland	**M**ount **K**ilimanjaro
BODIES OF WATER	**N**ile **R**iver	**G**uantánamo **B**ay
PARKS, FORESTS	**E**astside **P**ark	**S**herwood **F**orest
ROADS, STREETS, HIGHWAYS	**A**venue **H**	**H**ighway 10
OTHER GEOGRAPHICAL NAMES	**Y**ucatán **P**eninsula	**O**kefenokee **S**wamp

EXERCISE A In each of the following phrases, strike through each error in capitalization and write the correct form above it. If the item contains no error in capitalization, write *C* after it.

Example 1. the ~~c~~aribbean ~~I~~sland of Guadeloupe (corrections written above: C, i)

1. the largest Ocean, the Pacific
2. floating down the Blanco river
3. the western border of Wyoming
4. on Thirty-Eighth street
5. on the other side of the Lake
6. in Madison township
7. sailing on lake Buchanan
8. a view of mount McKinley
9. Niagara falls in Western New York
10. a trip to new Zealand

EXERCISE B In each of the following sentences, strike through each error in capitalization and write the correct form above it.

Example 1. Pablo and Victor rode a train through Copper ~~c~~anyon in Mexico. (correction written above: C)

11. Turn East on Route 56, and follow it until you reach the Town of Oak Grove.
12. Which United States Rivers flow into the Gulf Of Mexico?
13. Do you agree that the railroads were a significant factor in the settlement of the west?
14. The Canary islands were so named because wild dogs (called *canes* in Latin) roamed them.
15. You can hunt for diamonds at a place just North of the town where I grew up.
16. My grandfather lived in egypt twenty years ago.
17. Miami is located in Dade county, near the southernmost tip of Florida.
18. Many of Georgia O'Keeffe's paintings depict the American southwest.
19. Abby's family is planning to go to Zion national park in July.
20. The town of Grand gulf is a few miles south of Vicksburg on the Mississippi river.

Copyright © by Holt, Rinehart and Winston. All rights reserved.

NAME ______________ CLASS ______________ DATE ______________

Proper Nouns C

12d. Capitalize proper nouns and proper adjectives.

(3) Capitalize the names of organizations, teams, institutions, and government bodies.

EXAMPLES Anti-Defamation League — Los Angeles Lakers
Johns Hopkins Hospital — Justice Department

(4) Capitalize the names of historical events and periods, special events, and holidays and other calendar items.

EXAMPLES War of the Roses — Spanish Inquisition
Middle Ages — March of Dimes Telethon
Cinco de Mayo — Tuesday

EXERCISE Most of the following phrases are capitalized incorrectly. Write the items correctly on the lines provided. Write a C on the line if the item is correctly written.

Example 1. the 1936 summer olympics *the 1936 Summer Olympics*

1. the Biltmore hotel ______________
2. on saturdays and sundays ______________
3. chief of the Central intelligence agency ______________
4. a celebration on the Fourth of july ______________
5. at James Bowie high school ______________
6. spend the summer at the beach ______________
7. the battle of Gettysburg ______________
8. the local post office ______________
9. in M. D. Anderson hospital ______________
10. the War Of Independence ______________
11. Cedar Valley community college ______________
12. the last sunday in december ______________
13. the underground railroad ______________
14. the Cleveland browns ______________
15. democratic principles ______________
16. Cannes film festival ______________
17. Young Men's Christian Association ______________
18. the hundred years' war ______________
19. members of the united nations ______________
20. the age of Enlightenment ______________

Copyright © by Holt, Rinehart and Winston. All rights reserved.

NAME ______________________ CLASS ______________ DATE ______________

Proper Nouns D

12d. Capitalize proper nouns and proper adjectives.

(5) Capitalize the names of nationalities, races, and peoples.

EXAMPLES **S**wiss **H**mong **C**omanche

(6) Capitalize the names of religions and their followers, holy days and celebrations, holy writings, and specific deities.

EXAMPLES **T**aoism **P**resbyterians **Y**om **K**ippur
Koran **B**ook of **I**saiah **P**oseidon

EXERCISE A In each of the following phrases, strike through each error in capitalization and write the correct form above it. If the item contains no error in capitalization, write *C* after it.

Example 1. to ~~a~~(A)thena, ~~G~~(g)oddess of wisdom

1. a sixteenth-century arabic philosopher
2. a group of haitian immigrants
3. on easter Sunday
4. the hopi language
5. shinto priests in Japan
6. Shiva, the hindu goddess
7. South africans from Johannesburg
8. the old testament of the Bible
9. from mercury, the Roman messenger of the Gods
10. the Onondaga people

EXERCISE B In each of the following sentences, strike through each error in capitalization and write the correct form above it.

Example 1. Did you know that ~~q~~(Q)uinquagesima ~~s~~(S)unday means the fiftieth day before ~~e~~(E)aster?

11. The spanish conquistadors applied the name *Inca* to a native american people in present-day South America.
12. The new methodist minister is australian.
13. In hinduism, the god vishnu is regarded as the preserver of the universe.
14. On what day of the week does christmas fall this year?
15. One of the mormons' sacred scriptures is called the *book of mormon*.

Copyright © by Holt, Rinehart and Winston. All rights reserved.

Proper Nouns E

12d. Capitalize proper nouns and proper adjectives.

(7) Capitalize the names of businesses and the brand names of business products.

BUSINESSES	**A**merica **O**nline, **I**nc.	**L**ittleton **H**ardware
BUSINESS PRODUCTS	**B**en & **J**erry's ice cream	**K**ellogg's cereal

(8) Capitalize the names of ships, trains, aircraft, spacecraft, and other vehicles.

SHIPS	*Titanic*	*Bounty*
TRAINS	*Tom Thumb*	*Trans-**S**iberian **E**xpress*
AIRCRAFT	*Spirit of **S**t. **L**ouis*	*The **G**reat **B**alloon of **N**assau*
SPACECRAFT	*Challenger*	*Enterprise*
OTHER VEHICLES	**T**oyota **C**amry	**C**hevrolet **C**orvette

EXERCISE In each of the following sentences, strike through each error in capitalization and write the correct form above it. If the sentence contains no error in capitalization, write *C* after it.

Example 1. Do you like your ~~s~~ S ony tape player?

1. In 1928, two Australian and two American fliers flew an airplane called the *southern cross* 11,910 kilometers from Oakland, California, to Sydney, Australia.
2. Has Anna Maria decided to buy a compaq or a Dell Computer?
3. Charles Darwin was employed as a naturalist aboard the sailing vessel the *beagle.*
4. Arnulfo is going to test drive a new Dodge Truck.
5. The first manned mission to orbit the moon was *apollo 8.*
6. Did you know that the origins of reebok international ltd., the athletic shoe company, go back to 1890?
7. The British engineer George Stephenson designed the *Rocket,* a locomotive that traveled twenty-four miles per hour while hauling a coach filled with passengers.
8. The first Harley-Davidson Motorcycle, built in 1903, was basically a motor-equipped bicycle—the rider had to pedal uphill.
9. Ahmed's uncle Ibrahim has applied for a job at Amoco corporation.
10. In December 1986, an ultralight experimental aircraft called *voyager* completed the first non-stop flight around the world without refueling.

Copyright © by Holt, Rinehart and Winston. All rights reserved.

Proper Nouns F

12d. Capitalize proper nouns and proper adjectives.

(9) Capitalize the names of buildings and other structures.

BUILDINGS	**S**ears **T**ower	**M**useum of **A**nthropology
OTHER STRUCTURES	**B**ear **M**ountain **B**ridge	**G**reat **W**all of **C**hina

(10) Capitalize the names of monuments, memorials, and awards.

MONUMENTS	**S**an **J**acinto **M**onument	**I**ndependence **A**rch
MEMORIALS	**A**lbert **M**emorial	**A**rc de **T**riomphe
AWARDS	**G**olden **G**lobe	**C**apezio **A**ward

MECHANICS

EXERCISE In each of the following sentences, strike through each error in capitalization and write the correct form above it.

Example 1. I have a photograph of my sister standing beside Trevi ~~f~~ F ountain in Rome.

1. Who won the academy award for best director in 1998?
2. Green Bay Packer Paul Vernon Hornung had won the Heisman trophy in 1956 when he was on the University of Notre Dame team.
3. Is a visit to the white house included in your tour of Washington, D.C.?
4. In New Jersey can be found several Monuments that commemorate the American Revolution.
5. The Aswan dam is located in southern Egypt.
6. Is Mr. Ling going to the kennedy center to see the Alvin Ailey Dance Theater?
7. You're sure to see some well-known twentieth-century artists at the Hirshhorn museum.
8. Gregory Hines received a tony award in 1992 for his work in the Broadway production of *Jelly's Last Jam.*
9. We're planning to visit the alamo while in San Antonio; it's a former Franciscan mission and now a state monument.
10. You shouldn't leave New York City before going to the Empire state building.

Copyright © by Holt, Rinehart and Winston. All rights reserved.

NAME CLASS DATE

Proper Nouns G

12d. Capitalize proper nouns and proper adjectives.

(11) Capitalize the names of planets, stars, constellations, and other heavenly bodies.

PLANETS	**J**upiter	**V**enus
STARS	**P**roxima **C**entauri	**B**etelgeuse
CONSTELLATIONS	**D**raco	**T**aurus

12e. Do not capitalize the names of school subjects, except course names that include a number and the names of language classes.

EXAMPLES **p**hysics **G**eometry II **J**apanese

MECHANICS

EXERCISE In each of the following sentences, strike through each error in capitalization and write the correct form above it. If the sentence contains no error in capitalization, write *C* after it.

Example 1. On winter nights the constellation ~~o~~rion greets me. *O*

1. The first-magnitude giant star beta orionis is also called rigel.
2. Patricia is going to sign up for Calculus if the Algebra II class is full.
3. The cluster of stars that we know as the pleiades was named by the ancient Greeks after the "Seven Sisters" of mythology.
4. How many courses of Latin have you taken?
5. In his art 301 class, Mr. Holtzman tends to concentrate on the Renaissance era.
6. Which is greater, the distance between Venus and earth or between earth and Mars?
7. The star algol in the constellation Perseus is an eclipsing variable star.
8. The second-century astronomer Ptolemy named the twelve signs of the zodiac for constellations.
9. A requirement for that german course is Ms. Torres's class called Foundations of Language I.
10. Does it amaze you, as it does me, that people living thousands of years ago gazed at the same Moon that we do?

Copyright © by Holt, Rinehart and Winston. All rights reserved.

Proper Nouns Review

EXERCISE Most of the following phrases are capitalized incorrectly. Write the items correctly on the lines provided. Write *C* if the item is written correctly.

Example 1. denzel Washington as a jamaican police officer

Denzel Washington as a Jamaican police officer

1. frances perkins, the first female member of the cabinet
2. Ethiopian culture
3. going to Eastern California
4. the National Science foundation
5. Actors Edward james Olmos and sidney Poitier
6. japanese paper folding
7. Bill Yellowtail, jr.
8. paddling a canoe down the Suwannee river
9. dr. Jemison, an Astronaut
10. famous asian American cellist Yo-Yo Ma
11. two miles West of Denver
12. the headquarters of the Chrysler corporation
13. the third friday in march
14. the Constellations aries and virgo
15. the prestigious student of the year Award
16. the space shuttle *Discovery*
17. a bowl of breyer's Ice Cream
18. an islamic holy man
19. the war between the states
20. mount Vernon, home of George Washington

Copyright © by Holt, Rinehart and Winston. All rights reserved.

MECHANICS

Personal Titles and Titles Showing Family Relationships

12f. Capitalize titles.

(1) Capitalize a person's title when the title comes before the person's name.

EXAMPLES **L**ieutenant **T**homas-**W**ilkes **S**enator **J**oseph **B**iden the **p**ilot of the Boeing 747

(2) Capitalize a word showing a family relationship when the word is used before or in place of a person's name, unless the word is preceded by a possessive.

EXAMPLES **A**unt **I**rma **G**randpa **J**orgensen my **c**ousin Vliet Rosie's **f**ather

EXERCISE In each of the following sentences, strike through each error in capitalization and write the correct form above it. If the sentence is correctly written, write *C* after it.

Example 1. My first ~~Cousin~~ *c*ousin Maribel is a flight attendant.

1. Did you know that former senator Phil Gramm is the son of an army Sergeant?

2. The last person to leave the party was my seventy-year-old Grandmother.

3. We saw Ex-president Jimmy Carter at a baseball game last night.

4. Lucy's Uncle Percy is writing his autobiography.

5. In 2000, who was the governor of Missouri?

6. The defense wishes to call lieutenant Michael O'Reilly to the stand.

7. The committee is headed by Former Justice Billig.

8. Thank you, professor, for presenting your views on the topic.

9. I fully expect aunt Josie to join in the protest.

10. The Captain of the ship has called the entire crew on deck.

11. Every Judge has an office at the courthouse.

12. The Secretary-Treasurer of the Ecology Club can give you a check.

13. Was John Major prime minister before or after Margaret Thatcher?

14. At last count, cousin Edna had fourteen cats and three dogs.

15. Ask your Father if you can borrow his car this afternoon.

16. The archbishop and father Banks have known each other for twenty years.

17. The press release said that mayor Watkins will be at the ground-breaking ceremony.

18. The Community Services Division is sending sergeant Raymond to talk to the students.

19. Nominations for Club President and Vice President are still open.

20. Will she be a Doctor when she graduates from medical school?

Copyright © by Holt, Rinehart and Winston. All rights reserved.

NAME ________________ CLASS ________________ DATE ________________

Titles and Subtitles

12f. Capitalize titles.

(3) Capitalize the first and last words and all important words in titles and subtitles.

BOOKS, PERIODICALS	*The **A**dventures of **T**om **S**awyer, **T**he **W**all **S**treet **J**ournal*
CHAPTERS, OTHER PARTS OF BOOKS	"**U**nit 2: **A** **G**allery of **C**haracters"
POEMS, SHORT STORIES	"**T**he **R**um **T**um **T**ugger," "**T**o **B**uild a **F**ire"
PLAYS	***O**ur **T**own*
HISTORICAL DOCUMENTS	**G**ettysburg **A**ddress
MOVIES, RADIO AND TV SERIES	***M**y **F**avorite **M**artian, **M**asterpiece **T**heater*
VIDEOS AND VIDEO GAMES	***A**ncient **C**ivilizations: **T**he **G**reeks*
COMPUTER PROGRAMS AND GAMES	***M**yst*
COMIC STRIPS	***D**ilbert*
WORKS OF ART	***T**he **P**ersistence of **M**emory* [painting]
MUSICAL COMPOSITIONS	***N**ew **W**orld **S**ymphony*
AUDIOTAPES AND CD'S	***K**ind of **B**lue*

EXERCISE In each of the following sentences, strike through each error in capitalization and write the correct form above it.

Example 1. I look forward to seeing ~~*p*~~P*eanuts* in my daily newspaper, *The Marlville* ~~*g*~~G*azette.*

1. The PBS series *Sister Wendy's Story Of Painting* included a discussion of Millet's *the gleaners.*
2. Have you heard a CD called *Reggae: past, present, and future*?
3. For tomorrow's class, read the chapter titled "the Consequences of urbanization."
4. My little brother's favorite poem is Shel Silverstein's "sarah cynthia sylvia stout would not take the garbage out."
5. Ray Bradbury's "All Summer In A Day" is about a family who lives on Venus.
6. In addition to writing the book *What To Listen For In Music,* the American composer Aaron Copland wrote the music for the film *of mice and men.*
7. Child actress Judy Garland played Dorothy in *The wizard of oz.*
8. George Bernard Shaw wrote the play *Arms and The Man* and the political essay *The Intelligent Woman's guide to socialism and capitalism.*
9. American colonists were vehemently opposed to the stamp act, which required them to buy revenue stamps to put on all official documents.
10. Leonard Bernstein, winner of the 1985 Grammy Lifetime Achievement Award, wrote the musical *west side story* in 1957.

Copyright © by Holt, Rinehart and Winston. All rights reserved.

NAME ______________________ CLASS ______________ DATE ______________

for CHAPTER 12: CAPITALIZATION **pages 362–363**

Abbreviations A

12g. Generally, abbreviations are capitalized if the words that they stand for are capitalized.

Abbreviate given names only if the person is most commonly known by the abbreviated form of the name. Capitalize initials.

EXAMPLES **C. S.** Lewis, writer **D. W.** Griffith, film director

Abbreviate and capitalize social titles whether used before the full name or before the last name alone.

EXAMPLES **M**s. Fu **D**r. Edward Jenner

You may abbreviate and capitalize civil and military titles used before full names or before initials and last names. Spell them out before last names alone. Capitalize the title whether or not it is abbreviated.

EXAMPLES **G**en. **P.G.T.** Beauregard **G**eneral Beauregard

Abbreviate and capitalize titles and academic degrees that follow proper names.

EXAMPLES Jesse L. Jackson, **Jr.** Marcia Futschik, **D.D.S.**

Acronyms are usually capitalized and written without periods.

EXAMPLES **VCR** **IRS** **DVD** **MVP**

MECHANICS

EXERCISE Most of the following phrases contain errors in the use of abbreviations and capitalization. Write the items correctly on the lines provided. If the item is correctly written, write C.

Example 1. Native American artist r. c. Gorman *Native American artist R. C. Gorman*

1. my vet, Roberto Guzmán, d.v.m. ______________
2. the boxer Cassius Marcellus Clay, Jr. ______________
3. the t.v. in the living room ______________
4. American novelist E. l. Doctorow ______________
5. the rev. Martin Luther King, jr. ______________
6. my neighbor, Mister Garofolo ______________
7. a policy of the A. C. L. U. ______________
8. the speaker, Dr. Jeanne Li, Ph.D. ______________
9. a presentation by Prof. Cox ______________
10. Lisa's podiatrist, Cedric Evins, M.D. ______________

Copyright © by Holt, Rinehart and Winston. All rights reserved.

NAME ______________________ CLASS ______________ DATE ______________

for **CHAPTER 12: CAPITALIZATION** *pages 363–366*

Abbreviations B

12g. Generally, abbreviations are capitalized if the words that they stand for are capitalized.

In regular text, spell out names of states, other political units, and every word in an address. Abbreviate them in tables, notes, bibliographies, and in letter and envelope addresses.

TEXT They live at 34 Elm Street in Sacramento, California.
ENVELOPE 34 Elm **St.**
Sacramento, **CA** 90009.

Abbreviate the era designations *A.D.* and *B.C.*, as well as the designations for the two halves of the day measured by clock time, *A.M.* and *P.M.*

EXAMPLES **A.D.** 1280 100 **B.C.** 8:15 **A.M.** 7:30 **P.M.**

In regular text, spell out names of months and days. Abbreviate them in tables, notes, and bibliographies.

TEXT I leave for Belgium on Wednesday, November 22.
NOTE **Wed., Nov.** 22

In regular text, spell out names of units of measurement. Abbreviate them in tables and notes when they follow a numeral.

TEXT The speed limit here is sixty miles per hour.
TABLE 60 **mph**

MECHANICS

EXERCISE Most of the following sentences contain errors in capitalization and abbreviations. Cross out each error and write the correct form above it. If the sentence is correct, write *C* after it.

Example 1. The table says "25 ~~feet.~~" ft

1. Julio needs to leave for school by eight A.M. today.

2. The recipe calls for 2 tsp of olive oil.

3. The bibliography entry ends with "15 Jan. 1998:10."

4. In the A.D. first century, when Romans occupied Britain, London was already an important town.

5. When Mr. and Ms. Appelbaum lived in the U.S., they visited eight national parks.

6. In 51 b.c., when Cleopatra was about seventeen years old, she succeeded to the throne of Egypt with her brother Ptolemy XIII.

7. The Juárez family lived at 260 Mesquite Ave. in Phoenix, Ariz., for ten years.

8. The experiment requires 3 milliliters of boric acid.

9. Only two of the five states you mentioned are west of the Mississippi River: ND and NV.

10. The letter's inside address is "Ithaca, N.Y."

Copyright © by Holt, Rinehart and Winston. All rights reserved.

Titles and Abbreviations Review

12f. Capitalize titles.

12g. Generally, abbreviations are capitalized if the words that they stand for are capitalized.

EXERCISE Most of the following phrases contain errors in abbreviation or capitalization. Write the items correctly on the lines provided. Write *C* if an item is correct.

Example 1. the movie *Anna And The King* the movie *Anna and the King*

1. e. b. White, author of *Charlotte's Web* ________

2. my Great-Uncle Norbert ________

3. the m.t.v. channel ________

4. our good friend, Mister Lepage ________

5. the novel *All Quiet on the Western Front* ________

6. the house at 601 E. Republic St. ________

7. found in the unit titled "A world at war" ________

8. Barbara Eastman, ph.d. ________

9. lacking 5 cups of sugar ________

10. the recently released CD, *Love In Winter* ________

11. in the sixth century A.D. ________

12. an appointment with Dr. Kelly Thomas, m.d. ________

13. by three P.M. in the afternoon ________

14. an interview with Sen. Hutchinson ________

15. with Cousin Etta and her friend Hallie ________

16. the Former Speaker of the House Sam Rayburn ________

17. the Daily Newspaper *USA Today* ________

18. the Shakespearean play *As you like it* ________

19. jobs at the I.r.s. ________

20. in 960 B.C. ________

Copyright © by Holt, Rinehart and Winston. All rights reserved.

NAME ______ CLASS ______ DATE ______

Review A: Capitalization

EXERCISE Each of the following twenty items consists of a pair of expressions. In most cases, either the expression in Column A or the one in Column B is correctly capitalized. On the line provided, write the letter of the column containing the correct expression. If neither expression is correct, write *N* on the line.

	A	B
Example B	**1.** lake Michigan	Lake Michigan

	A	B
____	**1.** her Aunt from north Dakota	her aunt from North Dakota
____	**2.** the eastern end of lake Erie	the Eastern end of lake Erie
____	**3.** Yosemite, one of our national parks	Yosemite, one of our National Parks
____	**4.** a new Ford truck	a new Ford Truck
____	**5.** the New World's Spanish explorers	the New World's Spanish Explorers
____	**6.** studying Art, English Literature, and French	studying art, English Literature, and French
____	**7.** the Swiss towns of the Middle ages	the Swiss towns of the middle Ages
____	**8.** our High School and Malcolm Academy	our high school and Malcolm Academy
____	**9.** Spenser and other Elizabethan poets	Spenser and other Elizabethan Poets
____	**10.** a speech by Governor Grasso	a speech by governor Grasso
____	**11.** on Fifth avenue near Central park	on Fifth Avenue near Central park
____	**12.** Hoover dam	Hoover Dam
____	**13.** states in the Far West	states in the far West
____	**14.** two miles West of Route 106	two miles west of Route 106
____	**15.** a Freshman at the university of Michigan	a freshman at the university of Michigan
____	**16.** George Eliot's *The Mill On The Floss*	George Eliot's *The Mill on the Floss*
____	**17.** senator Nims and another senator	Senator Nims and another senator
____	**18.** an article about ex-Senator Margaret Chase Smith	an article about Ex-Senator Margaret Chase Smith
____	**19.** staying at the hotel Biltmore	staying at the Hotel Biltmore
____	**20.** the editor of *The New Yorker*	the Editor of *The new Yorker*

Copyright © by Holt, Rinehart and Winston. All rights reserved.

NAME CLASS DATE

for **CHAPTER 12: CAPITALIZATION** *pages 342–366*

Review B: **Capitalization**

EXERCISE Most of the following sentences contain errors in capitalization and abbreviation. Cross out each error, and write the correct form above it. If the sentence is correct, write *C* above it.

Example 1. The business card says "Ruby Donahue, ~~d.v.m.~~" D.V.M.

1. Last Summer Ricardo became Captain of the school's basketball team, the Reagan rockets.
2. In 1900, the Standard Oil company held virtually a monopoly position in the petroleum-refining industry of the U.S.
3. According to tradition, Joseph Priestley, the famous English Scientist, coined the name *rubber:* he is supposed to have discovered that the substance could "Rub out" pencil marks.
4. One of the oldest known handbooks on Mathematics is an Egyptian papyrus scroll dating from about 1700 B.C.
5. Was it Theodore Roosevelt who said, "Speak softly and carry a big stick"?
6. The Greek Gods supposedly dwelt on the peaks of Olympus, a mountain range in the Central part of Greece.
7. Today's assignment in history IV is to read Chapter 11, "The Beginning Of The Industrial Revolution," in *History In Perspective.*
8. Candace, Prof. Donatello told us that the correct answer was "2 tsp."
9. Please send this v.c.r. to 88 Forty-Fifth St. in Terre Haute, IN.
10. The point is, the koran has been sacred to Muslims for many centuries.
11. You can take latin or one of three Modern Languages at our High School.
12. Turn left, or East, on Central ave.
13. Should the closing be "sincerely" or "very truly yours"?
14. Please get some tape when you go to edam's corner store.
15. Which planet, Jupiter or Saturn, has more Moons?
16. The important question is, what do we do now?
17. Right this minute, i'd like to be on an island somewhere in the Caribbean sea.
18. When my Mom and Dad were young, school didn't start until after Labor day.
19. We'll stop at Nasa's Johnson Space Ctr. on our way to the gulf coast.
20. Gina heard him say he was "Deathly afraid of roller coasters."

MECHANICS

Copyright © by Holt, Rinehart and Winston. All rights reserved.

Review C: Capitalization

EXERCISE A The following sentences contain errors in capitalization and abbreviations. Cross out each error and write the correct form above it.

Example [1] Hawaii became the fiftieth state of the ~~union~~ U on ~~Aug~~ August. 21, 1959.

[1] dear mauricio,

[2] Here I am, back on dry land, sorely missing the Pacific ocean and wishing I were still about 3,000 mi West of Reno. **[3]** Now i understand why you told me you would give the Moon and stars to be able to move back to the Island of Kauai—its beauty is the stuff of dreams.

[4] We landed at Hanamaulu at 2:00 P.M. on a Thurs., and the fun didn't stop until we left ten days later. **[5]** we hiked across lava flows, visited the Waikiki aquarium in Honolulu, and saw waterfalls in Puaa Kaa state park on Maui. **[6]** We also spent time at the polynesian cultural center on Oahu. **[7]** We went to a *luau*—it's a hawaiian feast—where I watched people dancing the *hula*. **[8]** (Did you know that the *hula* used to be performed not only for entertainment, but also as a Religious exercise to honor the goddess laka?) **[9]** We spent our final day on Oahu so that my Dad could take us to the USS *Arizona* memorial at Pearl Harbor.

[10] The question I leave you with is, how are you and I going to save enough money so that we can go to Hawaii together the day after we graduate from High School?

EXERCISE B In the following word groups, cross out each error in abbreviations or capitalization and write the correct form above it.

Example 1. a letter addressed to ~~Doctor~~ Dr. and Mrs. Nelson

11. tour the Headquarters of the Fbi

12. well-known norse myths

13. New Year's day holiday

14. the company name is Neville & assoc.

15. Theodore Roethke's poem "The far field"

16. at the intersection of Broad ave. and Fifty-Sixth St.

17. to meet us in, Oh, ten min.

18. near the Lake on the West side of town

19. dear prof. Barrientos:

20. one of my favorite Mexican Restaurants

MECHANICS

Copyright © by Holt, Rinehart and Winston. All rights reserved.

Using End Marks

An *end mark* is used to indicate the purpose of a sentence.

13a. A statement (or declarative sentence) is followed by a period.

13b. A question (or interrogative sentence) is followed by a question mark.

13c. An exclamation (or exclamatory sentence) is followed by an exclamation point.

13d. A request or command (or imperative sentence) may be followed by either a period or an exclamation point.

STATEMENT Joan Didion writes thought-provoking essays**.**

QUESTION Do you enjoy Steven Spielberg's movies**?**

EXCLAMATION The house is on fire**!**

REQUEST Please open your book to page 137**.**

COMMAND Go, team, go**!**

EXERCISE A On the line provided, write *S* if the sentence is a statement, *Q* if it is a question, *E* if it is an exclamation, *R* if it is a request, or *C* if it is a command. Then, add the appropriate end mark to the sentence.

Example ___S___ **1.** She called after us, "See you soon**.**"

______ **1.** Have you ever read Robert Frost's poem "Fire and Ice"

______ **2.** Unable to open the door, Sofia called loudly for help

______ **3.** Watch out, Tony

______ **4.** Please read JoBeth Hall's column

______ **5.** What an incredible catch he made

EXERCISE B Ten punctuation marks have been omitted from the following passage. Add the missing end marks.

Example Becca sighed as she looked up from her drawing and rubbed her eyes**.**

"I've been working on this comic strip for hours" she exclaimed She glanced at the clock Yikes How could it already be 4:30 The strip was due to the paper by 5:00 Becca knew that all she needed was a good punchline How could she come up with a good idea "I know," she thought. "I'll just have the dog slip on a banana peel" She giggled

Copyright © by Holt, Rinehart and Winston. All rights reserved.

Abbreviations A

13e. Many abbreviations are followed by a period.

Abbreviate given names only if the person is most commonly known by the abbreviated form of the name. Leave a space between two initials, but not between three or more.

Abbreviate social titles whether used before the full name or before the last name alone.

Abbreviate civil and military titles used before full names, but spell them out before last names used alone.

Abbreviate titles and academic degrees that follow proper names.

EXAMPLES T**.** S**.** Eliot J**.** K**.** Rowling J**.**R**.**R**.** Tolkien
Mr**.** Mark Lane Mrs**.** Kingley Dr**.** Franklin
Gen**.** Omar Bradley *but* General Bradley
Yvgeny Solsak, Jr**.** Jenna Mason, M**.**D**.**

MECHANICS

EXERCISE A Correct the following sentences by adding periods to abbreviations as needed.

Example 1. Dr**.** Jarman, what is your diagnosis?

1. Was W E B Du Bois an early civil rights leader?

2. Now that I've graduated, I sign my name "Jayson Byars, M Ed."

3. Address your letter of thanks to Mr and Mrs Tsao.

4. The students rose and applauded when Sen Brenda Gomez was introduced.

5. Have you read any of D H Lawrence's works?

EXERCISE B For the city paper, you are making a list of guests of honor at a recent fund-raiser for the children's hospital. Using the information given below, list each person's name and any titles, using appropriate abbreviations.

Example 1. Thom and Fiona Marks, philanthropists *Mr. and Mrs. Marks*

6. Shawna Brown, doctor at the hospital ____________________

7. Les Simont, president of the hospital ____________________

8. T Mays, Junior, patient at the hospital ____________________

9. Señora Carlotta Sanchez, patient's mother ____________________

10. Jon Katz, professor at the city's college ____________________

Copyright © by Holt, Rinehart and Winston. All rights reserved.

NAME _______________ CLASS _______________ DATE _______________

Abbreviations B

13e. Many abbreviations are followed by a period.

After spelling out the first use of the names of agencies and organizations, abbreviate these names. Acronyms, words formed from the first (or first few) letters of a series of words, are written in capital letters without periods.

In regular text, spell out names of states and other political units. Abbreviate them in tables, notes, bibliographies, and letter and envelope addresses.

EXAMPLES NPR (National Public Radio)
NATO (North Atlantic Treaty Organization)
110 Forbes Dr., Lewisville, TX 75067

MECHANICS

EXERCISE Write the complete mailing addresses of the places given in parentheses. Use the phone book if you do not already know the addresses and ZIP codes of each place. Use appropriate abbreviations and punctuation.

Example 1. (a local club) *Hillsburg YMCA*
200 Buttercup Blvd.
Hillsburg, TX 78613

1. (your address) _______________
____
____

2. (your school) _______________
____
____

3. (the nearest hospital) _______________
____
____

4. (a local business) _______________
____
____

5. (a nonprofit agency) _______________
____
____

Copyright © by Holt, Rinehart and Winston. All rights reserved.

Abbreviations C

13e. Many abbreviations are followed by a period.

EXAMPLES Was the year A.D. 2000 the beginning of a new millennium?
Meeting: Tues., Mar. 14
cc, ft, in., mph, doz
Does water boil at one hundred degrees centigrade?

EXERCISE A Abbreviate the following, using numerals and periods where appropriate.

Example 1. ten inches *10 in.*

1. sixteen feet by twelve feet
2. Monday, October 12
3. Friday at 8:30 in the morning
4. one hundred pounds
5. two dozen
6. 5:00 in the afternoon
7. three feet, five inches wide by four feet, two inches long
8. teaspoon
9. nineteenth century A.D.
10. fifteen miles per hour

EXERCISE B Convert the abbreviated instructions into complete sentences.

Example 1. add 1 tbsp sugar *Add one tablespoon of sugar.*

11. Ingredients for grilled cheese sandwich: 2 slices bread, 1 slice cheese, 1 tsp butter, 1 tbsp mayonnaise
12. spread 1 tbsp mayonnaise on inside of bread, top with cheese
13. heat griddle with 1 tsp butter
14. grill sandwich at 250°C for 2 min each side
15. serve with 8 oz cold milk

Copyright © by Holt, Rinehart and Winston. All rights reserved.

Abbreviations D

13e. Many abbreviations are followed by a period.

EXERCISE A Abbreviate the following items on the lines provided.

Example 1. one dozen *1 doz*

1. two feet and three inches ______
2. 2:00 in the afternoon on Monday, November 2 ______
3. Mister Joseph Chen ______
4. *anno Domini* 2003 ______
5. Senator Kata Rodriguez ______
6. 10 in the morning, Sunday, April first ______
7. Professor Kyle Mannon ______
8. eight square kilometers ______
9. Doctor Martin Luther King, Junior ______
10. Oak Street and Maple Avenue ______

EXERCISE B Abbreviate the following words and phrases on the lines provided.

Example 1. two miles *2 mi*

11. Doctor Angela Mehran ______
12. 2:00 in the afternoon ______
13. Robert Edward Lee Middle School ______
14. Society for the Prevention of Cruelty to Animals ______
15. fifteen miles per hour ______

Copyright © by Holt, Rinehart and Winston. All rights reserved.

End Marks and Abbreviations

13a. A statement (or declarative sentence) is followed by a period.

13b. A question (or interrogative sentence) is followed by a question mark.

13c. An exclamation (or exclamatory sentence) is followed by an exclamation point.

13d. A request or command (or imperative sentence) may be followed by either a period or an exclamation point.

13e. Many abbreviations are followed by a period.

EXERCISE Each of the following sentences is missing its end mark. Some sentences also have inappropriately abbreviated words. Add an end mark to each sentence. Then, on the line provided, write out any inappropriately abbreviated words. If no correction of abbreviations is necessary, write C.

Example 1. Planning a party for four-yr-olds is certainly a challenge! *four-year-olds*

1. When my little sister turned four, I agreed to help plan her birthday party ______
2. After all, what could be so difficult about having three little friends over for cake and ice cream ______
3. Two wks before the party, we bought all the supplies at the grocery store on Main St ______
4. The day before the party, which was scheduled for Sat, we picked up the brightly iced cake that read, "Happy Birthday to Our Big Girl" ______
5. My little sister was thrilled when her three friends arrived with presents ______
6. They came at 9:00 A.M., and that's when the trouble started ______
7. We had bought cartoon trading cards for party favors, even though we knew that Rafe Miller, M.D., our pediatrician, thinks they are not good toys for little kids ______
8. We found out why when one kid began to cry because his card pack was missing his favorite character, Squirrely Squirrel, Junior ______
9. Sounds of crying and yelling could probably be heard all the way to the state of WA ______
10. Just then, my sister surprised me by saying, "Here, KC, you can have my Squirrely" ______

Copyright © by Holt, Rinehart and Winston. All rights reserved.

MECHANICS

Commas A

13f. Use commas to separate items in a series.

EXAMPLES He recycled the newspapers, washed his car, and cut the grass.
He enjoys Bach, Mozart, and Beethoven.

13g. Use a comma to separate two or more adjectives preceding a noun.

EXAMPLE I had a long, quiet talk with Aunt Bea.

EXERCISE A Add commas as needed to the following sentences. If the sentence is already punctuated correctly, write *C* on the line provided.

Example ______ **1.** The ball flew over the fence, bounced on the driveway, and landed on the roof.

______ **1.** In early spring, daffodils irises tulips and crocuses bloom.

______ **2.** Did Bob Rafael or Bart start as quarterback after the half?

______ **3.** The company put an intriguing classified ad in Sunday's paper.

______ **4.** I like Renee because she is such a dependable sensitive person.

______ **5.** Vermont has green rolling valleys and lofty pine-crested mountains.

______ **6.** I have visited Mississippi Louisiana and New Mexico.

______ **7.** He cooked me chicken fajitas with jalapeño peppers nopales and avocado.

______ **8.** Prague was a graceful pastel city.

______ **9.** Ahmed, Sheryl Fred and Suzi went to the library; but Harriet Kate and Jim ran.

______ **10.** My dog Daisy is brown black and white.

EXERCISE B The following paragraph contains several errors in the use of commas. Proofread the paragraph to correct all the errors, inserting commas where necessary. If a sentence is already correct, write *C* above it.

Example **[1]** Kim just finished reading an interesting, informative book by Lillie Patterson.

[11] Lillie Patterson has worked as a teacher librarian and children's author. **[12]** As a child, Patterson lived with her grandmother in South Carolina. **[13]** Her grandmother was an interesting well-read person, who instilled in Patterson her early love for books. **[14]** Patterson has written biographies poems and nonfiction articles for children. **[15]** The subjects of her biographies have included Frederick Douglass Booker T. Washington and Dr. Martin Luther King, Jr.

Copyright © by Holt, Rinehart and Winston. All rights reserved.

NAME ______________________ CLASS ______________ DATE ______________

for **CHAPTER 13: PUNCTUATION** *pages 382–383*

Commas B

13h. Use a comma before a coordinating conjunction (*and, but, for, nor, or, so,* or *yet*) when it joins independent clauses.

EXAMPLES I had practiced the concerto, yet I felt nervous before the concert.
We wanted to buy tickets, but the concert was sold out.

EXERCISE A Add commas as needed to the following sentences. If the sentence is already punctuated correctly, write *C* on the line provided.

Example ______ **1.** Did ancient peoples see dinosaur fossils, and could they have mistaken them for dragon bones?

______ **1.** Fire-breathing dragons never really existed but most ancient peoples believed in them.

______ **2.** Dragons appeared in legends and they were often portrayed as fire-breathing monsters.

______ **3.** According to legend, Saint George killed a dragon and saved a princess who was being sacrificed.

______ **4.** Beowulf killed the monster Grendel yet Beowulf was later killed by a dragon.

______ **5.** Chinese legends differ from Western ones for in Asian cultures the dragon is revered as sacred.

EXERCISE B On the line provided, rewrite each pair of sentences below as a compound sentence or as a simple sentence with a compound subject, verb, or object. Add conjunctions and commas as needed.

Example **1.** I had a cold yesterday. I feel better today.

I had a cold yesterday, but I feel better today.

6. We planned a picnic. It rained.

____

7. Shawndra practiced her speech. She felt confident.

____

8. I may go to Tulane next year. I may go to Ohio State.

____

9. We'll wait for you at the theater. Don't be late.

____

10. I thought we would make it to the game on time. The traffic was terrible.

____

MECHANICS

Copyright © by Holt, Rinehart and Winston. All rights reserved.

NAME CLASS DATE

Commas C

13i. Use commas to set off nonessential subordinate clauses and nonessential participial phrases.

A *nonessential* (or *nonrestrictive*) clause or participial phrase contains information that is not necessary to the meaning of the sentence.

NONESSENTIAL CLAUSE Behruz, **who is a track star,** was accepted at Yale.

NONESSENTIAL PHRASE Millicent, **hoping for a scholarship,** works hard.

EXERCISE Write *N* above the underlined clause or phrase if it is nonessential or *E* if it is essential. Then, add commas as needed.

Example 1. Kim Fong, who owns this restaurant, is my neighbor. (N)

1. Only dogs that are on leashes are allowed in the park.
2. Theseus who was a figure in Greek myths battled the Minotaur.
3. All people found guilty will be fined or sent to jail.
4. The playwright whom I admire the most is August Wilson.
5. All trains using Track 4 will be slightly delayed.
6. Dr. Kyoshi is the only man I know who likes opera as much as I do.
7. He cuts his lawn which is full of dandelions only once a month.
8. I recently spoke to a woman who had lived for two years in Taiwan.
9. The bread that we brought to the dinner party was fresh and hot.
10. Fifteen flags rippling in the breeze could be seen from the hilltop.
11. Samantha whom I've known since we were both two is my best friend.
12. I've always liked people who are considered eccentric.
13. The island that was covered with poppies was called Delos.
14. My dog is the one splashing in the mud puddle.
15. South Indian food which is sometimes served on a banana leaf is delicious.
16. The man wearing the hat gave up his seat on the bus for the elderly woman.
17. My little sister crowing like a rooster woke the guests.
18. The girl wearing the fedora wandered along the sidewalk.
19. My father who was Hungarian taught me to cook.
20. The performance that I enjoyed the most involved break dancing.

Copyright © by Holt, Rinehart and Winston. All rights reserved.

Commas D

13j. Use a comma after certain introductory elements.

(1) Use a comma after *yes, no,* or any mild exclamation such as *well* or *why* at the beginning of a sentence.

(2) Use a comma after an introductory participle or participial phrase.

(3) Use a comma after two or more introductory prepositional phrases or after one long introductory prepositional phrase.

(4) Use a comma after an introductory adverb clause.

EXAMPLES **Yes,** I want to perform in a musical.
Hoping for a role, she auditioned for the director.

EXERCISE A Add a comma where it is necessary in each of the following sentences. If the sentence is already punctuated correctly, write *C* on the line provided.

Example ______ **1.** When the rain started**,** we rushed into the store.

______ **1.** Walking as fast as possible we reached the store just before it closed.

______ **2.** In the scene at the end of *Casablanca* Rick says goodbye to Ilsa.

______ **3.** Planting onions or garlic next to your roses will benefit them greatly.

______ **4.** In a minute the train from Phoenix should arrive on Track 3.

______ **5.** Often mistaken for an actor my uncle Pierre is really handsome.

______ **6.** Whenever I see an old Fred Astaire film I regain my interest in dancing.

______ **7.** Why let's take dancing lessons together.

______ **8.** No I really have neither the time nor the talent.

______ **9.** At the corner of Fourteenth Street and Broad Street you'll see a beautiful fountain.

______ **10.** When Principal Carson retired my uncle took over the job.

EXERCISE B On the line following each of these introductory elements, add words and punctuation marks to form a complete sentence.

Example **1.** After the rain had stopped *, we went outside.*

11. Well ______

12. Because I enjoy adventure movies ______

13. At the top of the hill behind the school ______

14. While sitting in the restaurant ______

15. In June ______

Copyright © by Holt, Rinehart and Winston. All rights reserved.

Commas E

13k. Use commas to set off an expression that interrupts a sentence.

(1) Use commas to set off nonessential appositives and appositive phrases.

(2) Words used in direct address are set off by commas.

(3) Parenthetical expressions are set off by commas.

EXAMPLES Penelope Fitzgerald**, a Booker Prize winner,** wrote that novel.
Eubie, you are a terrific tennis player. Thank you**, Mallory.**
After all, we did win the championship.

EXERCISE A Add commas as necessary to the following sentences. If the sentence is already punctuated correctly, write *C* on the line provided.

Example ______ **1.** Jan, as you probably know, traveled to India last year.

______ **1.** Michael Jordan will be remembered I am sure as a great basketball player.

______ **2.** Joseph right now I don't have time to play catch.

______ **3.** The poet Carl Sandburg lived in Chicago.

______ **4.** Edmund Spenser an Elizabethan poet wrote *The Faerie Queene.*

______ **5.** Tennessee Williams wrote the play *A Streetcar Named Desire.*

______ **6.** The character's name was Indiana Jones not Oklahoma Jones!

______ **7.** Tawny's cousin a freshman just joined a fraternity at Arizona State.

______ **8.** Nikki have you got any ideas that you'd like to share with us?

______ **9.** Alfred Nobel the man who established the Nobel Prize was a scientist.

______ **10.** Nobel by the way was the person who invented dynamite.

EXERCISE B On the lines provided, write complete sentences containing the parenthetical expressions given. Punctuate your sentences correctly.

Example 1. nonetheless *Nonetheless, I'm going to dance.*

11. nevertheless ______________________________

12. however ______________________________

13. as if ______________________________

14. in fact ______________________________

15. naturally ______________________________

Copyright © by Holt, Rinehart and Winston. All rights reserved.

NAME ______________________ CLASS ______________ DATE ______________

Commas F

13f. Use commas to separate items in a series.

13g. Use a comma to separate two or more adjectives preceding a noun.

13h. Use a comma before a coordinating conjunction (*and, but, for, nor, or, so,* or *yet*) when it joins independent clauses.

13i. Use commas to set off nonessential subordinate clauses and nonessential participial phrases.

13j. Use a comma after certain introductory elements.

13k. Use commas to set off an expression that interrupts a sentence.

EXERCISE All of the following sentences contain a comma error. On the line provided, write the word preceding the error, and add the correct punctuation.

Example 1. Randy please lend me some paper. Randy,

1. We took our problem to our class advisor who had several helpful suggestions. ______
2. Pedro and Juan set the table for their father and mother were busy preparing the dinner. ______
3. After she listened to their explanation, the principal smiled nodded, and then sent the students back to class. ______
4. Yes our second composition assignment is due tomorrow. ______
5. Although he was born on Friday the thirteenth Sasha has never been superstitious about the number thirteen. ______
6. I had worked with her at the resort for three summers and I admired her determination to put herself through college. ______
7. John Buse, the president of our class asked me that same afternoon to sell tickets for the benefit concert. ______
8. Mowing the lawn at 6:00 A.M. may keep gardeners cool but it can aggravate their neighbors. ______
9. Jaime said in fact, that we could depend on his help at the car wash. ______
10. Ella, what do you think of the bland neutral color of this carpet? ______

Copyright © by Holt, Rinehart and Winston. All rights reserved.

Commas G

13l. Use commas in certain conventional situations.

(1) Use commas to separate items in dates and addresses.

(2) Use a comma after the salutation of a personal letter and after the closing of any letter.

(3) Use a comma to set off a title, such as *Jr., Sr.,* or *M.D.,* that follows a person's name.

EXAMPLES On Sunday, June 14, 2009, my sister graduated from college.

13 Oak Street, Oldtown, VA

Dear Sam, Dear Ms. Kaczowka,

Yours truly, Sincerely,

Ken Gardner, Jr. Luisa D. Eduardo, M.D.

EXERCISE A Add commas as necessary to the following sentences. If the sentence is already punctuated correctly, write *C* on the line provided.

Example ______ **1.** The final essay is due on May 12, 2009.

______ **1.** Rafael's address is 13 Henry Avenue Akron OH 44301.

______ **2.** On August 9 1954 my grandfather was born in San Juan Puerto Rico.

______ **3.** Marissa Valdez Ph.D. will be our guest on the fifth of October.

______ **4.** Harold P. Levinson Jr. opened a law office at 5 Dale Street in Ames Iowa.

______ **5.** The town of Boxford celebrated its bicentennial on 6 June 1966.

EXERCISE B Proofread the following letter, and add commas where necessary.

Example June 17, 2009

Dear Mr. Roosevelt:

On August 24 2010, I will be leaving to attend Ohio State University. Therefore, I will be terminating my employment at Bob's Diner as of August 22. I look forward to working for you again during my winter vacation, which begins on December 15. Meanwhile, please send my final paycheck to Box 1415 Ohio State University Columbus OH 43212.

Sincerely

Eugene Goldstein Jr.

Copyright © by Holt, Rinehart and Winston. All rights reserved.

NAME CLASS DATE

Commas H

13f. Use commas to separate items in a series.

13g. Use a comma to separate two or more adjectives preceding a noun.

13h. Use a comma before a coordinating conjunction (*and, but, for, nor, or, so,* or *yet*) when it joins independent clauses.

13i. Use commas to set off nonessential subordinate clauses and nonessential participial phrases.

13j. Use a comma after certain introductory elements.

13k. Use commas to set off an expression that interrupts a sentence.

13l. Use commas in certain conventional situations.

13m. Do not use unnecessary commas.

MECHANICS

EXERCISE Most of the following sentences contain a comma error. Add or delete commas as necessary. If a sentence is already correct, write *C* before the item number.

Examples 1. Oh, I didn't know he had been invited to the party.

2. In the room the children were sitting at their desks and, reading quietly.

1. Jim and Pedro sat enthralled during the long, exciting, basketball game.
2. I drove to the lake with my sister and several of her friends soon joined us there.
3. Mr. Haynes, who was once a professional baseball player gave us some tips about hitting and fielding.
4. On April, 6, 1917, the United States entered World War I.
5. By the way, did you know that, the Robertsons have moved to Palo Alto, California?
6. Sacagawea, the famous interpreter and explorer was a Shoshone.
7. The reporters many of whom had covered the trial from the very first day said that the defense lawyers had handled the case extremely well.
8. As soon as Alaqua arrived in Seattle, she called her parents, who had been waiting anxiously, to hear from her.
9. *Moby-Dick,* which is now considered one of the outstanding American novels of the nineteenth century, was not very highly regarded by most nineteenth-century critics.
10. Ambassador Williams returning from her successful mission, was met at the airport by a crowd of reporters and press photographers.

Copyright © by Holt, Rinehart and Winston. All rights reserved.

Review A: **End Marks and Abbreviations**

EXERCISE Identify each sentence below. On the line provided, write *S* if the sentence is a statement, *Q* if it is a question, *E* if it is an exclamation, *R* if it is a request, or *C* if it is a command. Then, add the appropriate question marks, exclamation points, and periods to the sentence.

Example ___C___ **1.** Step back immediately!

______ **1.** Are you satisfied with your hiking boots

______ **2.** Stay in your seats

______ **3.** Please order me a sandwich when our server comes

______ **4.** I decided to take tae kwon do next year at our YMCA

______ **5.** All papers must have bibliographies

______ **6.** All the world's a stage

______ **7.** Have you ever read T S Eliot's poem "The Hollow Men"

______ **8.** Your car is rolling into the river

______ **9.** What time is it

______ **10.** As soon as you have a chance, read Anna Quindlen's column in *Newsweek* called "The Last Word"

______ **11.** Stop that dog fight

______ **12.** May I answer that question

______ **13.** Drive carefully

______ **14.** I'd like to invite Uncle Rafael to my graduation

______ **15.** Didn't Carolyn Kizer write the poem "The Ungrateful Garden"

______ **16.** What did Elsa have in mind when she said that

______ **17.** Please walk down to the corner store for a loaf of bread

______ **18.** The British poet Alfred Tennyson wrote "The Kraken"

______ **19.** Do you want to walk to the concert with me

______ **20.** What a fantastic singer Leontyne Price is

Copyright © by Holt, Rinehart and Winston. All rights reserved.

Review B: Commas

EXERCISE A Most of the following sentences contain a comma error. Either a needed comma has been omitted or an unnccessary comma has been included. Add or delete commas as necessary. If the sentence is already correct, write *C* above it.

Example 1. Texarkana, Texas, is just across the Arkansas line.

1. Writing letters to the editor, is one of my favorite activities.
2. Yes if you are sure you want to enroll in the program, Bernie, by all means do so.
3. They decided to increase the size of the theater, for they always had to turn away customers.
4. Emma Lazarus, who wrote the sonnet engraved on the pedestal of the Statue of Liberty was born in New York City.
5. The miners carried picks, shovels, and pans, along the banks of the creek where gold had been discovered Lost Creek.
6. When the quarterbacks threw touchdown passes, their fans cheered wildly.
7. No one in the band, it seemed to me had ever played better than on that gray, cold day.
8. Listening to the news on the radio I failed to notice that my cousin had left the house.
9. My morning routine, which includes brushing my teeth and washing my face, helps me shake off my sleepiness and get ready for the day.
10. Viewers who enjoy sitcoms will like the series, that features a Martian running a diner.

EXERCISE B Most of the following sentences contain a comma error. Either a needed comma has been omitted or an unnecessary comma has been included. Add or delete commas as necessary. If the sentence is already correct, write *C* above it.

Example 1. She is the player, who won a tournament last week against her old rival.

11. When the cold, lonely, winter, evenings came we would huddle near the fireplace.
12. The surgeon's face showed no emotion but she felt anxious as she performed the operation.
13. "How would you like to go to the game with me tomorrow?" she asked taking me by surprise.
14. The man who had a window seat chose to move to an aisle seat when he began to feel airsick.
15. On the contrary the first attempts to improve farming techniques yielded few positive results.

Copyright © by Holt, Rinehart and Winston. All rights reserved.

Review C: End Marks and Commas

EXERCISE Add end marks and commas to the following sentences as needed.

Example 1. Many stories are told of the Civil War general**,** Robert E**.** Lee**,** in that picture.

1. All school buses needing repairs will be out of service next week
2. That song was sung by either Nancy Wilson or Natalie Cole
3. No I never heard Billie Holiday sing; was she good Clive
4. Sitting on that rickety chair I felt very nervous
5. I like films starring Humphrey Bogart so I know I'd enjoy *The African Queen*
6. Isn't George P. Steiner Sr the comptroller of Baldwin Corp
7. Is Emilio R Gustavo Jr still a corporate attorney with Ames, Johnson & Co
8. Before he could say another word the doorbell rang
9. I went swimming in the ocean visited Hal and played soccer
10. The Dixtro Co opened an office at 4 Rikes Blvd Chicago IL 60606
11. We walked on the beach collected some shells and had a long pleasant talk
12. Dave Barry, once a staffer for a local newspaper became a syndicated columnist
13. "Is writing a newspaper column challenging" wondered Pat
14. On Saturday June 6 2009 my sister moved to Chester County in Pennsylvania
15. Are you sure that a flowered bright-red scarf will go with this dress
16. Well look at the picture and try to find me
17. People who don't bother to vote shouldn't complain about the outcome of the election
18. Working hard should help you achieve the goals that you have set for yourself
19. "After you're finished with your chores do you want to go to a movie Bill"
20. Neither the coach nor the players are happy

MECHANICS

Copyright © by Holt, Rinehart and Winston. All rights reserved.

Semicolons A

14a. Use a semicolon between independent clauses that are closely related in thought and are not joined by a coordinating conjunction *(and, but, for, nor, or, so,* or *yet).*

EXAMPLE Terrence is a talented musician**;** he played a violin concerto at the concert.

14b. Use a semicolon between independent clauses joined by a conjunctive adverb or a transitional expression.

EXAMPLES I was full**; however,** Ian gave me more soup.
I am annoyed**; in fact,** I'm getting angry.

MECHANICS

EXERCISE A Insert semicolons where they are needed in the following sentences.

Example 1. Juanita went home right after softball practice; she was hoping to get a phone call.

1. The wind is fierce it sounds like a locomotive.

2. The workers were dissatisfied therefore, they considered a strike.

3. We are eager to go on vacation the past few weeks have been strenuous.

4. Tony has accomplished quite a lot on the other hand, Janis hasn't.

5. Begonias thrive in the shade marigolds need more sun.

EXERCISE B Some of the following sentence pairs contain closely related ideas that can be combined into one sentence punctuated with a semicolon. Others are unrelated and should remain as two separate sentences. On the lines provided, combine the related sentences. If the sentence pair should not be combined, write *C* on the line.

Example 1. The producers are meeting. Please do not disturb them.

The producers are meeting; please do not disturb them.

6. We were late for the game. As a result, we missed the kickoff.

____

7. Jules is the yearbook editor. He also works on the school newspaper.

____

8. The soup is delicious. Have all the guests arrived?

____

9. She stops by the library every Saturday morning. The bakery opens at 7:00.

____

10. Many events have been scheduled. For example, there are two concerts coming up.

____

Copyright © by Holt, Rinehart and Winston. All rights reserved.

Semicolons B

14c. You may need to use a semicolon (rather than a comma) before a coordinating conjunction to join independent clauses that contain commas.

EXAMPLE She completed several tasks on her list, including weeding the flower beds, mowing the yard, and trimming the shrubs; but she put off her indoor chores until a rainy day.

14d. Use a semicolon between items in a series if the items contain commas.

EXAMPLE Their children's birth dates are December 3, 1966; August 24, 1968; September 24, 1970; and June 20, 1979.

EXERCISE Insert semicolons where they are needed in the following sentences.

Example 1. The women on the tour bus came from Memphis, Tennessee; Aberdeen, Mississippi; Jackson, Mississippi; and Little Rock, Arkansas.

1. Among the people who contributed to the book are Dr. Newman, who did the research Ms. Lewis, who provided the photographs and Mr. Jung, who wrote the introduction.
2. Her best friends' birth dates are December 31, 1994 February 10, 1995 and March 21, 1995.
3. He was busy raking the yard, cleaning the gutters, and pulling out items for his garage sale, which he intended to have the next Saturday but he longed to submerge himself in a novel.
4. The members of the committee who helped the most are Sharon, who handled the publicity Betty, who led the finance subcommittee and Bart, who built all the booths.
5. We did not, for the most part, want to be identified with that organization, its leaders, or its cause nor did we want to sign the petition.
6. Stan realized that spilling juice on his keyboard is, of course, what damaged his computer that he should never, ever leave a drink sitting close to it again and that he was lucky to find a replacement keyboard so quickly.
7. The finalists were from Grand View, Idaho Big Horn, Wyoming and Sunburst, Montana.
8. On her day off, she had plans to take a cooking course, visit a friend, and tutor a third-grade student and after all that, she might take in a movie.
9. In 1992, the candidates vying for president were George Herbert Walker Bush, who was the current president William Jefferson Clinton, who was the governor of Arkansas and Ross Perot, who had never held public office.
10. We hope to visit Lexington, Charlottesville, and Harrisonburg, Virginia and if we have any time remaining, we would like to drive on to Gettysburg, Pennsylvania.

Copyright © by Holt, Rinehart and Winston. All rights reserved.

Semicolons Review

14a. Use a semicolon between independent clauses that are closely related in thought and are not joined by a coordinating conjunction *(and, but, for, nor, or, so,* or *yet).*

14b. Use a semicolon between independent clauses joined by a conjunctive adverb or a transitional expression.

14c. You may need to use a semicolon (rather than a comma) before a coordinating conjunction to join independent clauses that contain commas.

14d. Use a semicolon between items in a series if the items contain commas.

MECHANICS

EXERCISE Insert semicolons where they are needed in the following sentences. If the sentence is correct as written, write *C* after the sentence. Hint: In some sentences, semicolons will replace commas.

Example 1. He was tired and greatly in need of a warm place to rest; nevertheless, he refused to ask anyone for help.

1. Her grandparents had their first date on September 5, 1955, became engaged on February 14, 1957, and were married on June 28, 1958.

2. Some people can play musical instruments by ear without formal training others need years of lessons and practice to play an instrument well.

3. He started first grade in Waycross, Georgia attended junior high in Thomasville, Georgia finished high school in Macon, Georgia and ended up in Memphis, Tennessee, for college.

4. Sandy excelled in Latin that is, she won numerous honors.

5. He stayed up until 4 A.M., consequently, he slept through his 7 A.M. alarm.

6. Irving Berlin composed hundreds of songs, including "God Bless America," "Easter Parade," and "Always" but "White Christmas" may be his best-known song.

7. I must answer his letter straightaway otherwise, I'm afraid that I will forget.

8. Forty years ago, Jane broke her arm by falling off a horse, this time she lost her balance on some steps.

9. Bonnie designs most of her clothes for example, she sewed the lovely coat and dress that she wore Sunday.

10. On Tuesday, she should pick up her dry cleaning, and she must vote.

Copyright © by Holt, Rinehart and Winston. All rights reserved.

NAME ______ CLASS ______ DATE ______

Colons A

14e. Use a colon to mean "note what follows."

(1) Use a colon before a list of items, especially after expressions like *as follows* and *the following.*
(2) Use a colon before a long, formal statement or quotation.
(3) Use a colon between independent clauses when the second clause explains or restates the idea of the first.

EXAMPLES I was asked to bring the following**:** a flashlight, bedroll or sleeping bag, and a tarpaulin.

Dr. Martin Luther King, Jr., concluded the "dream" references of his famous speech with these words**:** "I have a dream that one day every valley shall be exalted and every mountain shall be made low. . . ."

The weather was perfect for sailing**:** The sky was clear, the wind was strong and constant, and the bright sunlight kept us warm.

EXERCISE Insert colons where they are needed in the following sentences. If a sentence is already correct, write *C* on the line provided.

Example ______ **1.** The newly elected officers are as follows: Miriam, Mona, Alice, and Nancy.

______ **1.** Hikers need the following sturdy boots, light clothing, and a waterproof jacket.

______ **2.** The actor gave me this advice Learn your lines, be on time, and don't get emotional.

______ **3.** The members of the band are Carroll on lead guitar, Melvin on rhythm guitar, David on upright bass, and Ron on drums.

______ **4.** The protests had a positive effect They grabbed the governor's attention.

______ **5.** President Franklin D. Roosevelt issued his famous statement about fear in his first inaugural address "So, first of all, let me assert my firm belief that the only thing we have to fear is fear itself. . . ."

______ **6.** The ballet troupe will perform in the following cities New York, Chicago, and London.

______ **7.** These words are from Eleanor Roosevelt's first autobiography "No one can make you feel inferior without your consent."

______ **8.** There is one thing I am sure about now At that point in my life, I should not have let my friends influence me so much.

______ **9.** Stella has two annoying habits entering my room without knocking and borrowing my things without asking.

______ **10.** We have no school on these holidays New Year's Day, Martin Luther King Day, Presidents' Day, and Memorial Day.

Copyright © by Holt, Rinehart and Winston. All rights reserved.

NAME CLASS DATE

Colons B

14f. Use a colon in certain conventional situations.

(1) Use a colon between the hour and the minute.
(2) Use a colon between a chapter and verse in referring to passages from the Bible.
(3) Use a colon between a title and a subtitle.
(4) Use a colon after the salutation of a business letter.

EXAMPLES 2:36 P.M. Psalms 118:24 *The Years of Lyndon Johnson: The Path to Power*
Dear Reader: Dear Mr. Branham:

EXERCISE Insert colons where they are needed in the following sentences.

Example 1. The text of the pastor's sermon was Genesis 3:1–21.

1. Both Matthew 6 28 and Luke 12 27 refer to the lilies of the field.
2. The letter began, "Dear Sir or Madam I am writing on behalf of my son."
3. She intends to be ready by 8 30 in the morning.
4. He would like to depart by 7 15 tomorrow evening.
5. My paper was titled "The Rain Forest Harvest of Shame."
6. Their flight left on time at 7 12 A.M.
7. Her father often quoted Micah 6 8.
8. In theory, I should be at my desk by 8 15.
9. You should take the 3 32 train to Columbus, where you will catch the 5 07 to Dayton.
10. The imagery in Isaiah 11 6 always intrigued her.
11. He decided to name his paper "Satchmo Musical Shaper of the Twentieth Century."
12. Jamie's letter began, "Dear Mr. Clark Please find enclosed two copies of my résumé."
13. Worship began with a congregational reading of Psalms 96 1–6.
14. I arrived at 7 37, about five minutes after the movie began.
15. I enjoyed the article "Cats Can They Be Trained?"
16. Her friends asked her to read I Corinthians 13 1–13 at their wedding.
17. The invitation says that the brunch is to begin at 10 30.
18. The lyrics of that song are taken from Ecclesiastes 3 1–8.
19. One of the albums she received for her birthday was Wynton Marsalis' *Standard Time, Vol. 5 The Midnight Blues.*
20. I promised that I would be prompt for our 12 45 lunch date.

Copyright © by Holt, Rinehart and Winston. All rights reserved.

NAME ____________ CLASS ____________ DATE ____________

for **CHAPTER 14: PUNCTUATION** *pages 402–406*

Semicolons and Colons

14a–f. Review pages 402–406 of your textbook for rules regarding the use of semicolons and colons.

EXERCISE A Insert semicolons and colons where they are needed in the following sentences. Hint: In some sentences, semicolons will replace commas.

Example 1. These trees, which have lost most of their leaves, are still healthy; but they will require pruning.

1. Sharon's alarm is set for 6 30 A.M.
2. Most tickets for the event are sold out however, there is a waiting list for remaining seats.
3. Eight pounds, three ounces, seven pounds, four ounces, and eleven pounds, four ounces are the current weights of my cats.
4. The following items are required at this course spikeless golf shoes, collared shirts, and one set of clubs per player.
5. The living room carpet has been vacuumed, the kitchen floor is being scrubbed right now.

EXERCISE B In the following business letter, insert colons and semicolons where they are needed. There should be a total of ten colons and semicolons added in order to punctuate the letter correctly.

Example My schedule has changed; as a result, I will need to change my Wednesday flight.

Dear Mr. Livingston

We have checked into connecting flights for you through the following cities Birmingham, Alabama Jackson, Mississippi New Orleans, Louisiana and Houston, Texas. The flight that seems to suit your schedule best is the one that departs Houston at 9 05 A.M. and arrives in Dallas at 9 55 A.M. (You would need to be at the airport no later than 8 00.)

We would like to know if this is agreeable with you otherwise, we will examine the remaining flight options. One thing is certain We need to make your reservation soon in order to secure a low fare.

Very truly yours,

Tim Horne

Copyright © by Holt, Rinehart and Winston. All rights reserved.

NAME ______________________ CLASS ______________ DATE ______________

for **CHAPTER 14: PUNCTUATION** pages 408–410

Italics (Underlining) A

14g. Use italics (underlining) for titles and subtitles of books, plays, long poems, periodicals, works of art, films, radio and television series, long musical works and recordings, videos, video and computer games, and comic strips.

EXAMPLES *Treasure Island* *Aeneid*
Sports Illustrated *Madonna of the Pomegranate*
The Wizard of Oz *Rose Is Rose*

MECHANICS

EXERCISE Underline all words that should appear in italics in the following sentences.

Example 1. She recently read The Wind in the Willows for the first time.

1. Rodgers and Hammerstein wrote the musicals South Pacific and Carousel.
2. The presidential candidates were on television last night on 60 Minutes.
3. Philadelphia once had an afternoon newspaper called the Evening Bulletin.
4. Grant Wood's painting American Gothic hangs at the Chicago Institute of Art.
5. She was quite sad when Charles Schulz, the creator of Peanuts, died.
6. Tina Brown left The New Yorker to begin Talk magazine.
7. One of her greatest thrills was seeing Leontyne Price in the opera Aida.
8. Mr. Edwards enjoys listening to All Things Considered weekday afternoons on NPR.
9. Darrell is proud that he has seen the movie Frequency three times at the theater and nine times on video.
10. She planned her evenings around reruns of Friends.
11. A Lesson Before Dying is among the selections for the book club.
12. For the past three Januarys, she had promised herself that she would read Shakespeare's Twelfth Night.
13. He could become absorbed in the games Myst and Riven for hours on his computer.
14. Her grandmother has subscribed to Good Housekeeping for over thirty years.
15. The 1939 movie Gone with the Wind won eight Academy Awards, including Best Picture.
16. Chagall's painting The Birthday and the story behind it touched her.
17. Stephen Vincent Benét wrote the narrative poem John Brown's Body in 1928.
18. La Bamba, the movie based on Ritchie Valens' life, both inspired and saddened them.
19. Thornton Wilder won his first of three Pulitzer Prizes for The Bridge of San Luis Rey.
20. John F. Kennedy, Jr., founded George magazine.

Copyright © by Holt, Rinehart and Winston. All rights reserved.

NAME ______________________ CLASS ______________ DATE ______________

Italics (Underlining) B

14h. Use italics (underlining) for the names of trains, ships, aircraft, and spacecraft.

EXAMPLES *Delta Queen* *Challenger* *Spirit of St. Louis*

14i. Use italics (underlining) for words, letters, symbols, and numerals referred to as such and for foreign words that have not been adopted into English.

EXAMPLES What does the expression *voila res gestae* mean? You left out an *s* in *Mississippi.*

EXERCISE Underline all words or letters that should appear in italics in the following sentences.

Example 1. In Spanish, the phrase loco poco describes someone who is slightly crazy.

1. Amtrak runs a train called the California Zephyr from Chicago to San Francisco.
2. The Yiddish word shlemil means "a foolish or unlucky person."
3. I often have difficulty keeping the words affect and effect straight in my mind.
4. The Titanic was supposedly unsinkable, yet the ship sank in 1912.
5. In German, v is pronounced like the English f, and w sounds like the English v.
6. The Latin phrase et cetera is the source of the abbreviation etc.
7. The Wright brothers' airplane, the Flyer, was the first successful engine-driven, heavier-than-air machine.
8. Semper fidelis, the motto of the United States Marine Corps, means "always faithful."
9. After an important victory, Julius Caesar reported to the Roman Senate, "Veni, vidi, vici [I came, I saw, I conquered]."
10. The Rapido carries passengers between Toronto and Montreal at an average speed of about eighty miles per hour.

Copyright © by Holt, Rinehart and Winston. All rights reserved.

NAME ______________________ CLASS ______________ DATE ______________

for CHAPTER 14: PUNCTUATION pages 408–410

Italics (Underlining) Review

14g. Use italics (underlining) for titles and subtitles of books, plays, long poems, periodicals, works of art, films, radio and television series, long musical works and recordings, videos, video and computer games, and comic strips.

14h. Use italics (underlining) for the names of trains, ships, aircraft, and spacecraft.

14i. Use italics (underlining) for words, letters, symbols, and numerals referred to as such and for foreign words that have not been adopted into English.

EXAMPLES He first studied *Hamlet* in college and has re-read it every year since.

The song "The City of New Orleans" is about the actual train the *City of New Orleans*, which runs south from Chicago to New Orleans.

Mary's casual, *c'est la vie* attitude was admirable in the face of such adversity.

MECHANICS

EXERCISE Underline all words or letters that should appear in italics in the following sentences.

Example 1. When they were boys, they were allowed to tour the USS Enterprise while it was docked near Boston.

1. What do the abbreviations SS and HMS stand for?
2. Tim likes to read The Washington Post regularly on the Internet.
3. Her mother recalled the Challenger tragedy, although she did not see the explosion on television as it happened.
4. His letter was ex animo, meaning "from the heart."
5. He always misspells vacuum by putting in an extra c and omitting a u.
6. She liked the novel Sense and Sensibility and looks forward to seeing the film.
7. She recalled reading the first issue of People over thirty years ago.
8. Kathleen was drawn to Winslow Homer's paintings of storms, especially Hurricane, Bahamas.
9. Although we liked the comic strip, we grew weary of her always quoting something from Doonesbury.
10. The original movie of The Women was cast entirely with females.

Copyright © by Holt, Rinehart and Winston. All rights reserved.

NAME ______________________ CLASS ______________ DATE ______________

Quotation Marks A

14j. Use quotation marks to enclose a ***direct quotation***—a person's exact words.

(1) A direct quotation generally begins with a capital letter.
(2) When a quoted sentence is interrupted by an expression that identifies the speaker, the second part of the quotation begins with a lowercase letter.
(3) A direct quotation is set off from the rest of the sentence by a comma, a question mark, or an exclamation point, but not by a period.
(4) When used with quotation marks, other marks of punctuation are placed according to the following rules:

- Commas and periods are placed inside closing quotation marks.
- Semicolons and colons are placed outside closing quotation marks.
- Question marks and exclamation points are placed inside closing quotation marks if the quotation is a question or an exclamation. Otherwise, they are placed outside.

EXAMPLES Nara said she was "quite upset" with the test results.
He jumped into the taxi and said, "Follow that car!"
"I'm confident," Luís said, "that we will win the championship."
Gloria said, "There's a special exhibit at the art museum."
"What is it?" I asked.
"Quite honestly," she confessed, "I would prefer to be alone."
He said, "No, I won't"; I, on the other hand, said, "Yes, I will."
Hank asked, "Where are you going?"
What kind of an answer is "I don't care"?

EXERCISE Add quotation marks as needed to the following sentences. Many sentences will also require the insertion of end marks.

Example 1. "If you really want to know," she interrupted, "ask Sherry."

1. I describe my aunt Luna by saying, Her words are candy, but her actions are cod liver oil

2. Teresa hollered across the yard, Have you seen my car keys

3. He ran down the street yelling, Wait for me

4. The first step in cooking ratatouille, my teacher said, is to clean and salt the eggplant

5. Who said, Beauty seen is never lost

6. Clare warned, If you keep eating, you'll ruin your supper; she sounded like my mother.

7. Colleen stopped me to inquire, When have you heard from Ken

8. If you ask me, Ned asserted, that board is too thick to use for your shelves

9. The poem begins, Who has seen the wind

10. He shouted his admonition: Don't put your fingers near the fan

Copyright © by Holt, Rinehart and Winston. All rights reserved.

Quotation Marks B

14j. Use quotation marks to enclose a ***direct quotation***—a person's exact words.

(5) When writing dialogue, begin a new paragraph every time the speaker changes, and enclose each speaker's words in quotation marks.
(6) When quoting a passage that consists of more than one paragraph, place quotation marks at the beginning of each paragraph and at the end of only the last paragraph in the passage.
(7) Use single quotation marks to enclose a quotation within a quotation.

EXAMPLES The painter Whistler did a portrait of a man. Afterward, artist and subject looked at the picture together. "Well," said the subject, "you can't call that a great work of art."

"Perhaps not," replied Whistler. "But then you can hardly call yourself a great work of Nature."

"At nine o'clock this morning," read the news story, "someone entered the Mill Bank, broke through the steel doors guarding the bank's vault, and escaped with an undisclosed amount of cash.

"No arrests have been made at this point. However, state police are confident the case will be solved."

"Why would you say, 'Might makes right'?" the former boxer asked.

EXERCISE A Add quotation marks as needed to the following dialogue. Additionally, insert the paragraph symbol (¶) before any word that should begin a new paragraph.

Example **[1]** "Have you heard of a philosopher named Diogenes?" Lola asked.

[1] The Greek philosopher Diogenes the Cynic lived in a huge barrel. **[2]** One day, Alexander the Great peered in to see the great philosopher. **[3]** Is there anything that I can do for you? Alexander asked. **[4]** Yes, answered Diogenes. **[5]** I'd like you to stop blocking my light.

EXERCISE B Add quotation marks as needed to the following passage. Additionally, insert the paragraph symbol (¶) before any word that should begin a new paragraph.

Example **[1]** "We are extremely grateful," said Mr. McAllister, "for the firefighters' help."

[6] The call came into Woodhaven Fire Station at 9:07. Firefighters reacted immediately and were at the McAllister residence within four minutes. **[7]** That's an unusually quick response time considering there are still some patches of ice on the streets, but when you hear someone say, There's smoke pouring out of my attic, it's an incentive, stated Chief Grant Hughes. **[8]** I have nothing but praise for the local firefighters, offered Ed McAllister. **[9]** Not only did they save my house, they rescued our family's dog. **[10]** Chief Hughes smiled modestly and shrugged.

Copyright © by Holt, Rinehart and Winston. All rights reserved.

Quotation Marks C

14k. Use quotation marks to enclose titles (including subtitles) of short works, such as short stories, short poems, essays, articles and other parts of periodicals, songs, episodes of radio and television series, and chapters and other parts of books.

14l. Use quotation marks to enclose slang words, invented words, technical terms, dictionary definitions of words, and any expressions that are unusual in standard English.

EXAMPLES I laugh out loud every time I read "Why I Live at the P.O."
Chapter 4 of *The Life of John Muir* is titled "To the Sierras."
In Philadelphia, a submarine sandwich is called a "hoagie."
The word *commodious* means "spacious; having plenty of room."

EXERCISE Add quotation marks to the following sentences as needed. Some sentences may also require the addition of end marks.

Example 1. My favorite patriotic song is "America, the Beautiful."

1. Thurber's short story The Night the Bed Fell is very funny.
2. Is Chapter 3 of *Winter Tales* called Up the Creek
3. The title of my essay is What Is the Point of Arguing
4. The Sanskrit word *ahimsa* means reverence for life; a principle of nonviolence.
5. He told me of a BBC Radio 2 program on a jazz composer; specifically, he mentioned the episode The Romance and the Reality
6. Your assignment is to read the excerpt from Emerson's essay titled Nature.
7. For years, people incorrectly coined the word *prioritize*, but it is now in the dictionary, meaning to arrange (items) in order of priority.
8. He compared the grimness of his relatives' house to the House of Usher, referring, of course, to Poe's short story The Fall of the House of Usher
9. Rebecca's pet peeve is the conversion of nouns to verbs; for example, she really dislikes hearing anyone say partnering
10. Stephen decided to memorize The Road Not Taken, a poem by Robert Frost.

Copyright © by Holt, Rinehart and Winston. All rights reserved.

Quotation Marks Review

14j. Use quotation marks to enclose a ***direct quotation***—a person's exact words.

14k. Use quotation marks to enclose titles (including subtitles) of short works, such as short stories, short poems, essays, articles and other parts of periodicals, songs, episodes of radio and television series, and chapters and other parts of books.

14l. Use quotation marks to enclose slang words, invented words, technical terms, dictionary definitions of words, and any expressions that are unusual in standard English.

EXERCISE Add single and double quotation marks to the following sentences as needed. Some sentences may also require the addition of capitalization and end marks.

Example 1. "Are you sure Mr. Jones said, 'Your papers will be due next Friday'?" asked Tameka.

1. Sherry inquired, have you read the story The Open Window

2. Emily Dickinson's Success is counted sweetest is one of Ellen's favorite poems.

3. *Arizona* means little springs, she explained.

4. The only tough part of the interview occurred when he asked, what do you see yourself doing in fifteen or twenty years

5. Halle said, I'm sure I have some royal blue thread; then, she proceeded to dig for it in the drawer.

6. Please finish your paper, he pleaded, so you can go to the movie with me

7. He quoted from Nelson Mandela's 1994 inaugural speech: Our deepest fear is not that we are inadequate. Our deepest fear is that we are powerful beyond measure. It is our light, not our darkness, that frightens us.

8. Mom said, Not tonight, he reminded me with a frown.

9. That a man can influence a woman with jewels I find opalling, he teased.

10. The last thing I remember is someone shouting, look out

Copyright © by Holt, Rinehart and Winston. All rights reserved.

NAME CLASS DATE

for **CHAPTER 14: PUNCTUATION** *pages 408–416*

Italics (Underlining) and Quotation Marks

14g. Use italics (underlining) for titles and subtitles of books, plays, long poems, periodicals, works of art, films, radio and television series, long musical works and recordings, videos, video and computer games, and comic strips.

14h. Use italics (underlining) for the names of trains, ships, aircraft, and spacecraft.

14i. Use italics (underlining) for words, letters, symbols, and numerals referred to as such and for foreign words that have not been adopted into English.

14j. Use quotation marks to enclose a direct quotation—a person's exact words.

14k. Use quotation marks to enclose titles (including subtitles) of short works, such as short stories, short poems, essays, articles and other parts of periodicals, songs, episodes of radio and television series, and chapters and other parts of books.

14l. Use quotation marks to enclose slang words, invented words, technical terms, dictionary definitions of words, and any expressions that are unusual in standard English.

MECHANICS

EXERCISE A Add underlining and quotation marks as needed in the following items.

Example 1. Katherine Mansfield's story "A Dill Pickle"

1. Yeats's poem When You Are Old
2. his weekly column in The Washington Post
3. the ship Titanic
4. the Gershwin tune I've Got Rhythm
5. Carson McCullers's play The Member of the Wedding

EXERCISE B Add underlining and quotation marks as needed in the following sentences.

Example 1. I was so impressed with the movie Persuasion, based on Jane Austen's novel, that it inspired me to read the book.

6. O. Henry's story The Ransom of Red Chief is included in the movie O. Henry's Full House.
7. Mr. Darcy's proposal to Elizabeth Bennet comes in Volume Two, Chapter XI of Pride and Prejudice; in consecutively numbered editions, however, it is in Chapter XXXIV.
8. A portion of James Baldwin's book The Fire Next Time first appeared in The New Yorker in November 1962 as A Latter from a Region in My Mind.
9. The Latin term res ipsa loquitur means the thing speaks for itself, the instructor reminded us.
10. The poem Lucinda Matlock is found in Edgar Lee Masters' Spoon River Anthology.

Copyright © by Holt, Rinehart and Winston. All rights reserved.

NAME ____________ CLASS ____________ DATE ____________

Ellipsis Points

14m. Use ellipsis points to mark omissions from quoted material and pauses in a written passage.

ORIGINAL	Winning isn't everything; it is the only thing.
WITH OMISSION	Winning . . . is the only thing.
PAUSE	"Let's see, . . . where was I?" Alexis said, trying to find her place.

EXERCISE On the lines provided, rewrite these quoted passages, omitting the parts that appear in italics. Use ellipsis points to indicate where the material has been omitted.

Example 1. "Know whence you came. *If you know whence you came,* there is really no limit to where you can go."
"Know whence you came. . . . [T]here is really no limit to where you can go."

1. "I'd like to learn to dance, *but I have two left feet!*" she said.

____

____

2. "Open your eyes to the opportunities around you. *Never give up and* never say 'I can't.'"

____

____

3. "Donnie came over. *He has a ticket for you.* He left a note on the door."

____

____

4. "Wishes, *even those that seem impossible,* can come true."

____

____

5. "Well, *for the first time in my life,* I'm almost speechless," Ashley replied.

____

____

Copyright © by Holt, Rinehart and Winston. All rights reserved.

NAME ______________________ CLASS ______________ DATE ______________

Apostrophes A

14n. Use an apostrophe to form the possessive of nouns and indefinite pronouns.

(1) To form the possessive of most singular nouns, add an apostrophe and an *s*.
(2) To form the possessive of a plural noun ending in *s*, add only the apostrophe.

Plural nouns that do not end in *s* form the possessive by adding an apostrophe and an *s*.

EXAMPLES

a bird's nest	a year's pay	a table's leg
the birds' nests	two years' pay	most of the tables' legs
a children's book	the geese's nest	the men's cars

EXERCISE On the lines provided, rewrite the following Phrases using possessive nouns.

Example 1. the mane of a horse *the horse's mane*

1. a vacation of two weeks ______________________
2. the den of the wolves ______________________
3. teacher of her children ______________________
4. cat of my niece ______________________
5. home of Bess ______________________
6. the complaints of the constituents ______________________
7. trophies of the amateurs ______________________
8. agility of Jesse ______________________
9. sale of the decade ______________________
10. the nest of the mice ______________________
11. the coat of the sheep ______________________
12. the backyard of the Joneses ______________________
13. the clarity of the audio ______________________
14. the heel of Achilles ______________________
15. lights of Paris ______________________
16. the rays of the sun ______________________
17. poems of Keats ______________________
18. the identities of the women ______________________
19. gift of her sons ______________________
20. the brilliance of the stars ______________________

Copyright © by Holt, Rinehart and Winston. All rights reserved.

Apostrophes B

14n. Use an apostrophe to form the possessive of nouns and indefinite pronouns.

(3) Do not use an apostrophe with possessive personal pronouns or with the possessive pronoun *whose.*

(4) To form the possessive of an indefinite pronoun, add an apostrophe and an *s.*

EXAMPLES I recognized **his** profile.
Whose phone number did you give me?
Everyone's attitude improves once he or she has eaten.

EXERCISE A From the choices in parentheses, underline the word that completes each sentence correctly.

Example 1. The Garcias' house is much newer than *(our's, ours).*

1. *(You're, Your)* painting is beautiful.

2. These are *(their, they're)* reports.

3. Which of those books is *(her's, hers)*?

4. The car has been sitting here for days because one of *(its, it's)* tires is flat.

5. Do you know *(who's, whose)* dog it is?

EXERCISE B On the line provided after each sentence, write the possessive form of the underlined words. If an underlined word is already in the correct possessive form, write a C on the line.

Example 1. No one attitude has improved as much as his has. No one's; C

6. Nobody else mail was sent to their address. ______

7. She shared everyone opinion that the team would win. ______

8. We would like to make our plans soon. ______

9. No one opinion matters more to me than hers. ______

10. This is somebody else notebook. ______

11. He gathered everybody tickets. ______

12. Somebody fingerprints are all over this mirror. ______

13. They must be somebody else; they're not mine. ______

14. It's anybody guess who they are. ______

15. Surely, they're your. ______

Copyright © by Holt, Rinehart and Winston. All rights reserved.

Apostrophes C

14n. Use an apostrophe to form the possessive of nouns and indefinite pronouns.

(5) Generally, in compound words, in names of organizations and businesses, and in word groups showing joint possession, only the last word is possessive in form.
(6) Form the possessive of each noun in a word group showing individual possession of similar items.
(7) Use an apostrophe to form the possessives of words that indicate time, such as *minute, hour, day, week, month,* and *year,* and of those that indicate an amount in cents or dollars.

EXAMPLES the Council on Policy and Development's recommendation
my sister-in-law's assistance
his aunt and uncle's house
a night's sleep
Marie's and Annie's test scores
a dollar and a quarter's worth

EXERCISE Revise each of the following word groups to express the same meaning with a possessive noun or pronoun.

Example 1. rest of not a minute *not a minute's rest*

1. members of NATO ______
2. input of her mother-in-law ______
3. efforts of Yvonne, Daphne, and me ______
4. plans for a week ______
5. schedule for National Public Radio ______
6. uniforms of Randy and Kevin ______
7. conference of the attorney general ______
8. worth of three dollars ______
9. fund-raiser of the Boy Scout Council ______
10. administration of Clinton and Gore ______

Copyright © by Holt, Rinehart and Winston. All rights reserved.

NAME _______________ CLASS _______________ DATE _______________

Apostrophes D

14n. Use an apostrophe to form the possessive of nouns and indefinite pronouns.

EXAMPLES Maya Angelou's poetry fifteen dollars' worth babies' toys
Josi's and my report everybody's ideas its tail

EXERCISE A Using apostrophes correctly, write the singular possessive and the plural possessive of each of the following nouns.

Example 1. girl *girl's* *girls'*

	Singular Possessive	Plural Possessive
1. lady	______	______
2. brother-in-law	______	______
3. dime	______	______
4. committee	______	______
5. gentleman	______	______

EXERCISE B On the line provided after each sentence, write the possessive form of each underlined item. If an underlined item is correct as it appears, write a *C* on the line.

Example 1. She has everybody phone number on her list. *everybody's; C*

6. His two sisters-in-law birthdays are both in February. ______

7. It is really nobody else business. ______

8. He volunteered his time to the NAACP legal efforts. ______

9. If Ray decides to go, he can use somebody ticket. ______

10. Whose blouse is it, yours or hers? ______

11. A week vacation was among that doctors orders. ______

12. Whether he intends to come is anybody guess. ______

13. Beverly and Bob house has a spectacular view. ______

14. Brad and Terry cars are both white. ______

15. That project is among the city council proposals. ______

Copyright © by Holt, Rinehart and Winston. All rights reserved.

NAME ____________ CLASS ____________ DATE ____________

Apostrophes E

14o. Use an apostrophe to show where letters, numerals, or words have been omitted in a contraction.

EXAMPLES she's you're they'll who's
don't couldn't weren't

EXERCISE On the line provided after each sentence, write the correct contraction for the underlined words.

Example 1. He would have called if there had been a problem. *would've*

1. We have an obligation to participate in the program. ____________
2. You are a very smart little girl. ____________
3. Do not plant these seeds until there is no chance of frost. ____________
4. Terry has not got a clue as to his own conduct. ____________
5. I cannot accept the package COD. ____________
6. Ed said he could have gone with her. ____________
7. It is important to be prepared. ____________
8. Angela said that they are due tomorrow. ____________
9. He will buy all the camping gear soon. ____________
10. Was not that your mother going in the back door? ____________
11. Sheila cannot decide whether to go or stay. ____________
12. Who is in charge here? ____________
13. I have several suggestions to offer. ____________
14. She would rather be home knitting. ____________
15. You have not had a chance to explore. ____________
16. We will be vigilant. ____________
17. That is the only ingredient you need. ____________
18. Would not you rather sit in a more comfortable chair? ____________
19. No matter how much he tried, he could not forget about her. ____________
20. That is not the best approach. ____________

Copyright © by Holt, Rinehart and Winston. All rights reserved.

NAME ______________________ CLASS ______________ DATE ______________

for **CHAPTER 14: PUNCTUATION** *page 425*

Apostrophes F

14p. Use an apostrophe and an *s* to form the plurals of all lowercase letters, of some capital letters, of numerals, of symbols, and of words referred to as words.

EXAMPLES R.N.'s 3's Class of '57 *t*'s

EXERCISE In the following sentences, underline each word that requires an apostrophe and write the word correctly on the line provided. If a sentence is already correct, write *C* on the line.

Example 1. Sometimes my *rs* look like *vs*. *r's; v's*

1. He's crashed two CPUs by spilling water in them. ______

2. She has lost all her photo IDs. ______

3. Johnny could count by 2s but not by 3s. ______

4. They've made all As the past two years. ______

5. The police department had issued only a few APBs. ______

6. Carter knew his ABCs but got his *k*s and *l*s out of order. ______

7. All the members were either J.D.s or M.D.s. ______

8. They've bought two DVDs this week alone. ______

9. I have too many IOUs. ______

10. Few people like to hear *I told you so*s. ______

11. How many @s appear in an e-mail address? ______

12. How many TVs do you have in your house? ______

13. He had used too many *therefore*s in his essay. ______

14. Both of my cousins have B.A.s from the same university. ______

15. Sheila revised her paper to reduce the number of *and*s and *but*s. ______

16. The *G*s stand for "good," and the *E*s stand for "excellent." ______

17. Her extended family includes five R.N.s. ______

18. Henry's handwritten *8*s sometimes look like *0*s. ______

19. Spell out the word *and;* don't use *&*s. ______

20. Don't forget to dot your *i*s and cross your *t*s. ______

MECHANICS

Copyright © by Holt, Rinehart and Winston. All rights reserved.

Apostrophes G

14o. Use an apostrophe to show where letters, numerals, or words have been omitted in a contraction.

14p. Use an apostrophe and an *s* to form the plurals of all lowercase letters, of some capital letters, of numerals, of symbols, and of words referred to as words.

EXAMPLES '90s won't four o'clock weren't you'll
l's L.P.N.'s 5's *can*'s

EXERCISE Use apostrophes as needed to form contractions and plurals from the underlined words, letters, or numbers in the following sentences. If underlined words or terms are already correct, write *C* on the line.

Example 1. I had associated those styles with the 60s. I'd; '60s

1. I cannot distinguish her cursive *es* from her *is*. ______
2. We are proud of his As and Bs. ______
3. They had earned their J.D.s in 87. ______
4. There are twelve *nos* and thirteen *yess*. ______
5. Cross your *ts*; otherwise, they look like *ls*. ______
6. His 57 convertible is his pride and joy, is not it? ______
7. I am eager to listen to your old LPs. ______
8. She had earned three M.A.s before she was thirty. ______
9. His *hellos* do not sound very warm. ______
10. I had counted twelve *uhs* in his remarks. ______

Copyright © by Holt, Rinehart and Winston. All rights reserved.

Apostrophes Review

14n. Use an apostrophe to form the possessive of nouns and indefinite pronouns.

14o. Use an apostrophe to show where letters, numerals, or words have been omitted in a contraction.

14p. Use an apostrophe and an *s* to form the plurals of all lowercase letters, of some capital letters, of numerals, of symbols, and of words referred to as words.

EXERCISE A Using apostrophes correctly, write the singular possessive and the plural possessive of each of the following nouns.

Example 1. garden *garden's* *gardens'*

	Singular Possessive	Plural Possessive
1. woman		
2. father-in-law		
3. dollar		
4. association		
5. major general		
6. Hughes		
7. he		
8. minute		
9. kiss		
10. cowboy		

EXERCISE B Use apostrophes with the following items to make possessive nouns or pronouns, contractions, or plurals.

Example 1. *U* *U's*

11. Who is ______

12. D.D.S. ______

13. everybody ______

14. *7* ______

15. two of the clock ______

16. *Z* ______

17. will not ______

18. they have ______

19. 1990s ______

20. *p* and *q* ______

Copyright © by Holt, Rinehart and Winston. All rights reserved.

Hyphens A

14q. Use a hyphen to divide a word at the end of a line.

Do not divide a one-syllable word.
Divide a word only between syllables.
Divide a word that is already hyphenated only at the hyphen.
Do not divide a word so that one letter stands alone.

INCORRECT George's father owns a deli.

CORRECT George's father
owns a deli.

INCORRECT Let us provide the facts.

CORRECT Let us pro-
vide the facts.

INCORRECT There were twenty-two members.

CORRECT There were twenty-
two members.

INCORRECT The legend is a-
bout Theseus.

CORRECT The legend is
about Theseus.

MECHANICS

EXERCISE On the lines provided, write the following words with hyphens, showing how they could be broken at the end of a line. If a word should not be divided, write *no hyphen*.

Example 1. funny *fun-ny*

1. eighty-nine ____________________
2. middle ____________________
3. handbag ____________________
4. around ____________________
5. strength ____________________
6. skiing ____________________
7. emit ____________________
8. teeny-bopper ____________________
9. height ____________________
10. station ____________________
11. conscious ____________________
12. scientific ____________________
13. scent ____________________
14. feuding ____________________
15. twenty-five ____________________
16. settlement ____________________
17. all-purpose ____________________
18. against ____________________
19. hammering ____________________
20. financially ____________________

Copyright © by Holt, Rinehart and Winston. All rights reserved.

NAME ________________ CLASS ________________ DATE ________________

Hyphens B

14r. Use a hyphen with compound numbers from *twenty-one* to *ninety-nine* and with fractions used as modifiers.

14s. Hyphenate a compound adjective when it precedes the word it modifies.

14t. Use a hyphen with the prefixes *ex–*, *self–*, *all–* and *great–*; with the suffixes *–elect* and *–free;* and with all prefixes before a proper noun or proper adjective.

14u. Use a hyphen to prevent confusion or awkwardness.

EXAMPLES forty-eight actors a well-written poem ex-president re-sign the contract

EXERCISE On the lines provided, rewrite the following items, inserting hyphens where they are needed. If an item is already correct, write *C* on the line.

Example 1. a much appreciated gesture *much-appreciated*

1. a wooded island in the mid Pacific ________
2. a four fifths majority ________
3. a self fulfilling prophecy ________
4. a fully lined jacket ________
5. twenty senators elect ________
6. a noise free atmosphere ________
7. one fourth cup of molasses ________
8. their great grandmother ________
9. a much admired teenager ________
10. an anti European attitude ________
11. her ex husband ________
12. all school picnic ________
13. an all American basketball player ________
14. three fifths of the students ________
15. a full moon night ________
16. a half baked idea ________
17. a dramatic recreation of the event ________
18. a sugar free snack ________
19. a well attended banquet ________
20. a frost free refrigerator ________

Copyright © by Holt, Rinehart and Winston. All rights reserved.

NAME ______________________ CLASS ______________ DATE ______________

for CHAPTER 14: PUNCTUATION pages 426–428

MECHANICS

Hyphens Review

14q. Use a hyphen to divide a word at the end of a line.

14r. Use a hyphen with compound numbers from *twenty-one* to *ninety-nine* and with fractions used as modifiers.

14s. Hyphenate a compound adjective when it precedes the word it modifies.

14t. Use a hyphen with the prefixes *ex–*, *self–*, *all–* and *great–*; with the suffixes *–elect* and *–free*; and with all prefixes before a proper noun or proper adjective.

14u. Use a hyphen to prevent confusion or awkwardness.

EXERCISE A On the lines provided, write the following words with hyphens, showing how they should be broken at the end of a line. If a word should not be divided, write *no hyphen*.

Example 1. won't *no hyphen*

1. prefix ______
2. suffix ______
3. T-shirt ______
4. go-between ______
5. proofread ______
6. weight ______
7. trimming ______
8. president-elect ______
9. abate ______
10. rebate ______

EXERCISE B On the lines provided, rewrite the following items, inserting hyphens where they are needed. If an item is already correct, write *C* on the line.

Example 1. a well adjusted child *a well-adjusted child*

11. a two thirds approval ______
12. an ex football player ______
13. an anti Irish vote ______
14. a self starting approach ______
15. our great grandparents ______
16. an antiinflammatory medication ______
17. twenty two travelers ______
18. a well liked relative ______
19. reduce by one fourth ______
20. a smoke free lobby ______

Copyright © by Holt, Rinehart and Winston. All rights reserved.

Dashes

14v. Use a dash to indicate an abrupt break in thought or speech.

14w. Use a dash to mean *namely, in other words,* or *that is* before an explanation.

EXAMPLES This book—perhaps you've already read it—is excellent.
Five dollars—the exact price of a ticket—is missing from my bag.

EXERCISE Rewrite each of the following sentences, adding dashes as needed.

Example 1. The money in the treasury the collected membership dues will go toward our graduation trip. *The money in the treasury—the collected membership dues—will go toward our graduation trip.*

1. That movie perhaps you've already seen it is excellent.

2. Have you read his recent book the one in paperback?

3. We should pack rain gear tarpaulins, boots, and ponchos.

4. Please hand me the hammer and a oh, never mind.

5. Lucille Ball had three television series *I Love Lucy, The Lucy Show,* and *Here's Lucy.*

6. His answer the logic of which I couldn't follow seemed to satisfy the judges.

7. You should have no problem getting into the show there are plenty of free tickets.

8. The point is and you should listen closely to make sure everyone follows instructions.

9. Some of the earliest New Orleans jazz musicians King Oliver, Louis Armstrong, and Sidney Bechet, for instance found fame first outside that city.

10. The author of the play I can't recall her name won a Pulitzer Prize.

MECHANICS

Copyright © by Holt, Rinehart and Winston. All rights reserved.

NAME ______ CLASS ______ DATE ______

for **CHAPTER 14: PUNCTUATION** *pages 430–431*

Parentheses

14x. Use parentheses to enclose informative or explanatory material of minor importance.

EXAMPLES Suzanne Carl (**'**86) is head of the alumni association.
The property is 920 acres (one and a half square miles).
The trumpet player (have you met him?) lives in my neighborhood.
Joe helped me change my flat tire. (What a nice guy!)

MECHANICS

EXERCISE Rewrite each of the following sentences, inserting parentheses, end marks, and capital letters where necessary.

Example 1. Lyndon B. Johnson 1908–1973 was the thirty-sixth president of the United States.
Lyndon B. Johnson (1908–1973) was the thirty-sixth president of the United States.

1. Marilyn Bennett do you know her is my lawyer. ______

2. Rep. Patrick Kennedy D–Rhode Island was head of the committee. ______

3. We should plan to have dinner Monday night. (do you think your plane will arrive on time) ______

4. Your win way to go was extraordinary. ______

5. Of all the nominees four total I like him the best. ______

6. The Nile River see map on page 620 is the longest in the world. ______

7. The Luces Harry was in third grade with you are moving next door. ______

8. His letter how thrilled I was to receive it enclosed recent photos. ______

9. The photography exhibit January 28 through May 24 contains several of his pictures. ______

10. Lisa Richter is in your graduating class. (it is her sister that I knew from junior high) ______

Copyright © by Holt, Rinehart and Winston. All rights reserved.

Brackets

14y. Use brackets to enclose an explanation within quoted or parenthetical material.

EXAMPLE Please consult your map of the thirteen colonies (page 720 **[**Figure 1**]**).

Use brackets and the Latin word *sic* to indicate that an error existed in the original version of a quoted passage.

EXAMPLE "I'm so happy I can't hardly **[***sic***]** stand it," the new champion exclaimed.

EXERCISE On the line before each of the following sentences, write *C* if the sentence is already punctuated correctly or *I* if it is incorrect.

Example __C__ **1.** "This [the victory] means the world to me and my family," the mayor-elect stated.

______ **1.** "This championship is everything to the team and I (*sic*)," said the breathless coach.

______ **2.** "It [her father's death] caused the first lady considerable introspection," responded her press secretary.

______ **3.** For complete directions on knitting the cable sweater, see the instruction guide [page 218].

______ **4.** The new principal [have you met him?] has a son in the freshman class.

______ **5.** Lou Gehrig [baseball player (1903–1941)] was a courageous man.

______ **6.** She leaned toward me and stressed, "They [her two children] mean more to me than those awards ever will."

______ **7.** "He can just see for hisself [*sic*]," she vowed.

______ **8.** "I can never forget the day President Kennedy was assassinated. November 23 [*sic*], 1963, is forever etched in my mind," he explained.

______ **9.** Of Monet's [1840–1926] works, I am most drawn to his paintings of waterlilies.

______ **10.** For the path of General Sherman's troops, consult the "March to the Sea" map (page 344 [Figure 2]).

Copyright © by Holt, Rinehart and Winston. All rights reserved.

NAME ______ CLASS ______ DATE ______

for **CHAPTER 14: PUNCTUATION** *pages 430–432*

Dashes, Parentheses, and Brackets

14v. Use a dash to indicate an abrupt break in thought or speech.

14w. Use a dash to mean *namely, in other words,* or *that is* before an explanation.

14x. Use parentheses to enclose informative or explanatory material of minor importance.

14y. Use brackets to enclose an explanation within quoted or parenthetical material.

MECHANICS

EXERCISE A On the line before each of the following sentences, write *D* if the underlined words should be set off by dashes. Write *P* if they should be set off by parentheses. Write *B* if they should be set off by brackets.

Example ___P___ **1.** The Mississippi see map on page 26 is the longest river in the country.

______ **1.** Kirk Douglas born Issur Danielovitch has been a popular movie star for years.

______ **2.** W. C. Fields I love his movies was born in Philadelphia.

______ **3.** Harry Lillis Crosby (commonly called "Bing" 1903–1977) was a baritone.

______ **4.** Diana Ross remember her from the Supremes? starred in a film version of Billie Holiday's life.

______ **5.** "It the Miss Universe pageant has exceeded all my dreams," Miss Brazil gushed.

EXERCISE B Some of these sentences are punctuated correctly, and others are not. On the lines provided, revise each incorrect sentence. If a sentence is already correct, write *C* on the line.

Example **1.** The developer stated, "We will be pleased if the (City Council) members approve the plan." *The developer stated, "We will be pleased if the [City Council] members approve the plan."*

6. Thomas Paine [1737–1809] wrote the pamphlet *Common Sense.* ______

7. Chadds Ford—in southeastern Pennsylvania—is the home of Andrew Wyeth. ______

8. Marlene Dietrich's film *The Blue Angel* (1930) is, I believe, a classic. ______

9. The speaker quoted from the poem "The Hollow Men" (T. S. Eliot (1888–1965)). ______

10. The Dudleys do you know their son Jim? plan to be there. ______

Copyright © by Holt, Rinehart and Winston. All rights reserved.

NAME ____________ CLASS ____________ DATE ____________

Review A: Using Punctuation Correctly

EXERCISE A In most of the following sentences, a comma or no punctuation has been used where a semicolon or a colon should be. On the line provided, write the word preceding the error and add a semicolon or colon, whichever is needed. If a sentence is already correct, write C on the line. Hint: Some sentences contain more than one error.

Example 1. We had originally planned to leave on Sunday, however, we may not be able to get away until Tuesday. Sunday;

1. You should be able to define the following terms *irony, hyperbole, platitude,* and *stereotype.*

____

2. The game is scheduled for Saturday, in case of bad weather, it will be played on Sunday.

____

3. These students have won scholarships, Arcady Grant, Duke University, Shirley Isaacs, Stanford, and Carol Murphy, Notre Dame.

____

4. The youth director approves of our plans, in fact, she has offered to give us any help she can.

____

5. The basic ski equipment you will need includes the skis themselves, a pair of ski boots, and some ski poles.

____

EXERCISE B The following sentences require underlining (italics), quotation marks, and single quotation marks. Supply the necessary punctuation in each sentence. Be careful to show the correct position of quotation marks in relation to other punctuation.

Example 1. "For tomorrow's assignment, class, read Chapter 1 in the book Exploring Physics," said Mr. Abernathy.

6. Who wrote the poem Elegy in a Country Churchyard?

7. If I'd known that you were going to the party, Norris said, I'd have offered you a ride.

8. Aldous Huxley's essay Music at Night appears in the anthology Adventures in English Literature.

9. Salvador announced proudly, I've learned to play The Star-Spangled Banner on the piano.

10. Daphne told me that she had seen a movie version of the play Hamlet on television.

Copyright © by Holt, Rinehart and Winston. All rights reserved.

Review B: Using Punctuation Correctly

EXERCISE A In each of the following sentences, a comma or no punctuation has been used where a semicolon or a colon should be. On the line provided, write the word preceding the error and add a semicolon or colon, whichever is needed.

Example 1. The store appeared to be closed, therefore, we went home. closed;

1. The floor was strewn with wrenches, hammers, screwdrivers, and pliers, and drills, screws, and boxes of nails covered the table. ______
2. Hundreds of people shook the president's hand, thousands more lined the street and waved. ______
3. Many cities in the United States are named after European cities, for instance, Paris, Texas, is named after the capital of France. ______
4. You must bring three items on the day of the test your admission ticket, your birth certificate, and a sharpened pencil. ______
5. I have a new plan of action, divide and conquer. ______

EXERCISE B The following sentences call for the use of underlining (italics) and quotation marks. Supply the necessary punctuation in each sentence. Be careful to show the correct position of quotation marks in relation to other punctuation.

Example 1. Bill said, "I've finished reading The Scarlet Letter."

6. Ralph Ellison's essay Hidden Name and Complex Fate is included in his book Shadow and Act.
7. Is it true, she asked, that only the anthem O Canada would be sung in a World Series between Toronto and Montreal?
8. Celeste asked whether the word scissors is considered singular or plural.
9. I hope, she said, that you read the editorial in the Daily Record.
10. Do you know who wrote the line Where are the snows of yesteryear?

Copyright © by Holt, Rinehart and Winston. All rights reserved.

NAME ______________________ CLASS ______________ DATE ______________

Review C: Using Punctuation Correctly

EXERCISE A On the lines provided, rewrite the following passages, omitting the underlined parts. Use ellipsis points to indicate where the material has been omitted.

Example 1. Their friendship, tried and true, has lasted thirty-six years. *Their friendship . . . has lasted thirty-six years.*

1. It was a tall, aromatic red cedar tree. ______________________

2. True sympathy is sincere and never condescending. ______________________

____

3. Tony's here. He needs a ride. He's waiting on the porch. ______________________

____

4. April showers, /Cold and clear,/ Bring May flowers. ______________________

5. Do you want to come hiking with us? We will likely be gone three hours. I expect that we will be back long before dark. ______________________

____

EXERCISE B The following items involve the use of apostrophes, hyphens, dashes, parentheses, and brackets. Each item consists of three expressions. Two of the expressions are correct; one is wrong. Find the wrong expression, and on the line provided, write the expression correctly.

Example 1. (a) Shes a veterinarian. (b) Your 2's look like 7's. (c) Their apartment's on the third floor. *(a) She's a veterinarian.*

6. (a) a four-fifths majority (b) one half of the students (c) a magnificently-drawn picture

____

7. (a) Ohio map (p. 330 [Figure 1]) (b) Ohio River [p. 331 (Figure 1)] (c) "the Gettysburg Address of 1862 [*sic*]" ______________________

8. (a) They're all in the car. (b) He does'nt think we know. (c) The +'s and −'s are not clear.

____

9. (a) I thought—and still think—she knew the answer. (b) Representative Ferraro (New York) had opposed the measure. (c) His remarks were pro Italian. ______________________

____

10. (a) Sally's and my opinion (b) twenty minutes' work (c) a notebook that is your's

____

Copyright © by Holt, Rinehart and Winston. All rights reserved.

Good Spelling Habits

(1) Pronounce words carefully.
(2) Spell by syllables.
(3) Use a dictionary.
(4) Proofread for careless spelling errors.

Always re-read what you have written so that you can eliminate careless spelling errors, such as typos (*trail* for *trial*), missing letters (*goverment* for *government*), and the misuse of similar-sounding words (*except* for *accept*).

EXERCISE Proofread the following sentences, and identify any misspelled words. No proper nouns are misspelled. If you are unsure about the spelling of a word, use a dictionary. Cross out any misspelled word, and write the correctly spelled word above it. If a sentence has no spelling errors, write *C* after the sentence.

Example 1. ~~Latter~~ *Later* tonight we will watch my favorite Boris Karloff film.

1. The acter Boris Karloff was born in England in 1887.

2. In a career that spanned more than fifty years, Karloff became famous in films that repeatedly cast him as a villian.

3. In one of my favorits, *His Majesty, the American* (1919), Karloff played the evil leader of a gang of spies.

4. In one of his final films, *The Incredible Invasion* (1968), he played a scientist who's body was taken over by an alien from outer space.

5. Other frightning films in which Karloff appeared include *The Ghoul, The Mummy, The Raven, The Black Cat*, and *The Terror*.

6. Probly the most famous of all of Karloff's screen roles was in *Frankenstein*.

7. This film, based on a novell by Mary Shelley, was first released in 1931.

8. Movie versions of Frankenstein have since been made many times, but Karloff was the first person to bring the role of the monster to the screan.

9. The movie was so successful that sequels followed, including *The Bride of Frankenstein* (1935), *Son of Frankenstein* (1939), and *House of Frankenstein* (1944).

10. Karloff also starred in some humerous films that made fun of tipical monster movies, including *Abbott and Costello Meet the Killer: Boris Karloff*.

Copyright © by Holt, Rinehart and Winston. All rights reserved.

ie and *ei*

15a. Write *ie* when the sound is long *e*, except after *c*.

EXAMPLES	relief	grief	receipt	conceit
EXCEPTIONS	leisure	neither	either	species

15b. Write *ei* when the sound is not long *e*, especially when the sound is long *a*.

EXAMPLES	vein	reign	neighbor	freight
EXCEPTIONS	efficient	friend	soldier	review

MECHANICS

EXERCISE In the following sentences, cross out any misspelled word and write the correct spelling above it. If a sentence contains no misspelled words, write *C* after the sentence. All proper nouns are spelled correctly.

friend
Example 1. A ~~freind~~ showed me an article about an archaeological wonder.

1. In 1974 a terra-cotta army of artifacts, referred to as the Eighth Wonder of the World, was discovered in China.
2. More than seven thousand life-size soldeirs and horses were uncovered in the burial complex of China's first emperor Qin Shihuangdi.
3. As the excavations of the warriors continued, the site grew to the size of approximately four football feilds.
4. Archaeologists have diligently peiced together the crumbled clay figures and have re-created Shihuangdi's army.
5. By examining the terra-cotta figures, archaeologists have learned much about the anceint sculpting techniques used during the emperor's time.
6. Can you concieve of the amount of work involved in creating the army, which looked so terrifyingly real?
7. I beleive that in 1980 archaeologists found two horse-drawn, bronze chariots in a side tomb.
8. Scholars think that the soldiers were created either to escort the emperor into the afterlife or to celebrate his military victories.
9. According to Chinese history, Shihuangdi protected the secret of his terra-cotta army by feindishly burying alive anyone who knew about the burial complex.
10. Although the emperor was ruthless, he unified China by creating systems for writing, money, transportation, and wieghts and measures.

Copyright © by Holt, Rinehart and Winston. All rights reserved.

–cede, –ceed, and –sede

15c. The only English word that ends in –*sede* is *supersede*. The only words ending in –*ceed* are *exceed, proceed,* and *succeed.* Most other words with this sound end in –*cede*.

EXAMPLES re**cede** pre**cede** inter**cede** se**cede**

EXERCISE In the following sentences, cross out any misspelled word and write the correct spelling above it. If a sentence contains no misspelled words, write *C* after the sentence.

Example 1. Single-handedly, Mother ~~suceeded~~ *succeeded* in repairing our broken dishwasher.

1. Joel was about to conceed defeat when his opponent suddenly faltered.

2. In 1860, South Carolina was the first of the Southern states to secede from the Union.

3. To make her kitchen wheelchair-accessible, Melba will procede with her plan to lower the countertops and install tilt-out bins and roll-out shelves.

4. The school board will acceed to the request for additional teaching materials.

5. According to the exercise physiologist, Grandfather's heart rate while exercising should not excede 145 beats per minute.

6. A picture and a biography of the author can be found on the preceeding page.

7. In the 1898 Treaty of Paris, Spain granted Cuba its freedom, agreed to ceed Puerto Rico and Guam to the United States, and gave the Philippine Islands to the United States in exchange for $20 million.

8. Because your parents respect my judgment, let me interceed on your behalf.

9. At daybreak the valley's inhabitants were relieved to discover that the floodwaters had receeded.

10. Board games and conversation have superseded television as evening entertainment for our family.

Copyright © by Holt, Rinehart and Winston. All rights reserved.

NAME ____________ CLASS ____________ DATE ____________

Prefixes

A *prefix* is a letter or group of letters added to the beginning of a word to create a new word that has a different meaning.

15d. When adding a prefix, do not change the spelling of the original word.

EXAMPLES dis + similar = dis**similar** im + mature = im**mature**
over + eat = over**eat** un + natural = un**natural**

EXERCISE A On the line provided, spell correctly each of the following words by adding the prefix given.

Example 1. dis + position *disposition*

1. over + ride ____________
2. mis + state ____________
3. hyper + active ____________
4. re + entry ____________
5. dis + locate ____________
6. il + logical ____________
7. anti + social ____________
8. pre + date ____________
9. mis + spell ____________
10. dis + engage ____________
11. dis + embark ____________
12. im + passive ____________
13. re + fill ____________
14. dis + satisfied ____________
15. pre + dispose ____________
16. re + finance ____________
17. im + mobilize ____________
18. dis + continue ____________
19. mis + spend ____________
20. im + measurable ____________

EXERCISE B In the following sentences, cross out any misspelled word and write the correct spelling above it.

Example 1. Much to our ~~dissappointment~~ *disappointment*, the concert was canceled.

21. To overcome her irational fear of the water, Aunt May has enrolled in a swimming class.
22. Because of the weather, we were forced to depplane in Pittsburgh although our destination was Chicago.
23. The Paleolithic Age is the name given to the earliest part of human prehhistory, although the period is also known as the Old Stone Age or the Ice Age.
24. For centuries, humankind has searched the globe for potions that will guarantee imortality.
25. The largest human migration in modern history occurred between 1892 and 1954 when twelve million imigrants were processed at Ellis Island.

Copyright © by Holt, Rinehart and Winston. All rights reserved.

Suffixes A

15e. When adding the suffix *–ness* or *–ly,* do not change the spelling of the original word.

EXAMPLES keen + ness = **keen**ness habitual + ly = **habitual**ly

For most words that have two or more syllables and end in *y,* change the *y* to *i* before adding *–ness* or *–ly.*

EXAMPLES silly + ness = silli**ness** merry + ly = merri**ly**

EXERCISE A On the line provided, correctly spell out each of the following words by adding the suffix given.

Example 1. happy + ly *happily*

1. general + ly ______
2. lean + ness ______
3. friend + ly ______
4. truthful + ly ______
5. empty + ness ______
6. sly + ly ______
7. swift + ness ______
8. quick + ly ______
9. gentle + ness ______
10. joyous + ly ______
11. open + ness ______
12. royal + ly ______
13. wool + ly ______
14. careful + ly ______
15. steady + ly ______
16. mean + ness ______
17. coward + ly ______
18. plain + ness ______
19. heavy + ness ______
20. busy + ly ______

EXERCISE B In the following sentences, cross out any misspelled word and write the correct spelling above it.

Example 1. The ~~strenuoussness~~ *strenuousness* of the first day of practice did not hamper the players' enthusiasm.

21. Although it is socialy acceptable for Kuwaiti women to wear European clothes to work or outside the house, they usually wear a traditional *dara'a,* or housecoat, once they get home.
22. Thanks to the valiant efforts of the firefighters, the small child was returned safly to her mother.
23. Artist Gerardo Tena consistenttly wins prizes for his innovative Mata Ortiz pottery.
24. The suddeness of Rosa's arrival ruined our birthday surprise for her.
25. According to Buddhist thought, attaining happyness that relates to the mind and the heart requires training.

Copyright © by Holt, Rinehart and Winston. All rights reserved.

Suffixes B

15f. Drop the final silent *e* before adding a suffix that begins with a vowel.

EXAMPLES approve + al = **approv**al desire + ed = **desir**ed

EXCEPTIONS peace + able = peace**able** courage + ous = courage**ous**

15g. Keep the final silent *e* before adding a suffix that begins with a consonant.

EXAMPLES hope + less = hope**less** nice + ly = nice**ly**

EXCEPTIONS awe + ful = **aw**ful whole + ly = **whol**ly

EXERCISE A On the line provided, correctly spell out each of the following words by adding the suffix given.

Example 1. lie + ing *lying*

1. house + ing ______
2. serene + ly ______
3. polite + ness ______
4. involve + ment ______
5. seize + ure ______
6. enforce + able ______
7. lone + ly ______
8. tie + ing ______
9. cringe + ing ______
10. home + less ______
11. nature + al ______
12. accommodate + ion ______
13. immediate + ly ______
14. contrite + ness ______
15. definite + ly ______
16. care + ing ______
17. achieve + ment ______
18. separate + ion ______
19. require + ment ______
20. advantage + ous ______

EXERCISE B In the following sentences, cross out any misspelled word and write the correct spelling above it.

Example 1. My ~~fascinateion~~ *fascination* with the country of Senegal has fueled my research.

21. After tasteing a Senegalese dish of fish and rice called *cheb-ou-jen,* I want to try more of the country's traditional foods.
22. The relations between the seven major ethnic groups of Senegal are, in general, peacful.
23. Since gaining its independence from France in 1960, Senegal has noticed a declineing economy.
24. How amazeing that the Senegalese economy relies almost entirely on one export product: peanuts.
25. One of the most popular forms of amusment in Senegal is storytelling, which serves as a valuable vehicle for educating the children.

Copyright © by Holt, Rinehart and Winston. All rights reserved.

NAME ______________________ CLASS ______________ DATE ______________

Suffixes C

15h. For words ending in *y* preceded by a consonant, change the *y* to *i* before adding any suffix that does not begin with *i*.

EXAMPLES plenty + ful = plent**iful** defy + ing = def**ying**
EXCEPTIONS shy + ness = sh**yness** wry + ly = wr**yly**

15i. For words ending in *y* preceded by a vowel, keep the *y* when adding a suffix.

EXAMPLES obey + ed = obe**yed** annoy + ance = anno**yance**
EXCEPTIONS day + ly = da**ily** say + ed = sa**id**

EXERCISE A On the line provided, correctly spell out each of the following words by adding the suffix given.

Example 1. bossy + est *bossiest*

1. bounty + ful ______
2. deny + ed ______
3. comply + ance ______
4. industry + ous ______
5. convey + ed ______
6. pay + ment ______
7. duty + ful ______
8. dreary + ness ______
9. decay + ed ______
10. gray + est ______
11. cagey + ness ______
12. comedy + an ______
13. annoy + ed ______
14. rely + ing ______
15. harmony + ous ______
16. funny + est ______
17. pay + ed ______
18. deploy + ment ______
19. brassy + ness ______
20. lay + ed ______

EXERCISE B In the following sentences, cross out any misspelled word and write the correct spelling above it.

Example 1. I was more saddened than angered by my friend's ~~betraial~~. *betrayal*

21. The counselor told me to check the *Occupational Outlook Handbook* for a description of various jobs, the education required for each, and emploiment trends.
22. Is this Blackfoot ceremonyal headdress worn during the Sun Dance?
23. The guest speaker was a dignifyed gentleman with a white beard and a twinkle in his eye.
24. Dressed in white satin and lace, the bride carryed a beautiful bouquet of red roses and calla lilies.
25. Because we camped in an arid climate, Maxine constantly complained about the driness of her skin.

Copyright © by Holt, Rinehart and Winston. All rights reserved.

NAME ______________________ CLASS ____________ DATE ____________

for CHAPTER 15: SPELLING **page 447**

Suffixes D

15j. Double the final consonant before adding a suffix that begins with a vowel if the word both (1) has only one syllable or has the accent on the final syllable and (2) ends in a single consonant preceded by a single vowel.

EXAMPLES run + er = run**ner** propel + ing = propel**ling**

When a word satisfies both conditions but the addition of the suffix causes the accent to shift, do not double the final consonant.

EXAMPLES defer + ence = defe**rence** profit + eer = profi**teer**

MECHANICS

EXERCISE A On the line provided, correctly spell out each of the following words by adding the suffix given.

Example 1. shovel + ing *shoveling*

1. slim + er ______________
2. permit + ed ______________
3. hot + est ______________
4. forget + able ______________
5. differ + ence ______________
6. drip + ing ______________
7. mud + y ______________
8. feel + ing ______________
9. regret + ed ______________
10. remit + ance ______________
11. excel + ed ______________
12. skim + ed ______________
13. treat + ing ______________
14. mop + ing ______________
15. select + ing ______________
16. refer + ing ______________
17. grab + ed ______________
18. regret + able ______________
19. deter + ence ______________
20. prefer + able ______________

EXERCISE B In the following sentences, cross out any misspelled word and write the correct spelling above it.

Example 1. Thirty minutes has been ~~alloted~~ *allotted* for the reading comprehension test.

21. Throughout his e-mail message, Jose made several referrences to his upcoming trip to Guatemala.
22. Balance and muscle movement are controled by the part of the brain called the cerebellum.
23. The Wright brothers, inventors of the first practical airplane, built their first propeler in 1903.
24. To gather information for my research project, I scaned numerous newspaper and magazine articles.
25. Our community Meals on Wheels program benefitted not only the recipients of the meals but also the volunteers who delivered them.

Copyright © by Holt, Rinehart and Winston. All rights reserved.

ie and *ei*; *–cede*, *–ceed*, and *–sede*; Prefixes and Suffixes

Be careful when spelling words with *ie* and *ei* and in spelling words with *–cede*, *–ceed* and *–sede*.

EXAMPLES thi**ef** forf**eit** con**cede** pro**ceed** super**sede**

Be careful when spelling words to which prefixes and suffixes have been added.

EXAMPLES **il**legal **royal**ly **activ**ity **care**ful **sunn**ier **trimm**er

EXERCISE A Circle the one misspelled word in each of the following groups of words.

Example 1. handkerchief, immovable, busily, referrence

1. truely, propeller, spicier, freight

2. intercede, ilogical, funniest, noticeable

3. overrated, amusement, gentleness, procede

4. dissappointment, counterfeit, forgettable, ninety

5. paid, steadiness, couragous, excelled

EXERCISE B In the following sentences, cross out any misspelled word and write the correct spelling above it. Some sentences may have more than one misspelled word.

Example 1. Through Internet research, I ~~discoverred~~ *discovered* the ~~amazeing~~ *amazing* history behind Grandmother's Panamanian *mosqueta* brooch.

6. A *mosqueta*, created by artisticaly combineing gold and pearls, has become a symbol of Panama.

7. Although its origin is mysteryous, the brooch, resembleing a flower, was named *mosqueta*—the Spanish name for the white musk roses of the Mediterranean area.

8. Balboa was probably the first foriegner to know of Panama's pearl beds.

9. According to legend, on Balboa's famous trek across the Isthmus of Panama, he made the acquainttance of a Native American cheif whose costume consistted mainly of pearls.

10. One of the earlyest written records of Panamanian pearl jewelry was made in 1821 by a French engineer who was visiting.

11. He tells of women, prouddly wearing earrings and combs of gold and pearls, celebrateing Panama's independence from Spain.

12. Although the pearls were plentyful, acquireing the treasures of the deep was not an easy task.

13. In 1938, the red tide—a natural phenomenon caused by a reproduceing organism—destroied Panama's oyster beds and, regretably, the pearl supply.

14. In the 1950's, Panama's production of *mosquetas* was resummed, but the coveted peices of jewelry were made with cultured pearls imported from Japan.

15. Imported filigree wire was another innoveation that changed the creation of the *mosqueta*.

Copyright © by Holt, Rinehart and Winston. All rights reserved.

NAME ______________________ CLASS ______________ DATE ______________

for **CHAPTER 15: SPELLING** *page 449*

Plurals A

15k. Remembering the following rules will help you spell the plural forms of nouns.

(1) For most nouns, add *s.*

EXAMPLES regret—regret**s** African—African**s** cardinal—cardinal**s**

(2) For nouns ending in *s, x, z, ch,* or *sh,* add *es.*

EXAMPLES class—class**es** tax—tax**es** Valdez—Valdez**es**

(3) For nouns ending in *y* preceded by a vowel, add *s.*

EXAMPLES buoy—buoy**s** volley—volley**s** Saturday—Saturday**s**

(4) For nouns ending in *y* preceded by a consonant, change the *y* to *i* and add *es.*

EXAMPLES poppy—popp**ies** sky—sk**ies** intricacy—intricac**ies**

MECHANICS

EXERCISE A On the line provided, write the plural form of each noun below.

Example 1. birch *birches*

1. booth ______
2. dish ______
3. observatory ______
4. history ______
5. moustache ______
6. pouch ______
7. subsidy ______
8. luxury ______
9. Thursday ______
10. hierarchy ______
11. missionary ______
12. wrench ______
13. hermit ______
14. medley ______
15. ambush ______
16. Ruiz ______
17. alloy ______
18. temptress ______
19. minority ______
20. phalanx ______

EXERCISE B Circle the one misspelled word in each of the following groups of words.

Example 1. alibis, (faxs,) trolleys, replays

21. trenchs, commodities, monkeys, flashes
22. intermediaries, Mondays, fireflys, foxes
23. monuments, dresses, punches, theorys
24. queries, scratches, seagulles, quizzes
25. sculptresses, crucifixs, cemeteries, peaches

Copyright © by Holt, Rinehart and Winston. All rights reserved.

NAME CLASS DATE

Plurals B

15k. Remembering the following rules will help you spell the plural forms of nouns.

(5) For some nouns ending in *f* or *fe,* add *s.* For others, change the *f* or *fe* to *v* and add *es.*

EXAMPLES proof—proof**s** leaf—lea**ves** wife—wi**ves**

(6) For nouns ending in *o* preceded by a vowel, add *s.*

EXAMPLES ratio—ratio**s** cameo—cameo**s** folio—folio**s**

(7) For many nouns ending in *o* preceded by a consonant, add *es.*

For some common nouns, especially those referring to music, and for most proper nouns, add *s.*

EXAMPLES potato—potato**es** solo—solo**s** Bono—Bono**s**

EXERCISE A On the line provided, write the plural form of each noun below.

Example 1. imbroglio *imbroglios*

1. belief ____
2. scenario ____
3. waif ____
4. tomato ____
5. sheriff ____
6. video ____
7. carafe ____
8. piano ____
9. hairdo ____
10. loaf ____
11. reef ____
12. soprano ____
13. knife ____
14. tattoo ____
15. Calvino ____
16. studio ____
17. hoof ____
18. echo ____
19. stereo ____
20. innuendo ____

EXERCISE B In the following sentences, cross out any misspelled word and write the correct spelling above it. If a sentence contains no misspelled words, write *C* beside the sentence's number.

Example 1. We may take portable ~~radioes~~ *radios* with headphones on our camping trip.

21. If possible, leave the skins on potatos, for the skin is both nutritious and flavorful.
22. Giraffes may appear to move slowly, but they're able to run thirty-five miles per hour.
23. "Two halfs make a whole," I explained to my little sister, who is curious about fractions.
24. Female bottle-nosed dolphins bear single calfes, which swim and breathe minutes after birth.
25. At the beginning of this song, the altoes harmonize beautifully.

Copyright © by Holt, Rinehart and Winston. All rights reserved.

NAME ____________________ CLASS ____________________ DATE ____________________

Plurals C

The plurals of nouns are formed in different ways.

EXAMPLES computer—computer**s** waltz—waltz**es** alley—alley**s**
tri**l**ogy—trilog**ies** belief—belief**s** thief—thie**ves**
scenario—scenario**s** torpedo—torpedo**es** alto—alto**s**

EXERCISE A One word in each of the following groups of words is misspelled. In each group, cross out the misspelled word, and write the correct spelling above it.

Example 1. ~~proofes~~ *proofs*, addresses, Kelleys, convoys

1. languages, ditchs, quizzes, torpedoes

2. academys, essays, tornadoes, prescriptions

3. carafes, strategies, cameos, rooves

4. headdresses, studios, technicalitys, trenches

5. strawberries, ranchs, hairdos, midwives

6. democracies, assessments, tabooes, classes

7. ratioes, kidneys, lives, sorceresses

8. hooves, stereos, sphinxs, sororities

9. syringes, anthologies, videoes, sheriffs

10. Tuesdays, symphonys, echoes, loaves

EXERCISE B In the following sentences, cross out any misspelled word and write the correct spelling above it. Some sentences may have more than one misspelled word.

Example 1. The talented seamstresses used ribbon and ~~buttones~~ *buttons* to hide the fabric's ~~irregularitys~~ *irregularities*.

11. The curtain opened slowly to reveal three grand pianoes and two celloes but no performers.

12. Topped with fresh garlic and lemon zest, my favorite casserole contains thin layers of potatos, spinach, and tomatos.

13. Place the trophys on these shelfs.

14. Does Robert Tree Cody Red Cedar Whistle play flute soloes on the CD *White Buffalo*?

15. Hoping their enemys were retreating, the soldiers could hear the receding echos of gunfire.

16. The grass clippings, leafs, and dead branchs can be added to the compost pile.

17. In honor of our country's heros, how many monumentes have been erected in Washington, D.C.?

18. Unpacking the boxs in the attic, we found photoes depicting Grandmother's childhood in Japan.

19. The missionarys convinced the warring chieves to put aside their knifes and spears and to communicate peacefully.

20. I enjoy the contemporary songes of Sergio and Odair Assad, virtuosoes of the classical guitar.

Copyright © by Holt, Rinehart and Winston. All rights reserved.

NAME ______ CLASS ______ DATE ______

for **CHAPTER 15: SPELLING** page 450

Plurals D

15k. Remembering the following rules will help you spell the plural forms of nouns.

(8) The plurals of a few nouns are formed irregularly.

EXAMPLES child—child**ren** louse—**lice** goose—g**ee**se

(9) For a few nouns, the singular and plural forms are the same.

EXAMPLES grouse—grouse Chinese—Chinese clothes—clothes

MECHANICS

EXERCISE A On the line provided, write the plural form of each noun below.

Example 1. foot *feet*

1. mouse ______
2. woman ______
3. sheep ______
4. Vietnamese ______
5. scissors ______
6. bass ______
7. tooth ______
8. trout ______
9. corps ______
10. Swiss ______
11. shrimp ______
12. politics ______
13. salmon ______
14. gentleman ______
15. ox ______
16. chassis ______
17. species ______
18. Sioux ______
19. moose ______
20. aircraft ______

EXERCISE B In the following sentences, cross out any misspelled word and write the correct spelling above it. If a sentence contains no misspelled words, write *C* after the sentence.

Example 1. We finally had to fence our yard to deter the ~~wolfs~~. *wolves*

21. To practice his addition skills, my little brother rolls three dices and calculates the sum.
22. Are reindeer domesticated as a source of milk?
23. Although squashes are not usually eaten raw, the word *squash* is derived from the Narragansett Indian word *asquutasquash,* meaning "that which is eaten raw."
24. More than three hundred childs will compete in our region's Special Olympics this year.
25. For the fruit salad we will need pears, strawberries, grapefruits, bananas, and apples.

Copyright © by Holt, Rinehart and Winston. All rights reserved.

Plurals E

15k. Remembering the following rules will help you spell the plural forms of nouns.

(10) For most compound nouns, form the plural of only the last word of the compound.

EXAMPLES alarm clock—alarm clock**s** cheerleader—cheerleader**s**

(11) For compound nouns in which one of the words is modified by the other word or words, form the plural of the noun modified.

EXAMPLES bill of sale—bill**s** of sale hanger-on—hanger**s**-on

EXERCISE A On the line provided, write the plural form of each noun below.

Example 1. kiss of peace *kisses of peace*

1. ladybug ____________

2. choirmaster ____________

3. dogcatcher ____________

4. general assembly ____________

5. passer-by ____________

6. disc jockey ____________

7. firefighter ____________

8. chief of staff ____________

9. charge account ____________

10. air bag ____________

11. justice of the peace ____________

12. forty-five-year-old ____________

13. chamber of commerce ____________

14. chaise lounge ____________

15. post office ____________

16. commander in chief ____________

17. gearbox ____________

18. chief executive officer ____________

19. dockworker ____________

20. letter of advice ____________

EXERCISE B In the following sentences, cross out any misspelled compound noun and write the correct spelling above it. If a sentence contains no misspelled words, write *C* after the sentence.

Example 1. Both of the ~~dinners theater~~ *dinner theaters* in Ashland are featuring Shakespearean plays.

21. The bride is designing the gowns that her maid of honors will wear in the wedding.

22. What kinds of prizes will the contest's runner-ups receive?

23. In June my brother-in-laws are traveling to Jamaica to attend the Fisherman's Festival.

24. The young entrepreneurs, anxious to begin their lawn-care business, built several lean-tos for equipment storage.

25. At the garage sale we found two matching chests of drawers that were reasonably priced.

Copyright © by Holt, Rinehart and Winston. All rights reserved.

Plurals F

15k. Remembering the following rules will help you spell the plural forms of nouns.

(12) For some nouns borrowed from other languages, the plural is formed as in the original language.

EXAMPLES addendum—addend**a** crisis—cris**es**

A few nouns borrowed from other languages have two acceptable plural forms.

EXAMPLES vertex—vertex**es,** vert**ices** syllabus—syllabus**es,** syllab**i**

EXERCISE A On the line provided, write the plural form or forms of each noun below. Consult a dictionary, if necessary.

Example 1. atrium *antra, antrums*

1. alumnus
2. basis
3. apex
4. phenomenon
5. millennium
6. larva
7. seraph
8. vertebra
9. fibula
10. medium
11. alumna
12. radius
13. chateau
14. cactus
15. antenna
16. curriculum
17. ampulla
18. stigma
19. datum
20. octopus

EXERCISE B In the following sentences, cross out any misspelled noun and write the correct spelling above it. If a sentence contains no misspelled words, write *C* after the sentence.

Example 1. Covered with ~~verrueas,~~ *verrucae* or warts, my pet toad is endearingly ugly.

21. Using tables of contents and indexs can facilitate the research process.
22. Rosa is creating a book titled *School Quotations* in which she is including dictums from classmates and teachers.
23. Algaes serve a vital function in an ecosystem, but they can deplete the oxygen supply and can block light from plant life.
24. Is it necessary to memorize the molecular formulaes for tomorrow's test?
25. The International Food Fair featured several dishes made from cacti; my favorite was nopal cactus salad with cilantro.

Copyright © by Holt, Rinehart and Winston. All rights reserved.

NAME ______________________ CLASS ______________ DATE ______________

Plurals G

15k. Remembering the following rules will help you spell the plural forms of nouns.

(13) To form the plurals of numerals, most uppercase letters, symbols, and most words referred to as words, add an *s* or both an apostrophe and an *s*.

EXAMPLES 2—2**s,** 2**'s** 1300—1300**s,** 1300**'s** *T*—*T***s,** or *T***'s**

+—+**s,** +**'s** *but*—*but***s,** *but***'s**

To prevent confusion, add both an apostrophe and an *s* to form the plural of all lowercase letters, certain uppercase letters, and some words referred to as words.

EXAMPLES *k*—*k***'s** *I*—*I***'s** *her*—*her***'s**

MECHANICS

EXERCISE For each of the following sentences, write on the line provided the plural form of the noun in parentheses.

Example 1. *(A)* Did you make all ___A's___ this semester?

1. *(6)* Our new phone number, which is extremely easy to remember, has four ______________ in it.

2. *(i)* Marcia is in love again; she is dotting her ______________ by drawing little hearts.

3. *(and)* Watching my recorded speech has made me aware of how many ______________ I use.

4. (1990) Some historians believe that the ______________ were more turbulent than any other decade of the century.

5. *(u)* I often misspell *Uruguay,* for I forget that it has three ______________.

6. ($) Mother added ______________ to all the figures in the columns on the family's annual budget.

7. *(goodbye)* After saying their ______________ at the station, Rico's family boarded the train to San Francisco.

8. *(3)* My little sister, who is just learning to write, makes her ______________ backwards.

9. *(you)* Mr. Garcia suggested that I replace some of the ______________ in my paper with proper nouns that are more exact.

10. *(G)* Look through the ______________ in the telephone book to see if *Gernhardt* is listed.

Copyright © by Holt, Rinehart and Winston. All rights reserved.

NAME ______________ CLASS ______________ DATE ______________

Plurals H

The plurals of nouns are formed in different ways.

EXAMPLES tooth—tee**th** corps—corps post office—post office**s**
head of state—head**s** of state phenomenon—phenomen**a**
radius—radi**i**, radius**es** 2—2**s**, 2**'s** *B*—*B***'s** *so*—*so***'s**

EXERCISE A On the line provided, write the plural form or forms of each noun below.

Example 1. appendix *appendixes or appendices*

1. midshipman ______________
2. kickstand ______________
3. 7 ______________
4. tableau ______________
5. bill of sale ______________
6. *and* ______________
7. Portuguese ______________
8. parenthesis ______________
9. *F* ______________
10. louse ______________

EXERCISE B In the following sentences, cross out any misspelled noun and write the correct spelling above it. If a sentence contains no misspelled words, write *C* after the sentence.

Example 1. After saying their ~~*I dos,*~~ *I do's* the bride and groom recited a poem.

11. Two North American grouses, the blue grouse and the spruce grouse, are sometimes called "fool hens" because their fearlessness makes them easy to hunt.
12. Between the ages of six and twelve, humans generally lose their twenty deciduous, or baby, tooths.
13. Although my family owns six alarms clock, we still overslept this morning!
14. Most of the passer-bys stopped to examine the vendor's wares.
15. My peer editor suggested that I shorten the sentences in my paper by removing some of the *ands*.
16. How many female Wellesley College alumnae, besides Hillary Rodham Clinton, continued their education at Yale University Law School?
17. Coincidentally, my two sisters' mother-in-laws were born on the same day.
18. Although the Swisses in the exchange student program speak English, their native language is German.
19. Through several family crisises, Sue has managed to keep her sense of humor.
20. Between the vertebraes are intervertebral disks, which permit various movements of the spinal column.

Copyright © by Holt, Rinehart and Winston. All rights reserved.

NAME ____________ CLASS ____________ DATE ____________

Numbers

15l. Spell out a ***cardinal number***—a number that states how many—if it can be expressed in one or two words. Otherwise, use numerals.

EXAMPLES **fourteen** boxes **three hundred** animals **366** books

15m. Spell out a number that begins a sentence.

EXAMPLE **Thirty-five** short stories were submitted for publication.

15n. Spell out an ***ordinal number***—a number that expresses order.

EXAMPLE Natalie was the **fifth** finisher in the marathon.

15o. Use numerals to express numbers in conventional situations.

EXAMPLES page **63** April **6, 1993** **303** Davis Drive **3:25** P.M.

EXERCISE In the following sentences, cross out any number that has been written incorrectly and write the correct form above it. If a sentence contains no errors in the usage of numbers, write *C* after the sentence.

Example 1. ~~5~~ *Five* of my friends and I have joined a Sherlock Holmes club.

1. The name of our club, which has 35 members, is the Seattle Sherlockian Society.
2. So that everyone has a copy of the bylaws, I made 40 5-page booklets.
3. Through research we discovered that we are not alone in our fascination for Sherlock Holmes; approximately 7 Sherlockian societies exist in the San Francisco Bay area alone.
4. Because time was limited, we were able to visit only 15 Web sites dedicated to Sherlock Holmes, but many more exist.
5. Several members of our club plan to attend a Sherlockian conference in Chicago, Illinois, tentatively scheduled for July fifteenth, 2003.
6. Holmes's creator, Sir Arthur Conan Doyle, was born in Edinburgh in eighteen hundred fifty-nine.
7. Conan Doyle wrote 4 novels and fifty-six short stories featuring Sherlock Holmes.
8. Wouldn't you like to visit the Sherlock Holmes Museum at 221b Baker Street in London, England?
9. On the 1st floor of the museum, visitors can see the study—made famous by Doyle's stories—overlooking Baker Street.
10. Tonight at eight thirty P.M. my favorite Sherlock Holmes movie, *The Hound of the Baskervilles*, is playing on television.

Copyright © by Holt, Rinehart and Winston. All rights reserved.

Words Often Confused A

Review the Words Often Confused covered on pages 456–457 of your textbook for information on the correct spelling and usage of the following words:

all ready, already	*altar, alter*	*born, borne*
all right	*assure, ensure, insure*	*brake, break*
all together, altogether		

Exercise From the choice in parentheses, underline the correct word or words for each of the following sentences.

Example 1. The tailor will *(altar, alter)* the suit to fit.

1. I have *(all ready, already)* explored my options for summer employment.
2. The mission of the United Nations is to bring the world's people *(all together, altogether)* in peace and cooperation.
3. "I *(assure, ensure, insure)* you that the election results will be available before midnight," announced the incumbent's campaign manager.
4. Derek Walcott was *(born, borne)* on the island of Saint Lucia in 1930.
5. After a family vote we unanimously decided that leaving unwashed dishes in the sink overnight is not *(allright, all right)*.
6. Father, who taught me to drive, insisted that I never apply the *(brake, break)* with my left foot.
7. The huge, ornately carved *(altar, alter)* was the focal point of the church's décor.
8. Will a letter of introduction *(assure, ensure, insure)* me an interview?
9. The master of ceremonies will not begin the questioning until the contestants are *(all ready, already)*.
10. Did the casserole dish *(brake, break)* when you dropped it?

Copyright © by Holt, Rinehart and Winston. All rights reserved.

Words Often Confused B

Review the Words Often Confused covered on pages 457–459 of your textbook for information on the correct spelling and usage of the following words:

capital, capitol *coarse, course* *consul, council, councilor,*
choose, chose *complement, compliment* *counsel, counselor*
clothes, cloths *desert, desert, dessert*

EXERCISE From the choice in parentheses, underline the correct word for each of the following sentences. Notice that each sentence contains two sets of words in parentheses.

Example 1. I (*chose, choose*) to eat a light meal so I would feel hungry for (*desert, dessert*).

1. I will not (*desert, dessert*) my running partners although the marathon (*coarse, course*) is a difficult one.

2. Of (*coarse, course*), the (*capital, capitol*) of Belize is Belmopan.

3. Please (*complement, compliment*) the chef for this wonderful (*desert, dessert*).

4. These (*cloths, clothes*) are not effective for dusting because the fabric from which they are made is too (*coarse, course*).

5. On the steps of the (*capital, capitol*), Grandfather had his picture taken with the Japanese (*consul, council, counsel*), whose name is Tatsuo Tanaka.

6. With suitcase space so limited, do you (*choose, chose*) to pack more (*clothes, cloths*) to wear or more books to read?

7. The school (*councilor, counselor*) suggested that I look for a cautious, reticent friend to (*complement, compliment*) my impulsive, outspoken personality.

8. I accepted the wise (*consul, council, counsel*) of my parents concerning the type of (*cloths, clothes*) to wear for the job interview.

9. The entrepreneur's (*coarse, course*) mannerisms will hinder his efforts to acquire (*capital, capitol*) for his business.

10. Do you agree with the city (*consul's, council's, counsel's*) (*coarse, course*) of action to renovate the downtown area?

Copyright © by Holt, Rinehart and Winston. All rights reserved.

Words Often Confused C

Review the Words Often Confused covered on pages 459–461 of your textbook for information on the correct spelling and usage of the following words:

formally, formerly *lead, led, lead* *miner, minor*
its, it's *loose, lose* *moral, morale*
later, latter

EXERCISE From the choice in parentheses, underline the correct word or words for each of the following sentences. Notice that each sentence contains two sets of words in parentheses.

Example 1. My watch has stopped; *(its, it's) (later, latter)* than we think.

1. The valedictorian will *(lead, led)* the other seniors on stage, where their diplomas will be *(formally, formerly)* presented.
2. Because *(its, it's)* collar is too *(loose, lose)*, our dog often manages to escape and roam the neighborhood.
3. At halftime the captain *(lead, led)* a rousing cheer to boost the team's *(moral, morale)*.
4. *(Formally, Formerly)*, coal *(miners, minors)* suffered numerous occupational hazards; however, passage of the 1969 Federal Coal Mine Health and Safety Act provided health compensation and set safety standards.
5. When given the choice of *(loosing, losing)* or winning, I'll choose the *(later, latter)*.
6. Having no *(lead, led)* for my mechanical pencil is a *(miner, minor)* annoyance.
7. *(Its, It's)* never too late to ponder one's *(moral, morale)* obligations.
8. *(Later, Latter)* this afternoon our tour guide will *(lead, led)* us through the Mid-America All-Indian Center.
9. After an unsuccessful attack by poachers, the gorilla *(lead, led) (its, it's)* group to safety.
10. After witnessing a serious argument between my friends, I've decided that my *(moral, morale)* reflection is "Never *(loose, lose)* your sense of humor!"

Copyright © by Holt, Rinehart and Winston. All rights reserved.

NAME CLASS DATE

Words Often Confused D

Review the Words Often Confused covered on pages 461–463 of your textbook for information on the correct spelling and usage of the following words:

passed, past ***plain, plane*** ***quiet, quite***
peace, piece ***principal, principle*** ***stationary, stationery***
personal, personnel

EXERCISE From the choice in parentheses, underline the correct word for each of the following sentences. Notice that each sentence contains two sets of words in parentheses.

Example 1. It is (*plain, plane*) to see that the felon lacks (*principals, principles*).

1. Avoid using flashy, colorful (*stationary, stationery*) if you are writing a letter to the head of (*personal, personnel*).

2. For my woodworking project, I will need a (*plain, plane*), a level, some sandpaper, and several (*peaces, pieces*) of wood.

3. To find the school cafeteria, go (*passed, past*) the (*principal's, principle's*) office and turn right.

4. Josh meditates for an hour every morning; he claims that he needs this (*personal, personnel*) time to find (*peace, piece*) of mind before beginning a hectic day.

5. As I (*passed, past*) by the classroom door, I noticed how (*quiet, quite*) and attentive the children were.

6. Our yoga teacher can remain (*stationary, stationery*) on one leg for (*quiet, quite*) a long time.

7. Simplicity of dress, (*plain, plane*) living, and a strong desire for (*peace, piece*) characterize the more conservative Mennonite groups.

8. Riding a (*stationary, stationery*) bicycle is Alicia's (*principal, principle*) form of exercise.

9. A woman of (*principal, principle*), Grandmother made us (*quiet, quite*) aware of the difference between right and wrong.

10. "How much longer will we remain (*stationary, stationery*)?" asked the first passenger to board the (*plain, plane*).

MECHANICS

Copyright © by Holt, Rinehart and Winston. All rights reserved.

Words Often Confused E

Review the Words Often Confused covered on pages 463–464 of your textbook for information on the correct spelling and usage of the following words:

than, then	*to, too, two*	*who's, whose*
their, there, they're	*waist, waste*	*your, you're*

EXERCISE From the choice in parentheses, underline the correct word for each of the following sentences.

Example 1. My grandparents hope to revisit *(their, there, they're)* native country of Tibet.

1. Higher *(than, then)* any other region in the world, Tibet has an average altitude of 16,000 feet.
2. The country includes expansive areas of land *(to, too, two)* cold and windswept for the growth of any vegetation.
3. The Chinese invasion in 1951 resulted in cultural upheaval for the Tibetans, *(who's, whose)* way of life had been static for centuries.
4. Most Tibetans are Buddhists, and religion is an integral part of *(their, there, they're)* lives.
5. *(Who's, Whose)* the current Dalai Lama, or spiritual leader, of Tibetan Buddhism?
6. While traveling in Tibet, *(your, you're)* likely to eat yak meat, for it has been a staple of the Tibetan diet for thousands of years.
7. Little of the domesticated yak is *(waisted, wasted)*: Its milk is used for cheese and butter; the meat is eaten; the bones are made into jewelry and utensils; the hide and fur become clothes, rope, and tents; and the dried dung is used as fuel.
8. *(To, Too, Two)* instruments used in Tibet's religious music are the thigh-bone drum and the double-skull drum.
9. The *chuba,* a long-sleeved cloak fastened at the *(waist, waste)* with a colorful belt, is the national dress for both men and women.
10. *(Their, There, They're)* is much to learn about this fascinating country.

MECHANICS

Copyright © by Holt, Rinehart and Winston. All rights reserved.

Review A: Spelling Rules

EXERCISE A On the line provided, correctly spell out each of the following words by adding the prefix or suffix given.

Example 1. mis + state ___misstate___

1. un + known ______
2. glory + ous ______
3. service + able ______
4. endure + ing ______
5. real + ly ______
6. kindly + ness ______
7. true + ness ______
8. blue + ly ______
9. skim + ing ______
10. sly + ness ______

EXERCISE B On the line provided, write the plural form of each noun below.

Example 1. *so* ___so's___

11. son-in-law ______
12. spoonful ______
13. tomato ______
14. radio ______
15. symphony ______
16. *3* ______
17. mix ______
18. alumnus ______
19. leaf ______
20. species ______

EXERCISE C In the following sentences, cross out any misspelled word or number that has been written incorrectly. Write the correction above the word you have crossed out.

Example 1. Our small town has ~~15~~ *fifteen* churches.

21. Tanzania is not dominated by one cheif ethnic group; the estimated 120 black tribal groups generally live in peace.
22. When the interruptions cease, you can procede with your presentation.
23. The vocabulary test includes 20 5-syllable words.
24. 15 of my friends and family members will attend the Cinco de Mayo festival with me.
25. At the hieght of his popularity, this author wrote at least one book per year.

Copyright © by Holt, Rinehart and Winston. All rights reserved.

Review B: Words Often Confused

EXERCISE From the choice in parentheses, underline the correct word for each of the following sentences.

Example 1. "(*Its, It's*) a beautiful day!" exclaimed Juanita.

1. Our team should not (*loose, lose*) more than three or four games this season.
2. Several people have (*complemented, complimented*) Nichola on the fine article she wrote for the school paper.
3. The Sahara is a vast (*desert, dessert*) in Africa, covering more than three million square miles.
4. The conductor (*led, lead*) the band in a spirited rendition of the school song.
5. The Tonkawas were less numerous (*than, then*) most neighboring Native American groups.
6. A business letter should be written on conventional business (*stationary, stationery*).
7. One of the important jobs of the captain is to help maintain team (*moral, morale*).
8. The bus route takes you (*passed, past*) the Grand Canyon and several other scenic spots.
9. Miraculously, Chak Tong survived the thirty-foot fall with no injuries except (*miner, minor*) cuts and bruises.
10. The members of the tour were (*all ready, already*) to board the bus, but the tour director had not yet arrived.
11. Part of the order arrived today, but the rest will not be delivered until (*later, latter*).
12. The team members were seldom seen (*all together, altogether*) off the playing field.
13. No one seemed to know (*who's, whose*) paper had received the highest grade.
14. For as long as I can remember, Aunt Rosita has been a friend and (*councilor, counselor*) to me.
15. The new mayor was (*formally, formerly*) a grocery-store clerk and supermarket manager.
16. Donita suggested that I use a (*plain, plane*) to smooth the surface of the wood.
17. The disposal of nuclear (*waist, waste*) is an issue that has been discussed for decades.
18. If you wish to ask for a transfer, you should speak to Mr. Forsch in the (*personal, personnel*) department.
19. Wendel seems to wear expensive (*clothes, cloths*) to work.
20. It takes a certain amount of skill to (*brake, break*) an egg with one hand while turning pancakes with the other.

Copyright © by Holt, Rinehart and Winston. All rights reserved.

Review C: Spelling and Words Often Confused

EXERCISE A In the following sentences, cross out any misspelled word or any number that is used incorrectly. Write the correction above the word you have crossed out. Note that each sentence contains more than one error.

Example 1. At the ceremony ~~3~~ *three* war ~~heros~~ *heroes* were given ~~trophys.~~ *trophies*

1. Is there a possibillity that you can interceed on my behalf?
2. My freinds' ilogical arguement seemed comical to those of us witnessing it.
3. Inside the buryed wooden box we found several jeweled knifes.
4. The American Indian Movement, supported by many modern Sioux, has activly protested government treatment of Native Americans since the 1960s.
5. 6 justice of the peaces attended the seminar.
6. Is it socialy accepttable for the family's hier to travel abroad?
7. Conceeding defeat, the immpassive warriors laid down their sheilds.
8. The boxs in the basement were filled with photoes of my ancestors.
9. Childs in the small farming community merryly celebrated the 1st day of spring.
10. Because the water spot on the cieling is barely noticable, repainting the whole room seems unecessary.

EXERCISE B From the choice in parentheses, underline the correct word or words for each of the following sentences.

Example 1. Do not *(loose, lose)* sight of *(your, you're)* goals.

11. This wonderful *(desert, dessert)* *(complements, compliments)* the delicious meal.
12. Taxpayers have *(born, borne)* the cost of the queen's elegant *(cloths, clothes).*
13. The senators posed *(altogether, all together)* in front of the *(capital, capitol).*
14. This irrigated farmland was *(formally, formerly)* a dry *(desert, dessert).*
15. *(Its, It's)* a serious crime for a soldier to *(desert, dessert)* a battalion.
16. Wash the car and then use these soft *(cloths, clothes)* to polish *(its, it's)* chrome.
17. *(Who's, Whose)* in charge of raising enough *(capital, capitol)*?
18. By the time *(your, you're)* in first grade, I will *(already, all ready)* have completed high school.
19. Your wise *(council, counsel)* has helped to make me a *(moral, morale)* person.
20. Our school *(principal, principle)* *(lead, led)* the seniors in a rousing cheer.

Copyright © by Holt, Rinehart and Winston. All rights reserved.

NAME CLASS DATE

Review D: Spelling and Words Often Confused

EXERCISE In the following sentences, cross out all misspelled words, incorrectly used words, and incorrectly written numbers. Write the corrections above the words you have crossed out. Note that each sentence contains more than one error.

Example 1. ~~Whose voiceing~~ (*Who's voicing*) our complaints to the ~~editor in chiefs~~ (*editors in chief*)?

1. All 12 soldeirs should remain stationery until dismissed.
2. Although we stompped our feet, the deers proceded to eat you're flowers.
3. Congress past a bill to upphold the principal of civil rights.
4. Whose been chosen to reveiw the bill of sales?
5. Given the choice of runing a mile or doing calisthenics, I choose the later.
6. If he continues to loose wieght, his clotheing will not fit.
7. 1st your a junior and then a senior.
8. Annie's home videoes actualy look professionnal.
9. Of coarse, I appreciate a sincere complement.
10. Our school councilor owns two dance studioes.
11. Sillyness seemed innappropriate in the principle's office.
12. Will both sopranos conceed to singing soloes tonight?
13. I beleive we got their at 5 o'clock, but I'm not positive.
14. After checking the indexes of several anthologys, I found the poem.
15. Both runner-ups immediatly demanded a rematch.
16. I've all ready unpacked 6 20-pound boxes.
17. The chieves looked splendid in thier colorful headdresses.
18. I ensure you the performance exceded our expectations.
19. Its too early to go shoping; most of the stores are still closed.
20. You inncorrectly spelled *Venezuela* with 4 *es*.

MECHANICS

Copyright © by Holt, Rinehart and Winston. All rights reserved.

Sentence Fragments and Run-on Sentences A

EXERCISE Identify each of the following word groups by writing above it *F* if the word group is a sentence fragment, *R* if it is a run-on sentence, or *S* if it is a complete sentence.

Example 1. *F* Neither slavery nor involuntary servitude, except as a punishment for crime whereof the party shall have been duly convicted, within the United States.

1. The executive power shall be vested in a President of the United States of America, he shall hold his office during the term of four years.
2. The Senate of the United States shall be composed of two Senators from each state, and each Senator shall have one vote.
3. In order to form a more perfect union, do ordain and establish this Constitution for the United States of America.
4. All bills for raising revenue shall originate in the House of Representatives, the Senate may propose or concur with amendments as on other bills.
5. The right of citizens of the United States to vote shall not be denied or abridged by the United States or by any State on account of race, color, or previous condition of servitude.
6. The removal of the President from office or of his death or resignation, the Vice-President to become President.
7. The right of citizens of the United States, who are eighteen years of age or older, to vote.
8. He shall have power, by and with the advice and consent of the Senate, to make treaties.
9. Abridging the freedom of speech, or of the press.
10. New states may be admitted by the Congress into this union, no new state shall be formed or erected within the jurisdiction of any other state.

Copyright © by Holt, Rinehart and Winston. All rights reserved.

Sentence Fragments and Run-on Sentences B

EXERCISE On the short lines provided, identify each word group in the following paragraph as a sentence fragment *(F)*, a run-on sentence *(R)*, or a complete sentence *(S)*. Then, rewrite the paragraph, correcting sentence fragments and run-ons.

Example ___F___ **[1]** Clashes between political figures and religious leaders not uncommon even in ancient times. *Clashes between political figures and religious leaders were not uncommon even in ancient times.*

[1] ______ In Egypt, one such clash by Amenhotep IV, the pharaoh who ruled from about 1379 B.C. to 1362 B.C. **[2]** ______ Angering the polytheistic priests by teaching the existence of only one god, the sun, symbolized by a sun disk called the Aton. **[3]** ______ Amenhotep even changed his name to Akhenaton to honor the Aton. **[4]** ______ He moved the capital to Tell el Amarna from Thebes, there, the nobles and priests had become powerful. **[5]** ______ Egyptian wealth no longer pouring in to the priests at the great temple in Thebes. **[6]** ______ A fierce political struggle broke out between Akhenaton and priests and nobles who worshiped many gods. **[7]** ______ The pharaoh gradually learned that orders cannot change religious beliefs, when he died, the clash between church and state ended. **[8]** ______ His successor, Tutankhamen, proving his willingness to revert to the old system of beliefs. **[9]** ______ Well known today, Tutankhamen, whose life-sized gold funeral mask was discovered in his tomb in 1922. **[10]** ______ Dying at age eighteen, he nevertheless ruled long enough to move Egypt's capital city back to Thebes.

Copyright © by Holt, Rinehart and Winston. All rights reserved.

Subject-Verb Agreement A

EXERCISE A In each of the following sentences, underline the verb in parentheses that agrees in number with its subject.

Example 1. Either Carmen or Miranda, both of whom have fine voices, *(is, are)* a good choice for the leading role in the musical.

1. Both of the girls have sung in the choir for years, and each of them easily *(sing, sings)* the high notes.

2. *(Is, Are)* Josh or either of his brothers planning to audition?

3. Several of the roles *(do, does)* not require singing, except as part of a chorus.

4. The best dancer and singer in the class *(is, are)* certainly Julio.

5. The cast list, along with a schedule of rehearsals, *(have, has)* been posted outside the auditorium.

6. Students in the stagecraft class *(has, have)* already begun to design the sets and the lighting.

7. *(Doesn't, Don't)* that class also design and sew the costumes?

8. The stage manager, assisted by the props manager, *(makes, make)* sure that everything is running smoothly backstage.

9. According to the house manager, *(there's, there are)* a full house tonight.

10. Everyone waiting in the greenroom or in the wings *(seem, seems)* nervous and excited.

EXERCISE B In each of the following sentences, underline any verb that does not agree with its subject and write the correct form of the verb above the incorrect form. If all the verbs in a sentence are already correct, write *C* after the sentence.

Example 1. The children who want to learn volleyball is waiting in the gym. (*are*)

11. Cass and Trina don't like cafeteria food, so each of them bring a lunch from home.

12. Sometimes one of them prepares a lunch that they share.

13. For almost three years, the two of them has eaten lunch together nearly every day.

14. There are a little grove of trees outside the door of the cafeteria.

15. Many students in the senior class prefers to eat outside when the weather is pleasant.

Copyright © by Holt, Rinehart and Winston. All rights reserved.

COMMON ERRORS

NAME ______________________ CLASS ______________ DATE ______________

Subject-Verb Agreement B

EXERCISE A For each of the following sentences, decide whether the underlined verb agrees in number with its subject. If the verb form is incorrect, write above it the correct form. If the verb is already correct, write *C* above it.

Example 1. Each of the cars in the parade were (*was*) at least twenty-five years old.

1. The book that we requested last week through the interlibrary loan system have arrived.
2. She sometimes catches a ride to school with her neighbor, especially when the weather turn cold.
3. Neither the municipal swimming pool near our house nor the water park remain open past Labor Day.
4. Do either your younger brother or one of his classmates need any help understanding fractions and decimals?
5. Both Renata and Christina, her older sister, volunteers at the food bank twice a week after school.
6. Has the team manager or Coach Dodd told you about locker assignments?
7. Angie, together with Bianca and Zoe, have been selected to serve on the publicity committee.
8. The stuffing in the back of the chair and in one of the cushions need to be replaced.
9. All of the members of the band, including those who play tuba and sousaphone, marches in the pregame parade.
10. In addition to pencils, scratch paper, and a protractor, what other supplies are he expected to bring?

EXERCISE B In each of the following sentences, circle the subject of the underlined verb. Then, if the verb does not agree in number with its subject, write the correct form of the verb above the incorrect form. If the verb is already correct, write *C* above it.

Example 1. My whole family is worried because (one) of our cats seem (*seems*) to have disappeared.

11. Did you tell me he try to read at least one book a week?
12. Many students in the senior class participates in community service projects.
13. Has Julie told everyone what time the movie begins?
14. Less than 20 percent of the eligible voters has an opinion about that subject.
15. Soup and sandwich are the lunch special at that restaurant today.

COMMON ERRORS

Copyright © by Holt, Rinehart and Winston. All rights reserved.

NAME CLASS DATE

for **CHAPTER 16: CORRECTING COMMON ERRORS** *pages 170–176*

Pronoun-Antecedent Agreement A

EXERCISE A In each of the following sentences, circle the antecedent of the pronoun in parentheses. Then, underline the pronoun in parentheses that agrees with the antecedent.

Example 1. Every member of the club will have the opportunity to explain *(their, his or her)* position.

1. One of the girls who attended the meeting has given me a copy of *(their, her)* notes.

2. Officers of the student council will conduct an orientation session for *(its, their)* successors.

3. In *(their, its)* excitement about the lopsided victory, the crowd cheered and shouted for at least twenty minutes after the game ended.

4. Relations between the United States and *(their, its)* neighbors to the north and south have not always been cordial.

5. Anyone who wants to help decorate the senior class's float for the homecoming parade should put *(their, his or her)* name and phone number on this list.

6. Marcus, Sam, and Cody knew that *(he, they)* would do well on the final exam.

7. I've shown Simone and Nelda how to do these problems, but now the girls need to try to do them *(herself, themselves)*.

8. My grandmother and Aunt Louisa, who have never flown on an airplane, are taking *(their, her)* first flight next week.

9. Either the hedgehog or the opossum rolls *(themselves, itself)* up in a ball when threatened.

10. Neither Sam nor Zack remembered to write down *(his, their)* Social Security number.

EXERCISE B In each of the following sentences, underline any pronoun that does not agree with its antecedent. Then, write the correct pronoun above the incorrect pronoun. If a sentence is already correct, write C after it.

Example 1. The new political party held a convention to select their *(its)* nominees for office.

11. Each part of the country seems to have their own regional legends and folklore.

12. I don't like to use this kind of laptop as much as the one that Jaime bought because its keys are too small and closely spaced for my fingers.

13. My uncle and aunt attended the Olympic games when Los Angeles sponsored them.

14. Clarence, along with two other students, is planning to work for a year after their graduation.

15. Despite what their mother told them, two of the little girls forgot to wear her boots today.

COMMON ERRORS

Copyright © by Holt, Rinehart and Winston. All rights reserved.

Pronoun-Antecedent Agreement B

EXERCISE A In each of the following sentences, circle the antecedent of the underlined pronoun. Then, if the pronoun does not agree with its antecedent, write the correct pronoun above the error. If the pronoun is already correct, write *C* above it.

Example 1. Neither of the children wanted to have their hair brushed. *his or her*

1. The yearbook staff surprised their sponsor by dedicating the yearbook to her.
2. During the class picnic, some of the girls decided to have her picture taken.
3. Either Marcus or Alex can lend you his notes.
4. Over 75 percent of the tickets have been sold already, most of it to parents.
5. Does everyone who owns a dog understand that they must be kept on a leash at all times?

EXERCISE B On the lines provided, rewrite each of the following sentences to correct errors in pronoun-antecedent agreement.

Example 1. Each student in my class stayed up late to study because they wanted to do well on the test. *All the students in my class stayed up late to study because they wanted to do well on the test.*

6. Over a third of the tomato plants died because we forgot to water it. __________
7. Each finalist will have to pay their own airfare and other expenses. __________
8. Not one of the boys in that family has to be reminded to make their bed in the morning before breakfast. __________
9. Every member of the graduating class should congratulate themselves for having passed their final exams. __________
10. Nobody likes to be reminded about their faults or shortcomings. __________

COMMON ERRORS

Copyright © by Holt, Rinehart and Winston. All rights reserved.

Pronoun Forms A

EXERCISE A In each of the following sentences, underline the correct pronoun in parentheses.

Example 1. The man who lost his dog is *(him, he)*.

1. It's *(she, her)* who is driving the supervisor's limousine.
2. Were you going to administer the test to Daryl and *(I, me)*?
3. Carlos, Gina, Tammy, and *(he, him)* are going to watch that movie again.
4. It must be *(they, them)* who volunteer at the animal shelter.
5. Several Native American speakers *(who, whom)* you heard before are here.
6. The team members applauded more loudly than *(her, she)* and Coach Martinez.
7. *(Who, Whom)* was her secret admirer?
8. Give the leftover tickets to the band members and *(we, us)*.
9. Do you believe that Tranh is a better advisor than *(he, him)*?
10. *(Us, We)* seniors must resolve a number of questions about the future.

EXERCISE B In each of the following sentences, underline any incorrect pronoun and write the correct pronoun above it. If all the pronouns in a sentence are correct, write *C* after the sentence.

Example 1. He
Him and I are the only members of the class who can't go on the field trip tomorrow.

11. I think Diana dances much more gracefully than her.
12. Two of the bassoon players, Martina and him, have been selected to play in the city's student orchestra.
13. The librarian gave the reading list to whomever wanted a copy.
14. Mr. Cantu gave my brother and I a ride to the store this afternoon.
15. One of the graduate students has offered an hour of free tutoring to whoever signs up first.
16. My friends and me are going fishing this weekend.
17. The children who put up the signs about a lost puppy are them.
18. Do you have the list of people who we are inviting to the ceremony?
19. Mr. Kraft is a tough teacher, but we usually get interesting assignments from him.
20. The committee assignments were made by Samantha, who is the president of the club, and he.

Copyright © by Holt, Rinehart and Winston. All rights reserved.

Pronoun Forms B

EXERCISE In each of the following sentences, underline the correct pronoun in parentheses. Then, identify the use of the pronoun by writing above it *S* for *subject*, *PN* for *predicate nominative*, *DO* for *direct object*, *IO* for *indirect object*, *OP* for *object of a preposition*, or *A* for *appositive*.

Example 1. One of my aunts, either Aunt Ann or (*she*, *her*), will cook the Thanksgiving turkey this year.

1. Can you throw the ball any farther than (*he, him*)?
2. I hope you plan to wait a few minutes for (*we, us*) latecomers to catch up.
3. The news story featured three students—Lucy, Oscar, and (*he, him*)—who have unusual hobbies.
4. The article about careers in engineering interested Caroline as much as it interested (*he, him*).
5. (*Who, Whom*) would like to open the discussion?
6. Sandra says that she told (*him, he*) the combination to her locker.
7. The man whose hat blew away is (*he, him*).
8. Keith looked all over for his sunglasses, but he can't remember where he left (*they, them*).
9. Please offer Mrs. Crandall and (*she, her*) a glass of iced tea.
10. Although she is older than the McGinty twins, my sister enjoys playing with (*they, them*).
11. We believe that (*we, us*) twelfth-graders should have special privileges in the school.
12. Her father or her older brother picks (*her, she*) up from school every afternoon.
13. Despite our best efforts, the winners are once again (*them, they*).
14. In addition to (*she, her*) and her brother, the twins are also meeting us at the theater.
15. Their grandmother fixed (*they, them*) a hearty breakfast on Sunday mornings.
16. The person who collected and organized the information is (*me, I*).
17. I'll try to save one of the seats next to (*we, us*) for you.
18. (*Her, She*) and Nadine are in charge of arranging transportation to the beach.
19. My grandparents gave all of (*we, us*) copies of the family's photographs.
20. If you could describe (*he, him*) a little better, I might remember his name.

Copyright © by Holt, Rinehart and Winston. All rights reserved.

NAME ______ CLASS ______ DATE ______

Clear Pronoun Reference A

EXERCISE On the lines provided, rewrite each of the following sentences, correcting any unclear or inexact pronoun references. You may need to add or rearrange words to make the sentences clear.

Example **1.** Margarette won the tennis match, which made her happy.
Winning the tennis match made Margarette happy.

1. The boy blew out all the candles with one breath, which made all the children cheer. ______

2. One of the dams on the creek had a small crack, but that was not enough to cause the flood. ______

3. Our family's farm was affected by the drought in the 1930s, which ought to be obvious from this photograph. ______

4. Cassie and her grandmother talked for an hour on the phone, but she forgot to tell her about the missing puppy. ______

5. Shawn enjoys going out in the ski boat, although he hasn't been able to stay up on them very long yet. ______

6. It says in the instructions that you should never use this cleaning fluid near an open flame. ______

7. I prefer it when they bring the soup or salad before the main course. ______

8. Even though we waited in line at the ticket window for hours, we weren't able to get one. ______

9. The dog returned home before she had a chance to put up the notices or place an ad in the newspaper, which made her happy. ______

10. When the second sailboat rounded the buoy and sped toward the finish line, it became an exciting race. ______

COMMON ERRORS

Copyright © by Holt, Rinehart and Winston. All rights reserved.

Clear Pronoun Reference B

EXERCISE On the lines provided, rewrite each of the following sentences, correcting any unclear or inexact pronoun references. You may need to add or rearrange words to make the sentences clear.

Example 1. At the student council meeting, they announced the date of the annual awards dinner. *The date of the annual awards dinner was announced at the student council meeting.*

1. I love the poetry of Dylan Thomas, but I haven't read all of them.

2. In one dictionary source, it says that the two spellings are equally accepted.

3. We saw Antoinette's slides of her Costa Rican vacation, which made us all want to go there.

4. Roberto and his father agreed on the strategy he should use.

5. Your sprints are not very fast today, but it is probably due to your injury.

6. I have enjoyed reading all of his fiction, but the one I liked best was a mystery.

7. Of all the instruments she played, she enjoyed either piano or guitar the most, and she practiced it regularly.

8. When you see Francine and Teresa this afternoon, be sure to tell her how much I enjoyed her singing as well as her accompaniment.

9. The contest between Mac and Colin was over when he spelled the word *pterodactyl* correctly.

10. Whenever the children did their chores without being asked, this pleased their mother enormously.

COMMON ERRORS

Copyright © by Holt, Rinehart and Winston. All rights reserved.

Verb Forms A

EXERCISE A In each of the following sentences, underline the incorrect verb form and write the correct form above it.

Example 1. Magnificent architecture and engineering have putted [put] a number of cities at the top of the sightseer's list.

1. Builded in the early 1970s, the opera house in Sydney, Australia, stands out in the city's harbor.
2. The Woolworth Building in New York City has rose 792 feet straight up since 1913.
3. When Calgary, Canada, became the 1988 winter Olympics location, special buildings were constructing.
4. Some people have said that the Taj Mahal is the most beautiful building they have ever seed.
5. Countless visitors have took a tour of the Louvre in Paris.
6. Surely you payed a visit to Notre Dame while in France.
7. The great pyramids of Egypt seem to have standed since the beginning of time.
8. Tourists who have went to China would speak of the Great Wall.
9. Have you also heared of Hadrian's Wall, which the Romans built between what is now England and Scotland?
10. For many years visitors have get tours of the Empire State Building in New York City.

EXERCISE B On the lines provided, write the correct form of the verb in italics.

Example 1. *eat* I probably should have ___eaten___ something before the rehearsal.

11. *forget* Cheryl must have ______ that she was supposed to meet us after school.
12. *dive* He walked to the end of the board, bounced once, and ______ gracefully into the pool.
13. *drink* Before the hike, I ______ a pint of water and filled several water bottles.
14. *forgive* Clearly, she had not yet ______ her younger brother for embarrassing her in front of her friends.
15. *freeze* Despite the cold snap, the river never quite ______.

COMMON ERRORS

Copyright © by Holt, Rinehart and Winston. All rights reserved.

Verb Forms B

EXERCISE In each of the following sentences, underline any incorrect verb form and write the correct form above it. If all the verbs in a sentence are correct, write *C* after the sentence.

Example 1. The tickets should have costed (*cost*) us only ten dollars each, but we payed (*paid*) an extra fee to the ticket service.

1. I am sure that unkind remark hurted her feelings.

2. The hose must have froze and burst during last week's cold weather.

3. Someone his age really should have knowed better.

4. After the witness had been swore in, the defense attorney begun questioning her.

5. He had had the shoes so long that he had wore holes in the soles.

6. The driver who had barely avoided an accident was clearly shook.

7. Students, please turn your tests over and past them forward; time has ran out.

8. I would have wrote a longer essay, but I simply forget some of the names of the people.

9. By the time the rest of the decorating committee shown up, we had already blowed up most of the balloons.

10. The sweater shrunk to half its former size because she had throwed it into the dryer with the rest of the clothes.

11. Please bring the groceries in from the car and set them on the kitchen table.

12. She has arose before dawn every day this month.

13. He seems to have became more confident of his abilities during the past year.

14. The old book had laid on a shelf in a dark corner of the library for many years.

15. Although she hadn't seed her friend for several years, she find that they still had much in common.

16. He lay the book down on the arm of the couch, took off his glasses, and closed his eyes for a few minutes.

17. The little boy knowed he should not have did that.

18. Either I have leaved my keys somewhere, or they have fell out of my pocket.

19. Two of the children spread the picnic cloth on the ground beneath a tree, and three others unpacked the food and drinks.

20. For many years, those two brothers fight and argued, but now they got along.

Copyright © by Holt, Rinehart and Winston. All rights reserved.

NAME ______________________ CLASS ______________ DATE ______________

Verb Tense

EXERCISE A The verb tenses in the following paragraph are not used consistently and logically. On the lines provided, rewrite the paragraph to correct errors in the use of tense.

Example [1] In the twentieth century, musical experimentation becomes more common, and new sounds and forms began to emerge.

In the twentieth century, musical experimentation became more common, and new sounds and forms began to emerge.

[1] Some composers, such as Dmitri Shostakovich of Russia, wrote traditional symphonies of four distinct movements. **[2]** After 1945, serious musicians accept the innovative sounds of synthesizers and other experimental instruments. **[3]** Composers also allow musicians a greater role in determining the sound of a piece. **[4]** African American contributions to contemporary music had included rhythm and blues and soul music. **[5]** The rhythms of Latin America will have a growing and appreciative audience in recent times.

____

____

____

____

____

____

____

____

EXERCISE B In each of the following sentences, determine whether the tense of the underlined verb is correct. If the tense is incorrect, write the correct form above it. If the tense is correct, write *C* above it.

Example 1. When you reach the top of the mountain, could you see the ocean? *(reached)*

6. By this time next month, I received an admission or rejection letter from that college.
7. Every day before he goes to school, he fixed breakfast for everyone in the family.
8. If Mindy had studied a little harder, she would do better on the test.
9. I have looked everywhere for information on this topic, but I haven't found a single source.
10. When grandmother arrived at seven o'clock, we will all eat dinner together.

COMMON ERRORS

Copyright © by Holt, Rinehart and Winston. All rights reserved.

NAME CLASS DATE

Comparative and Superlative Forms of Modifiers

EXERCISE A In each of the following sentences, underline any error in the use of the comparative or superlative form of a modifier, and write the correct form above the incorrect form.

Example 1. Which of those two jackets have you owned longest? *longer*

1. I was able to finish the paper more quicklyer because I had organized my research notes.
2. The diamond in her ring is smaller but brilliant than the one in her mother's ring.
3. Did you enjoy the movie or the dinner afterward most?
4. Of all the grandchildren, Robert is the one with the darker hair.
5. If I hadn't felt so badly, I would have done best on the test.

EXERCISE B Each of the following sentences contains a double comparison, an unclear comparison, a double negative, or other errors in the use of comparative and superlative forms of modifiers. On the lines provided, rewrite each sentence to correct any errors in the use of modifiers.

Example 1. Many more people don't hardly realize that child labor is still an issue in the world today. *Many people don't realize that child labor is still an issue in the world today.*

6. Is it more harder to attend school or to work a fifteen-hour day? ______

7. If you had lived in England earlier as 1819, you wouldn't have had no more choice than any British child. ______

8. The Factory Act of 1819 addressed some of the worse conditions; children less than nine years old couldn't work in the cotton mills no more. ______

9. Children nine years old but more younger than eighteen couldn't be made to work greater than twelve hours a day in the textile factories. ______

10. Longer than workers in the textiles industry, mines were still allowed to employ boys under ten years old, as well as girls and women. ______

COMMON ERRORS

Copyright © by Holt, Rinehart and Winston. All rights reserved.

NAME ______________________ CLASS ______________ DATE ______________

Misplaced and Dangling Modifiers A

EXERCISE On the lines provided, rewrite each of the following sentences to correct the misplaced or dangling modifier.

Example 1. Steep and winding, the car had maneuvered through the hairpin turns on the mountain road. *The car had maneuvered through the hairpin turns on the steep and winding mountain road.*

1. Dr. Ortiz pioneered treatment in the laboratory for unusual viral infections. ______________________

2. Unhappy with dormitory costs, Sonia's choice was to live at home. ______________________

3. Before touring the U.S. Capitol, their first stop was the National Gallery of Art. ______________________

4. Few students pay attention to billboards on their way to school. ______________________

5. Wobbling and squeaking on every turn, John made slow progress on the old bike. ______________________

6. Historically interesting, everyone wants to see the Declaration of Independence. ______________________

7. The principal promised by Friday to announce the results. ______________________

8. After viewing a documentary on African wildlife, the possibility of travel interests me. ______________________

9. Sulima found a trumpet at a garage sale that only has one small dent. ______________________

10. To comprehend the principles of calculus, a background in algebra is recommended. ______________________

COMMON ERRORS

Copyright © by Holt, Rinehart and Winston. All rights reserved.

Misplaced and Dangling Modifiers B

EXERCISE On the lines provided, rewrite each of the following sentences to correct the misplaced or dangling modifier.

Example 1. Ms. Nguyen will finish grading the projects that we turned in during spring break.
During spring break, Ms. Nguyen will finish grading the projects that we turned in.

1. Kicking and screaming, the mother was clearly embarrassed by her child's behavior.

2. While waiting for the bus in the rain, all the traffic lights went out at the intersection.

3. To cook a complete dinner for twenty guests, careful planning is the first step.

4. Raining and dreary outside, we weren't able to go to the game.

5. Recently elected by the voters of our district, the Legislature welcomed its new member.

6. The woman was dismayed to realize that she had forgotten to take the package to the post office that she had wrapped so carefully.

7. Swooping and diving toward the water, the boys watched the pelicans.

8. I only forgot how to do this kind of problem, but all the others were easy.

9. After placing a classified ad in the newspaper, many phone calls were received about the job.

10. The parks and recreation department has set aside an area where people, without leashes, are allowed to walk their dogs.

COMMON ERRORS

Copyright © by Holt, Rinehart and Winston. All rights reserved.

Correct Use of Modifiers

EXERCISE On the lines provided, rewrite each of the following sentences to correct any errors in the use or placement of modifiers.

Example 1. My personal goal for this season is to score even more points than any player.
My personal goal for this season is to score more points than any other player.

1. Twisted and snarled in the branches of the tree, the little girl realized she couldn't hardly climb high enough to get her kite.

2. At the art museum I saw some of the more remarkable paintings I've ever seen.

3. Don't you know how to fold laundry no more better than that?

4. Walking to the corner to mail a letter, a lost puppy came up to Melissa's sister and wagged its tail.

5. Too exhausted from hours of cleaning out the garage, the movie no longer seemed so attractive.

6. Although he looks weller than he did yesterday, I'm sure he still don't feel so good.

7. Her gymnastics routine was more difficult than Maxine, but Maxine's was executed more careful.

8. Remind Alex when he finishes his homework he should meet us at the basketball court.

9. Flying at an altitude of twenty-seven thousand feet, the sunset on the clouds was most truly beautiful.

10. Mark won the competition because he worked more harder than anyone.

COMMON ERRORS

Copyright © by Holt, Rinehart and Winston. All rights reserved.

NAME _______________ CLASS _______________ DATE _______________

Standard Usage A

EXERCISE A In each of the following sentences, decide whether the underlined word or words are correct according to formal, standard English usage. If the usage is incorrect, draw a line through any words or letters that should be deleted or corrected and write the correct usage above it. If the usage is already correct, write *C* above it.

Example 1. You should ~~of~~ *have* remembered to turn off the water.

1. The trees have less leaves than they did even a few days ago.
2. The reason Jerome couldn't come with us is because he couldn't find his shoes.
3. Kris thought the comedian's jokes were kind of juvenile.
4. Although the car was ensured, the company wouldn't pay for the broken windshield.
5. When I went to visit her at the hospital, I took her a bouquet of flowers.
6. As Cole accepted the award, the audience stood and clapped for him.
7. I hope her comment wasn't an illusion to my new haircut.
8. Greta and myself will take responsibility for organizing the canned food drive.
9. I felt so nauseous all morning that I was sure I had caught the flu.
10. Clayton got these diagrams off a Web site.

EXERCISE B On the lines provided, rewrite the following sentences to correct any errors in formal, standard English usage.

Example 1. The screenplay was suppose to of been adopted from a well-known novel. *The screenplay was supposed to have been adapted from a well-known novel.*

11. Finally, her anxiety began to ease some, and she began to feel kind of better about herself. _______________

12. I read in the newspaper where some people will try and clean up the creek on Saturday. _______________

13. Them golden retrievers, who belong to the Campbells, are gentle, well-behaved dogs. _______________

14. Hopefully, this week our history teacher won't act like we don't have no other homework accept what she assigns. _______________

15. Your a lot more generous then I would of been in that situation. _______________

Copyright © by Holt, Rinehart and Winston. All rights reserved.

Standard Usage B

EXERCISE On the lines provided, rewrite the following letter, correcting any errors in formal, standard English usage.

Example **[1]** Being as she hadn't written to Gabriela in awhile, Carolyn set down to write her a letter. *Since she hadn't written to Gabriela in a while, Carolyn sat down to write her a letter.*

Dear Gabriela,

[1] Its been sort of a long time since I wrote you, so I thought I would try and catch you up on recent events in my life. **[2]** The reason I haven't written is because I've had alot of homework this semester. **[3]** In every class accept for chemistry, the teachers assign so much work that I don't have hardly no time for myself. **[4]** They act like we don't have anything else to do. **[5]** Yesterday, I was suppose to finish a paper, than work on my science project some and start drafting a kind of a speech that I have to give in class next week. **[6]** Hopefully, all this here hard work will have an affect on my grades this year!

[7] I hope your doing good at your new school and that your taking less classes then you did here. **[8]** I'd like to call you sometime, but we're liable to run up a huge phone bill. **[9]** Maybe we could meet somewheres this summer. **[10]** Until then, I guess we'll just have to adopt to the situation as well as we can. Take care.

Your friend,

Carolyn

Copyright © by Holt, Rinehart and Winston. All rights reserved.

COMMON ERRORS

Standard Usage C

EXERCISE A In each of the following sentences, underline the word or phrase that is used incorrectly according to the rules of formal, standard English usage. Then, write the correct usage above the incorrect usage.

number
Example 1. The children will be able to see a large amount of ducks and turtles in that creek.

1. You may recall that Benjamin Franklin discovered bifocals.
2. Winston Churchill is one of the most notorious heroes of England.
3. Clarence has less college options than his brother Charles.
4. Some of the Girl Scouts are liable to knock on your door next week.
5. That type movie often gives Bernice nightmares.
6. The teacher reacted like Clarence turned his work in late all the time.
7. The final exam in Biology II was alot easier than I expected it to be.
8. Charles borrowed me his bicycle because mine had a flat tire.
9. On Saturday morning, don't he have to mow the lawn, bundle the newspapers, wash the car, give the dog a bath, and etc.?
10. Frankly, they ought to of done it theirselves.

EXERCISE B In the following paragraph, underline any errors in formal, standard usage and write your corrections above the sentences.

doesn't *anymore*
Example [1] Taking care of a young child don't seem easy no more.

[11] Perhaps I shouldn't of been so confident that I could look after my toddler cousin and study for the economics test at the same time. **[12]** Somewheres I got the notion that the younger a child is, the less mischief he can get into. **[13]** Little Danny didn't hardly look at the teddy bear I had taken him before he attempted to eat the pages of my textbook. **[14]** Beside that, he grabbed my highlighter and proceeded to create some original hieroglyphics on the living room wall. **[15]** You may have guessed that I had to leave my studies go until I had no other responsibilities.

Copyright © by Holt, Rinehart and Winston. All rights reserved.

Capitalization A

EXERCISE A In each of the following sentences, circle any letter that should be capitalized.

Example 1. In the united states, the capital of a state is not necessarily its largest city; sacramento, for example, is not the largest city in california.

1. The resolution passed by the student council of jefferson county high school read: "resolved: that the student council supports an increase in the length of the lunch period from fifteen to thirty minutes."

2. On friday, some of us are going to el mercado, a tex-mex restaurant, to celebrate Matthew's eighteenth birthday.

3. The globe theatre, where many of shakespeare's plays were first performed, was in london, not in stratford-on-avon.

4. Many people are unaware that the continent of north america includes not only the united states (except for hawaii), but also canada and mexico.

5. How many doctors are members of the american medical association (ama)?

EXERCISE B In each of the following sentences, circle any letter that should be capitalized and draw a slash (/) through any letter that should be made lowercase.

Example 1. Some people mistakenly consider *gulliver's travels,* by jonathan swift, to be a mere Children's story.

6. Born in dublin, ireland, on november 30, 1667, and educated at trinity college, the young swift became known in london as a skillful writer of political and religious essays.

7. *Gulliver's travels,* swift's greatest satire, was originally published in 1726 under the title *travels into several remote nations of the world.*

8. The book's Hero, lemuel gulliver, travels to such strange lands as lilliput, where the tiny people are always at war, and laputa, populated by a people who are so intellectual that they ar utterly lacking in common sence.

9. In another Land, gulliver finds much to admire in the houyhnhnms, a race of decent and reasonable Horses.

10. soon, gulliver realizes that the seemingly virtuous houyhnhnms can barely tolerate th ner race on the island, the yahoos.

Copyright © by Holt, Rinehart and Winston. All rights reserved.

Capitalization B

EXERCISE A In each of the following sentences, circle any letter that should be capitalized.

Example 1. mr. fisher, our german teacher, has traveled extensively in europe.

1. many of my friends think that jane austen's books must be tedious, but I thought *emma* was a really funny novel.
2. Are we all going to grandma and grandpa cook's house during spring break?
3. their house is on the atlantic coast, not far from ocean city, maryland.
4. My mother's family emigrated from county mayo, ireland, during the great famine of the 1840s, which was caused by the complete failure of the potato crop.
5. Maria introduced her friends to her great-grandmother, sra. alvarez, who was born in mexico early in the twentieth century.

EXERCISE B In the following paragraph, circle any letter that should be capitalized and draw a slash (/) through any letter that should be made lowercase. If the capitalization in the sentence is correct, write C above the sentence.

Example **[1]** The Spanish civil war in the early Twentieth Century was as cruel as any other civil war.

[6] Both opposing forces, Republicans and Nationalists, were responsible for the deaths of many
lians. **[7]** The right-wing republicans were aided by germany and italy, while the nationalists
helped by the soviet union and a group of volunteers from fifty Nations, called the interna-
brigade. **[8]** Intellectuals and artists were in special danger. **[9]** Among the nonmilitary
ies was Federico García lorca, whose literary efforts had already made him known around
orld. **[10]** One of spain's most important modern writers, he was both a poet and a play-
. **[11]** His play *The house Of Bernarda alba* dealt with suffering under a dictatorship. **[12]** His
n *gypsy ballads* also won him popular acclaim. **[13]** The future dictator of Spain, gen.
Franco, began his uprising not long after the poetry collection's publication.
[14
ed while hiding at a friend's house, lorca was arrested and briefly imprisoned at
gran
5] Tragically, the gifted Writer Lorca died at the hands of his political enemies on
august
936.

Copyright © by Holt, Rinehart and Winston. All rights reserved.

NAME CLASS DATE

Commas A

EXERCISE In each of the following sentences, draw a caret (^) to show where any missing commas should be inserted.

Example 1. Students^for this problem you will need a calculator^some graph paper^and^of course^your pencils.

1. Ladies and gentlemen please join me in welcoming our guest speaker Derek Creighton-Jones who really needs no further introduction.
2. No thank you I never buy anything from a telephone salesperson.
3. Sharon and Randy can set up the tables and Ron can start blowing up the balloons.
4. The original Library of Congress established in 1800 under President John Adams lost its collection when the U.S. Capitol was burned by the British in 1814.
5. President Jefferson then retired offered his personal library which he had been collecting for fifty years as a replacement.
6. After years of renovation the beautifully restored Jefferson Building of the Library of Congress reopened to the public on May 1 1997.
7. This coming weekend we plan to scrape down the woodwork patch a few little holes in the walls and choose the paint color.
8. Coach Randall and the Physical Education Department director Dr. Etheridge have agreed on the schedule of practices.
9. Although many of my relatives live in the area around Des Moines Iowa my mother and father were both born in Illinois she in Cairo and he in Chicago.
10. Please be sure to bring your scripts to the first rehearsal which has been scheduled to begin promptly at 4:00 P.M. Thursday January 17.

Copyright © by Holt, Rinehart and Winston. All rights reserved.

Commas B

EXERCISE In each of the following sentences, draw a caret (^) to show where any missing commas should be inserted, and circle any unnecessary commas.

Example 1. Richard^whose family is originally from Scotland^competes in the annual Scottish Games(,)every year.

1. Late in the spring perhaps as late as, May 15 the school board will dedicate the new school.
2. Chloe, who was named, after her aunt prefers to be called by her middle name Ann.
3. According to this flier the parade starts at the intersection of Broad Street and Elm Avenue proceeds along Broad Street, to city hall, and ends at the civic center.
4. "Nicholas" his father said pointing, to the billboard "there's the playoff schedule."
5. Many old recipes my mother told us are less specific than the recipes, in modern cookbooks.
6. In my notes I've recorded, that the first sprouts appeared on April 12 2009 and the first bloom, appeared on June 1.
7. Uh-oh I finished the homework but I forgot to put it in my backpack, this morning.
8. The rehearsal ran late past ten o'clock so all of us feel a little sleepy today.
9. I was so tired that the cheerful, chirping of the birds which I usually enjoy was annoying.
10. The loud, plaid pattern of his coat clashed with the gray pinstriped fabric of his trousers.
11. Framed, and hung carefully above the fireplace the portrait was truly impressive.
12. By the way I hope you heard that the meeting we scheduled for Tuesday afternoon, has been postponed until Thursday.
13. You should address the letter, to Dr. Keith Inman Director of Admissions Chataway College, 1112 College Street Chataway NH 02011.
14. My uncle's dogs Lucy and Linus are purebred longhaired Chihuahuas.
15. Beverly likes broccoli, and green beans but for some reason she never eats salads.
16. That boy's name is Michel not Michael.
17. Did you have Ms. Rocha for biology or Mr. Price the same teacher, my brother had?
18. My little cousin's favorite book *Goodnight Moon* has been read so many times, that the pages are falling out.
19. Unless one of the candidates, receives a clear majority a runoff election will be held.
20. He's not in class this afternoon, because he had an appointment I think with the dentist.

Copyright © by Holt, Rinehart and Winston. All rights reserved.

Semicolons and Colons

EXERCISE In each of the following sentences, underline any word or number that should be followed by a colon, and draw a caret (‸) to show where a semicolon should be inserted. Some semicolons will replace commas.

Example 1. I cleaned out the refrigerator and checked all the cupboards, ‸ we're almost out of the <u>following</u>, milk, yogurt, eggs, bread, flour, mustard, and olive oil.

1. Every morning he looked for signs of rain, every afternoon the sun baked the soil a little more.
2. Your application package should contain the following, two completed copies of the application form, your essay, double-spaced and neatly typed, three letters of recommendation, preferably from teachers or former employers, and a self-addressed, stamped envelope.
3. This week's rehearsals have been scheduled as follows, 4 30 P.M. on Monday, Tuesday, and Wednesday, 6 30 on Thursday, and 6 00 on Friday.
4. This is exactly what the instructions say, Insert bolt A as shown on figure 2-C.
5. Michael is slightly older than his twin brother, Tom was born at 4 39 P.M., five minutes later than Michael.
6. My cousin Taylor is a talented athlete, he plays on both the football and baseball teams, runs three miles almost every day, and swims at least twice a week.
7. We have to be at the station by 6 15, the train leaves at 6 30.
8. To fulfill the district's minimum requirements for graduation, you will need these credits, four years of English, three years of math, three years of science, and three years of social studies.
9. Electives in fine and performing arts are also required, as are computer science courses, two years of a foreign language are strongly recommended.
10. Despite their efforts to decipher the old map, they could not locate the buried treasure, perhaps, after all, it would remain hidden forever.

COMMON ERRORS

Copyright © by Holt, Rinehart and Winston. All rights reserved.

NAME ______________________ CLASS ______________ DATE ______________

for **CHAPTER 16: CORRECTING COMMON ERRORS** pages 372–416

Quotation Marks with Other Punctuation A

EXERCISE On the lines provided, rewrite the following dialogue, inserting quotation marks and other punctuation as necessary. Be sure to start a new paragraph whenever the speaker changes.

Example **[1]** Reggie Teresa began could you please help me with these math problems

"Reggie," Teresa began, "could you please help me with these math problems?"

[1] Sure no problem **[2]** What kind of problems are they **[3]** Oh Teresa said just some problems converting fractions to decimals **[4]** I don't think I understood Ms. Minot's explanation very well **[5]** I think she said Divide everything by ten or maybe she said Multiply everything by ten or maybe oh I just don't know **[6]** Well, I doubt she said any of those things but let me show you **[7]** Get me a piece of paper and a pencil please. **[8]** Teresa ran from the room and came back with the items **[9]** I don't suppose you could well just do one or two or maybe even four or five of these problems could you **[10]** Teresa sighed Reggie barely suppressing a laugh how do you think that would help you learn to convert fractions to decimals

COMMON ERRORS

Copyright © by Holt, Rinehart and Winston. All rights reserved.

Quotation Marks with Other Punctuation B

EXERCISE A In each of the following sentences, insert a caret (^) to show where quotation marks should be inserted. If single quotation marks are required, write upside-down carets above the line to show where they go.

Example **1.** ^Children,^said Mrs. Thistlewick sternly,^who tied my shoelaces together?^

1. Martin's father took his glasses off, wiped his eyes, and said, I don't know whether to laugh or cry about that.

2. Are we supposed to read all of Chapter 16, The Cradle of Civilization, tonight? Crystal asked.

3. We certainly are, answered Cleo, but it's only thirty pages long.

4. Kim asked, Did I just make this up, or did Ms. Simpson really say, No homework tomorrow?

5. Isn't Maria one of the best known songs from *West Side Story*?

EXERCISE B On the lines provided, rewrite the following sentences, adding or deleting punctuation marks to correct punctuation errors and correcting the capitalization.

Example **1.** Here's someone who made progress against racial bias long before the Civil Rights Movement observed Clint. *"Here's someone who made progress against racial bias long before the Civil Rights Movement," observed Clint.*

6. Who's that Sun Mi wanted to know? ______

7. Charles Drew, who was a surgeon Clint said Saved many lives in the early part of the century by networking blood banks." ______

8. Sun Mi asked will that information help us get started on the Black History Month project? ______

9. Yes, Clint said "but not just because he's an accomplished African American. read this. ______

10. wow Sun Mi exclaimed it was only after Dr. Drew proved there was no scientific basis for labeling blood plasma according to ethnicity that the practice ceased in 1945. ______

COMMON ERRORS

Copyright © by Holt, Rinehart and Winston. All rights reserved.

Apostrophes

EXERCISE In each of the following sentences, insert a caret (‸) to show where an apostrophe should be inserted.

Example 1. Phillip‸s sister‸s book will be reviewed in Tuesday‸s newspaper.

1. They shouldve been able to complete the assignment in an hours time.
2. This Fridays game will probably be rained out; well have to play a makeup game next week.
3. Shed be better off if shed listened to her mother and fathers advice.
4. The Smiths farm is in a neighboring county, near Zekes grandmothers place.
5. Id like to eat at Joes Family Restaurant tonight; theyre famous for their chicken and dumplings.
6. Our buses will leave from the south parking lot at four o clock, and well return from the theater by ten o clock tonight.
7. Well be the class of 09.
8. Last winters big snowstorm badly damaged the barns roof.
9. If you order the special, youll be sure to get your moneys worth.
10. Did you hear that everyones bikes were smashed when the bus backed into the schools bike rack?
11. Cecilys parents business is located near the Peoples Drugstore on Main Street.
12. This teddy bears fur is torn and its missing an eye.
13. Whats the address of the girl whose grandmothers photograph was published in the paper?
14. After a few minutes rest, hell attempt the afternoons most difficult dive.
15. Casss distress was apparent to all of us.
16. Each members vote counts the same; no ones vote is more important than anyone elses.
17. Whos going to wake me up at four o clock in the morning so that Ill be at the airport on time?
18. Isnt Als painting style quite a bit different from everyone elses?
19. This week its Dan and Felicias turn to clean out the mices cage.
20. The yearbook staffs photograph was mislabeled, much to Mr. Gomezs chagrin.

Copyright © by Holt, Rinehart and Winston. All rights reserved.

All Marks of Punctuation Review A

EXERCISE Rewrite each of the following sentences, inserting necessary punctuation marks.

Example 1. What time is it asked Darius I certainly hope Im not late for the game
"What time is it?" asked Darius. "I certainly hope I'm not late for the game!"

1. This first slide could someone please get the lights? is of the waterfall near our campsite

______

2. I dont think I want to go to that store anymore caveat emptor is written above the doorway ______

______

3. Oh my laughed Cecil That means Let the buyer beware ______

______

4. How many of you have already read John Steinbecks novel The Grapes of Wrath ______

______

5. My great grandfather was one of the Oklahomans who migrated to California during the Dustbowl of the 1930s ______

______

6. Please do not bring any of the following items to camp expensive jewelry CD players cellular telephones or pagers ______

______

7. I wish you could have seen his face I almost burst out laughing when he realized it was a surprise party ______

______

8. Nash who is older than Neil is a left handed writer but he paints with his right hand ______

______

9. The Thirty Years War 1618–1648 which began as a civil war eventually involved most of Europe ______

______

10. No no no a thousand times no yelled the hot tempered conductor Youll have to do that part again sopranos ______

______

COMMON ERRORS

Copyright © by Holt, Rinehart and Winston. All rights reserved.

All Marks of Punctuation Review B

EXERCISE Rewrite the following letter, inserting appropriate punctuation marks as necessary.

Example [1] Booker Williams wrote a thank you note to Dr Lebowitz who had addressed some members of the senior class recently *Booker Williams wrote a thank-you note to Dr. Lebowitz, who had addressed some members of the senior class recently.*

May 2, 2009

[1] Dear Dr Lebowitz

[2] Im writing to thank you first of all for speaking to senior class members planning to attend Prairie Tech U next fall **[3]** In my opinion the best talk was yours **[4]** Your final comment about learning from our failures as well as from our successes Ive experienced a few of both was appreciated **[5]** What an inspirational speaker you are

[6] I have of course another reason for writing I am interested in knowing whether freshman leaders have been selected yet **[7]** My application for one of the positions should have reached your office by the March 31 12 00 PM deadline **[8]** I realize both that there were many applicants and that youre quite busy but I am hoping to find out before I complete the student loan process **[9]** I knew the first time I read about the position in your booklet What Awaits You at Prairie Tech U that I would enjoy taking on the extra duties I look forward to hearing from your office.

[10] Sincerely

Booker Williams

COMMON ERRORS

Copyright © by Holt, Rinehart and Winston. All rights reserved.

Spelling A

EXERCISE A In each of the following sentences, if either or both of the underlined words are misspelled, write the correct spelling above the incorrect spelling. If both underlined words are spelled correctly, write *C* after the sentence.

athletically
Example 1. If you're not athleticly inclined, you should probably try band.

1. In her judgement, the silliness has not abated.
2. Brenda excelled because she exercised all her muscles in a cross-trainning program.
3. It is hopeless to try to win their approveal now.
4. I wouldn't call Gerard concieted just because he made one referrence to his success in the chess tournament.
5. What a mischeivous little fellow your young neighbor is!
6. The drama club conceeds that its improvisation exercises can get a little wierd.
7. In a separate incident, a boulder seemed to propel itself down-hill, narrowly missing a cabin.
8. Government officials went about rewarding their allies by offering them additional supplies.
9. Several videoes are in the boxes over there.
10. These developement rules supercede the rules issued last year.

EXERCISE B In each of the following sentences, underline any misspelled word and write the word correctly above it. If all the words in a sentence are spelled correctly, write *C* after the sentence.

tendency *conclusions*
Example 1. Her tendancy to jump to conclusons was regrettable.

11. As the group of runners stumbleed toward the finish line, their exhaustion was apparent.
12. The awkward silence was more than noticable; it was embarasing.
13. The stubborness of the superintendent had certainly been a factor in the rebelion.
14. The mechanic insisted that the problem was in the carburetor.
15. The miniature golf course is a few blocks past Crenshaw Boulevard.
16. This anonymous letter, accordding to the police sergeant, is unmistakeably the work of a disgruntled former employee.
17. The regulators' responsibility is to protect the innocent from the unnscrupulous.
18. As the temperature rose, the recruits began to collapse.
19. There is no concievable reason this endeavor could fail.
20. The food at that restaurant is mediocre at best.

COMMON ERRORS

Copyright © by Holt, Rinehart and Winston. All rights reserved.

Spelling B

EXERCISE A In each of the following sentences, underline any misspelled or incorrectly used word or number and write the correct word or number above it. If all the words in a sentence are spelled and used correctly, write *C* after the sentence.

Example 1. This story is formulaic; both the heros [heroes] and the villains are uncomplicatted [uncomplicated] characters.

1. The choir director expects the sopranoes and the altoes to know they're parts by Wednesday.

2. His father, who was an alumni of the university, interceeded with the dean.

3. The attornies general of several states met to discuss the settlement yesterday.

4. Tornados have been seen in the area during the past few hours.

5. 27 students signed up for the calculus class.

6. Cursive *Z*s have always looked identical to *3*s to me.

7. Your assignment is to read pages two hundred fifty-seven through two hundred ninety-five.

8. The number of bookshelfs in this library is insufficeint.

9. Unfortunatly, the accident that occured last night was unavoidable.

10. The international financeir apparently considered the law no hindrance to his activitys.

EXERCISE B On the lines provided, write the plural form of each of the following items.

Example 1. cello *cellos*

11. thief ______

12. library ______

13. editor in chief ______

14. waltz ______

15. Hernandez ______

16. cameo ______

17. runner-up ______

18. phenomenon ______

19. 1970 ______

20. foot ______

21. cherub ______

22. DVD ______

23. trash ______

24. Sandy ______

25. ancestry ______

26. fox ______

27. theory ______

28. cactus ______

29. *i* ______

30. radio ______

COMMON ERRORS

Copyright © by Holt, Rinehart and Winston. All rights reserved.

NAME _______________ CLASS _______________ DATE _______________

Words Often Confused

EXERCISE A In each of the following sentences, underline the correct word in parentheses.

Example 1. In the (*course, coarse*) of the discussion, important objections to the plan were raised.

1. The immigrants had (*born, borne*) all their hardships with great dignity.
2. The red tie might better (*compliment, complement*) this pinstriped shirt, sir.
3. When I need your (*council, counsel*) about which alarm clock to use, I'll ask for it.
4. Both fruit and pastry were offered as dessert, and I chose the (*later, latter*).
5. Lydia says (*passed, past*) experience has taught her not to count on guessing the right answers.
6. Laws are changing about when a (*minor, miner*) can be tried as an adult in a court of law.
7. (*Who's, Whose*) LaMont taking to the church picnic?
8. Please explain what (*led, lead*) you to believe those books were in the basement.
9. Someone in the (*personal, personnel*) office will conduct the first interview.
10. Don't (*dessert, desert*) the trio now that we have performance dates!

EXERCISE B In each of the following sentences, underline any incorrect word and write the correct word above it. If all the words in a sentence are correct, write *C* above the sentence.

Example 1. I don't believe we have ever been formerly (formally) introduced.

11. I can't describe the affect the defeat had on the team's moral.
12. As soon as their finished talking to the career councilor, we'll join them for refreshments.
13. One of the fundamental principals of our democracy is the right of citizens to choose their representatives.
14. Jeff had all ready ensured his father that he would have the breaks adjusted.
15. The venture capitol firm has borne most of the company's financial losses.
16. When the city council meets next Monday, its agenda will include a discussion of the parks budget.
17. I had to go to the stationary store because I needed a single, large peace of a certain kind of paper.
18. Are you quite sure that one of you're fillings is lose?
19. If my plain leaves at four o'clock, than we need to leave for the airport by half past two.
20. When I past her the ball, she wasn't quiet ready.

Copyright © by Holt, Rinehart and Winston. All rights reserved.

NAME CLASS DATE

for **CHAPTER 16: CORRECTING COMMON ERRORS** pages 441–466

Spelling and Words Often Confused

EXERCISE In the following memorandum, underline each misspelled or misused word and write the correct spelling or word above the incorrect word. If all the words in a numbered word group are correct, write *C* above it.

Example **[1]** The senior class secretary had all ready (*already*) printed and delivered the memo to the assistant principle's (*principal's*) office.

[1] February 10, 2009

To: Ms. Carol Varner

[2] From: Senior Class Counsel

[3] Subject: Status of Courtyard Landscaping Project

[4] At it's first meeting last fall, the representatives of the senior class voted to landscape the courtyard outside the cafeteria as our classes gift to the school. **[5]** Spring, of coarse, is just around the corner, and we want to make every concieveable effort to finish the project by May. **[6]** Our goals, as you know, are to beautify our surrounddings, to camouflage some of the unssightly chain-link fence, and to lower noise levels. **[7]** The echoes of a hundred voices bounce off the brick walls and must be irritating for the counsilors who's offices overlook the courtyard.

[8] We have added compost to the soil in the planters and beds, and replaced the sundial that had fallen off it's pedestal. **[9]** We beleive the small trees, shrubs, and flowers we have chosen will compliment the building's design and colors. **[10]** Some of the students have familiarized themselfs with the plants that grow best in our region; none of the plants should require more then routine maintenance. **[11]** The planting will begin next Wednesday after school and will last until 6 o'clock or latter. **[12]** All together, we expect forty or fifty volunteers to work on the project. **[13]** With hard work and a minimum amount of capitol, we will transform our "dessert" into a lush garden. **[14]** It will certainly be a more pleasant and pieceful place then it is now.

[15] As we have discused in the passed, we'd like to hold a dedication ceremony early in May. **[16]** We'd like to invite both you and Mr. Raymond, the principle, to speak at the dedicateion. **[17]** Also, we all want you to know how much we've appreciated your council and your fund-raising expertise. **[18]** Thank's for all you're help. **[19]** The class is also grateful to the PTA.

[20] We twelvth graders—the Class of 09— are all ready looking foreword to the time when we can revisit our courtyard as alumnea!

COMMON ERRORS

Copyright © by Holt, Rinehart and Winston. All rights reserved.

NAME ______________________ CLASS ______________ DATE ______________

Review A: Usage

EXERCISE A Most of the following sentences contain a subject-verb or pronoun-antecedent agreement error. If a sentence contains an agreement error, underline the incorrect pronoun or verb and write the correct word or words above it. If the sentence is correct, write *C* after it.

Example 1. Benazir Bhutto, who became Pakistan's prime minister in 1988, stand (stands) out as the first woman to govern a Muslim country.

1. *Porgy and Bess,* in addition to *Othello,* is a drama in which the talented African American actor Paul Robeson starred.
2. Humphrey Bogart, along with Ingrid Bergman, increased their fame in a film story set in Casablanca, Morocco.
3. The Trail of Tears refer to the route of the Cherokee people on their forced march to a reservation west of the Mississippi in the 1830s.
4. *Heart of Darkness,* a novel well known among Joseph Conrad's works, concern the search for a corrupt adventurer in the interior of Africa.
5. For his and her science project, Alice and Casey tested several hundred students.

EXERCISE B On the lines provided, rewrite each of the following sentences, correcting any errors in the use of modifiers. You may need to rearrange or add words to make the meaning of a sentence clear.

Example 1. Rhonda's essay was much longer than Calvin, but his was the most thoughtful.
Rhonda's essay was much longer than Calvin's, but his was more thoughtful.

6. Long, low, and lonesome, the night was pierced by the whistle of a faraway train.
7. Covered with dirt and scratches from their struggle through the underbrush, the cool waters of the creek refreshed the weary hikers.
8. The screenwriter adapted the novel better than any other.
9. Recently arrived from Denmark, the class met the visiting professor.
10. You wouldn't hardly recognize him if you saw him; he's tall as his brother now.

COMMON ERRORS

Copyright © by Holt, Rinehart and Winston. All rights reserved.

Review B: Mechanics

EXERCISE On the lines provided, rewrite each of the following sentences, capitalizing letters and inserting punctuation as needed and correcting any misspelled or incorrect words.

Example 1. These red delicious apples are really juicy dont you want one of them in your lunch
These red delicious apples are really juicy; don't you want one of them in your lunch?

1. I'd really like to have a big salad tonite please bring these items from the store romaine lettuce, tomatoes, a red onion, and too cucumbers.

2. Last Wednsday afternoon I beleive it was wednesday but it may have been Tuesday the faculty met with the principle and discused plans for the new wing

3. The Gomezes cats name is mr tibbs.

4. Our journeys end finally in site we sighed with releif

5. According to the police report the victim of the hit and run accident told the oficer that he the victim doesnt remember what happened

6. Cecilia likes to read mysterys I told her she should try the novels of P D james including An unsuitable job for a woman

7. Let me see said the birdwatcher my book says that bird is called a two toed red feathered purple spotted something or other

8. Oh grandma what big tooth you have cried the little girl in the red hooded cape

9. My father still can recite tennysons poem The charge of the light brigade which he memorized when he was an eighth grader

10. Embarased, nick picked up the note cards he had dropped on the floor and said Ok um let me see where I was oh heres my place

Copyright © by Holt, Rinehart and Winston. All rights reserved.

NAME ______________________ CLASS ______________ DATE ______________

Review C: Usage and Mechanics

EXERCISE Revise the following paragraphs, correcting any errors.

Example **[1]** In 1942, few members of the public knew anything about penicillin; ~~less~~ fewer than ~~100~~ one hundred people in the united states had been treated with the drug.

[1] On saturday night november 28 1942 that situation began to change **[2]** Fire breaked out in the cocoanut grove a huge popular nightclub in boston of the nearly 1 thousand people packed into the club more than 400 died and hundreds more were injured **[3]** recent medical break-throughs helped save many lives the victims were given blood plasma injections the technology for separateing plasma was only four years old at the time and to combat infection sulfadiazine one of the sulfa drugs discovered in the 1930s and 1940s was administered

[4] Sulfa drugs however couldnt combat infection from Staphylococcus aureus a bacteria that often infected burn wounds and skin grafts at the time most burn patients who got a staph infection died **[5]** the drug that could fight staph infections was penicillin discovered by british scientist alexander fleming in 1928 but it was hard to manufacture and only a small supply existed reserved for the use of the u.s. military forces **[6]** An emergency supply of penicillin was driven from the production facility of the drugs manufacturer merck & co inc in new jersey three hundred sixty-eight miles to the massachusetts general hospital in boston

[7] The survival of the cocoanut grove fires victims focused national attention on the new wonder drug **[8]** Penicillin seemed to work miracles stopping infections that formally killed there victims and cureing pneumonia and blood infections **[9]** by 1945 however fleming penicillins inventor was warning against the overuse of the drug for he had all ready been able to grow bacteriums that were resistent to penicillin **[10]** in fact fleming predicted that as people started to take penicillin at home rather than in the hospital more drug resistant bacteria would develop fleming was worried that many people wouldnt take the drug properly

Copyright © by Holt, Rinehart and Winston. All rights reserved.